Basic
Chemical
Thermodynamics

Basic

Chemical

Thermodynamics

Jürg Waser

Professor of Chemistry
California Institute of Technology

1966

V. A. BENJAMIN, INC.   *NEW YORK   AMSTERDAM*

Basic Chemical Thermodynamics

Library of Congress Catalog Card Number 66–12703
Manufactured in the United States of America

The manuscript was put into production on July 19, 1965; this
volume was published on March 15, 1966

W. A. Benjamin, Inc.
New York, New York 10016

To the memory of
Roscoe Gilkey Dickinson (1894–1945),
in the spirit of whose teaching of thermodynamics
I have endeavored to write

Preface

Undergraduates in chemistry and related sciences should receive sound instruction in thermodynamics as early as possible. An excellent reason for this is the central position that thermodynamics assumes relative to all of chemistry—inorganic, organic, and biological. Its application permits, for example, a rigorous development of such important relationships as the mass-action law and the Nernst equation. A second reason for an early start is that the modern course in physical chemistry often consists of an introduction to statistical mechanics and quantum mechanics, with thermodynamics treated more cavalierly. A thorough introduction to thermodynamics is thus of great help when the subject is taken up again, and makes possible a much deeper development at that time. A prompt exposure followed later by a second round is also advantageous because the difficulties in thermodynamics are not in the mathematical formalism but in the logical fabric. At the time of the follow-up the ideas have become rooted in the students' minds and have developed consciously and subconsciously to a deeper understanding.

The present exposition of chemical thermodynamics grew out of freshman class notes at the California Institute of Technology. With the excellent preparation that today's entering college students have received, this text should be suitable for use with selected freshmen or sophomores. It could also be used on the junior level in a physical chemistry course that does not aim to make the students into expert thermodynamicists.

vii

The emphasis in this text is on ideas rather than on mathematical manipulation. The aim has been to impart the flavor of thermodynamics, but concepts that are hard to understand have not been ignored, and a special effort has been made to treat difficult points in some detail. Highlighted are enthalpy, free energy, and chemical potential in their application to the treatment of chemical equilibrium, phase transformation, and electrochemistry. The results of statistical mechanics are used to supplement conclusions reached by thermodynamic arguments and to further an intuitive understanding of entropy and of the $T \Delta S$ term in free energy. The last chapter contains a cross section of important applications, and one of the appendices treats the relationship between thermodynamic and statistical-mechanical entropy in some detail. The mathematics used is restricted to derivatives of $\ln x$ and of the powers of x, and to the related integrals. Some use of partial derivatives is made in the last section of Chapter 5 and in a few later instances, but no prior knowledge of this subject is required, because the general apparatus of partial differentials is not used and the complexities of partial molal quantities are avoided.

A word on notation may be in order, because it differs in two respects from that used in many other texts: (1) Work performed on a system is counted positive here and is thus treated the same way as heat. I believe this to be more consistent than to use opposite conventions for the signs of work and heat, even though this is still done in many texts. The convention used here is employed by such authorities as E. A. Guggenheim (*Thermodynamics*, Wiley-Interscience, New York, 1950), I. Prigogine and R. Defay (*Chemical Thermodynamics*, Longmans, Green, London, 1954), W. J. Moore (*Physical Chemistry*, 3rd ed., Prentice-Hall, Englewood Cliffs, N.J., 1964), and R. P. Feynman, R. B. Leighton, and M. Sands (*The Feynman Lectures on Physics, Vol. I*, Addison-Wesley, Reading, Mass., 1964). (2) Standard enthalpies and free energies of formation are denoted H_f^0 and G_f^0, even though in many modern standard works an additional Δ is used: ΔH_f^0 and ΔG_f^0. This Δ appears to me unnecessary, because it is part of, and thus contained in, the definitions of standard enthalpies and free energies. These quantities can by their nature have meaning only relative to a standard state, just as do standard half-cell emfs $\mathcal{E}^0$, where a Δ is by convention not used.

Molar quantities are indicated by a tilde $(\tilde{G})$, following the practice of A. A. Noyes and M. S. Sherrill (*Chemical Principles*, 2nd ed., Macmillan, New York, 1938).

ACKNOWLEDGMENTS

I wish to express my appreciation to many colleagues and students who have helped and encouraged me in the present undertaking. Their names would fill pages and my explicit thanks must be limited to a few. Particularly valuable have been the criticism and advice of Edward W. Hughes. I am also indebted for helpful suggestions to Richard M. Badger, Leo Brewer, William H. Corcoran, Joseph B. Dence, L. Carroll King, Cornelius Pings, William P. Schaefer, Brahama Datta Sharma, and Craig Spencer.

For competent editorial help and expert typing and draftsmanship my appreciation goes to Judith A. Stewart. Additional thanks are due to W. A. Benjamin, the publisher, and his staff for a handsomely produced book; in particular, the manuscript owes a great deal to a detailed and critical review by Caroline A. Lanford. I am further obliged to Science Bookcrafters, Inc., especially to Nancy Orban and Barbara Zeiders for expert editing and to Cecilia Duray-Bito for the artwork. Last, but not least, I am grateful to my wife for helpful editorial advice and for much forebearance and encouragement.

JÜRG WASER

Pasadena, California
January 1966

Note to Students

Thermodynamics is not a simple subject. The difficulties lie less in the mathematics than in the close reasoning involved. To learn about thermodynamics takes time and patience. Thus, if some of the material looks forbidding on first reading, give it a rest; a second perusal may show that it is not so difficult after all. This is, in fact, good general practice for any difficult subject: Read an extended portion rather rapidly, not worrying unduly about points that remain unclea. Follow up by a more careful, detailed study, jot down key words or phrases, retrace mathematical developments, and rework the examples provided. Close the book frequently and recapitulate in your own words. Remain critical and do not accept without question—authors of texts have been known to err. Ask your instructor about points that remain unclear. Above all, do not let the material frustrate you. It is useless to spend hours on a point or a problem that does not seem to yield. Do some other work, or relax, and return to the worrisome point later; your viewpoint may have changed.

If you have difficulties with the relatively few applications of calculus, perusal of the first-rate 214-page paperback by D. A. Greenberg, *Mathematics for Introductory Science Courses* (Benjamin, New York, 1965), may prove helpful.

JW

Contents

Energy-Conversion Factors

	Cal	J	liter-atm
1 cal	1	4.18	0.0413
1 J	0.239	1	0.00987
1 liter-atm	24.2	101.3	1

Physical Constants

$R = 0.0821$ liter-atm/mole-deg $= 8.31$ J/mole-deg $= 1.99$ cal/mole-deg
$k = 1.38 \times 10^{-23}$ J/deg $= 3.30 \times 10^{-24}$ cal/deg
$\mathfrak{F} = 96{,}500$ coulomb/mole $= 23{,}100$ cal/volt-mole

(See pages 28 and 29 for additional significant figures.)

1 Preliminary Aspects of Thermodynamics

In this chapter an exposition of the general aspects of thermody-namics is followed by characterizations of the different laws of this branch of science. Temperature and thermometers are ex-plained, and the Kelvin scale is defined. Thermodynamic concepts, such as system and surroundings, state variables, cyclic processes, and reversible and irreversible paths, are introduced. An extensive discussion of work, particularly of the volume-pressure type, is given. The chapter ends with a discussion of heat and of heat capacities that relate to different paths.

1–1   THE NATURE OF THERMODYNAMICS

Thermodynamics is the science of heat and temperature and, in particular, of the laws governing the conversion of heat into me-chanical, electrical, or other macroscopic forms of energy. It is a central branch of science with important applications in chemistry, physics, biology, and engineering.

An important characteristic of thermodynamics is that it per-mits the derivation of *relationships* among different laws of nature, even though the laws themselves are not a consequence of thermo-dynamics. For example, given Raoult's law of vapor-pressure lowering, other colligative properties of a solution—for example, the osmotic-pressure law—can be derived. Neither Raoult's law nor the osmotic-pressure law, however, is an individual consequence of thermodynamics. One or the other must be accepted on the basis of experiment, or derived from a detailed molecular theory of solutions.

Thermodynamics is a phenomenological theory, concerning **macroscopic** quantities such as pressure, temperature, or volume. It is both the strength and the weakness of thermodynamics that the relationships based upon it are completely independent of any microscopic explanation of physical phenomena (**microscopic** is used throughout to mean on the atomic and molecular level). The *strength* is that thermodynamic relationships are not affected by the changes to which microscopic explanations are subject even to-day. On the contrary, the conclusions of atomic and molecular theories *must not* contradict those of thermodynamics, so that thermo-dynamics can be used as a guide or as a touchstone in the develop-ment of microscopic theories. Much of thermodynamics was, in fact, developed at a time when many scientists did not believe in atoms and molecules, and long before detailed atomic theories were available.

The *weakness* is that thermodynamics does not provide the deep insight into chemical and physical phenomena that is afforded by microscopic models and theories. But to understand these theories a great deal of mathematics is required, whereas the more simple aspects of calculus suffice for thermodynamics.

Although thermodynamics is a completely self-contained mac-roscopic theory, it is nevertheless possible to find a microscopic in-terpretation of it in statistical mechanics, which provides consider-able insight and is of great value for a full understanding of thermo-dynamics.

Section 1–2 previews the laws of thermodynamics; a more detailed treatment will be presented later. The aim of this book is to present thermodynamic ideas and to impart their flavor, rather than to strive for great precision and completeness in the derivations.

1–2   THE LAWS OF THERMODYNAMICS

Several postulates, called the *laws of thermodynamics*, are basic to thermodynamics. Although these laws are consistent with the re-sults of all known experiments, this huge amount of observational material does not serve as *proof* but rather as *support*. The "laws" of thermodynamics are postulates, or axioms, as are all "laws" of nature.

The **first law** of thermodynamics states that to any system may be assigned an **energy** that remains constant when the system is isolated. Only when heat is transferred into or out of the system, or when work is performed by it or on it, does the energy of the system change, and then by an amount corresponding to the work or heat added or abstracted. The first law is intuitively easy to understand. The key is that the energy of a system is the energy of its molecules. When the system is heated by being in contact with a hotter body, interactions on the molecular level transfer energy from the hotter body to the molecules of the system; when work is performed on the system, energy is transferred to it on a macroscopic level. Temperature is a measure of the vigor of the random motion of atoms and molecules.

In many applications to chemistry, a modified energy, in which pressure-volume work is automatically taken into account, is far more useful than the energy itself. This is the **enthalpy,** and we shall place particular emphasis on the development and application of this concept.

The **second law** defines a quantity called the **entropy,** and states that the entropy of an isolated system never decreases. An intuitive quantitative understanding of the second law is much more difficult to obtain than a similar understanding of the first. In the microscopic interpretation, entropy is a measure of the *disorder* associated with the system on the atomic level. For example, other things being equal, the entropy of a crystalline substance is smaller than that of a liquid substance, because atoms are arranged in a highly ordered way in the crystal, whereas there is considerable disorder in the liquid. The disorder in a gas is larger yet; therefore so is the entropy. Under the second law, the disorder of an isolated system can only stay constant or increase.

If the system is not in equilibrium, changes tend to occur in the direction of increasing entropy. When the entropy of the isolated system has reached its maximum, equilibrium exists. It is therefore possible to give thermodynamic criteria for the direction in which a chemical reaction is liable to proceed. Unfortunately, it is not possible to establish by thermodynamics how *fast* a reaction proceeds toward equilibrium. In favorable cases this may be established by detailed molecular theories, but in general each case requires experimental investigation. Thermodynamics might thus more properly be called *thermostatics*, but "thermodynamics," coined in the early days of steam-engine theory, is undoubtedly more enticing.

Important chemical consequences of the second law may be derived most readily by considering the properties of quantities called **free energy** and **chemical potential,** which are related to the energy and the entropy of a system. These considerations permit, for example, the derivation of the mass-action law, of the relation between the temperature dependence of the mass-action constant and the heat of reaction, and of the Nernst equation. They further show that there are two forces that drive a reaction, one of them in the direction of the lowest possible energy, the other in the direction of the highest possible disorder. Which of the two forces is the more important turns out to depend on the temperature.

The **third law** states that at the absolute zero of temperature the entropy of an ordered crystal is zero, which would correspond to a state of complete order. This is also called the **Nernst heat theorem** after its discoverer. Often it is given less prominence than the first two laws.

Some authors feel that a separate theorem postulating the existence of temperature should be given the stature of a law. They have called it the **zeroth law** of thermodynamics; it is discussed in the next section. The discussion of the first, second, and third laws is more extensive and follows in later chapters.

1–3   TEMPERATURE AND THERMAL INTERACTIONS

Temperature and thermal interactions are concepts characteristic of thermodynamics, just as the concept of mass is characteristic of mechanics. It is therefore proper to introduce them in terms of observable phenomena.

Two bodies are said to be of *different* **temperature** if they change their properties when in contact with each other, even though interchange of matter, or mechanical, chemical, or electrical interaction, etc., is prevented. For example, when a hot metal wire is immersed in cold water the wire is found to shorten, and the water changes its density. When there are no further changes, it is said that there is equality of temperature—that **thermal equilibrium** exists. Interactions that cause equalization of the temperature but are not of mechanical, chemical, electrical, or similar nature are called **thermal interactions.** Such interactions may, of course, be the *source* of mechanical, electrical, or other changes, as was the case in the example.

It is found empirically that when two bodies A and B are separately at thermal equilibrium with a third body C, they are also at thermal equilibrium with each other. The third body C may thus also be used to compare the temperatures of A and B without bringing A and B into direct contact. This is the role of a **thermometer,** and any suitable physical property of C, for instance its volume or its electrical resistance, may be used to establish a **temperature scale.**

This state of affairs cannot be proved, nor is it self-evident. Rather, it is a postulate of thermodynamics: For any body there exists a quantity, called the temperature, such that two bodies having the same temperature are in thermal equilibrium when brought into contact. The usefulness of this postulate, like that of all tenable postulates of science, is that a large body of experience is in agreement with it, and that it permits the correlation of the results of many experiments.

The next step is the definition of a temperature scale that has universal character. A scale that is widely accepted is the **centigrade scale** (°C). Two points of this scale are easy to describe, because they are fixed by phase transformations of water—its boiling point at 1 atm pressure (100°C) and its freezing point when saturated with air of 1 atm pressure (0°C).

It is more difficult to find a universally convenient way to divide the interval between these fix points into 100 parts. One may subdivide the distance in a mercury thermometer between the marks at 100 and 0°C and extend this calibration uniformly over the entire temperature range in which mercury is liquid. This is satisfactory for many purposes but is not of universal character, because it depends on the thermal properties of mercury and of the glass used to make the thermometer. (The void in the glass containing the mercury expands with temperature like the glass.) It would, of course, be possible to agree by convention on a standard glass, and the temperature scale could be extended beyond the freezing and boiling points of mercury by agreeing on other standard substances.

Fortunately a much more natural way exists. Fundamentally, it is tied to thermodynamics, but it can also be related to the experimental fact that all *gases* approach the same *ideal behavior* at sufficiently low pressure. Helium and hydrogen approach this ideal behavior at pressures of 1 atm or 760 torr[1], but for other gases lower pressures are required. When the pressure is constant, all gases that behave ideally show the same fractional increase in volume for a given increase in temperature. The division into **degrees** of the **centigrade** scale may then be defined as follows: If V is the volume of a gas at a constant pressure small enough to permit the gas to behave ideally, and V_{100} and V_0 are its volumes at the boiling and freezing temperatures of water, the centigrade temperature t of the gas is

$$t = \frac{100\ (V - V_0)}{V_{100} - V_0} \tag{1-1}$$

Table 1–1 shows the *deviations* from the centigrade scale of thermometer scales based on the thermal expansion of several substances: Hg in two kinds of glass, pentane (mp, $-131.5°C$; bp, $36.2°C$), toluene (mp, $-95°C$; bp, $110.6°C$), $H_2(g)$, and $He(g)$. Both pentane and toluene boil before they reach $100°C$, so that aside from the ice point another temperature fix point must be introduced. This is the sublimation point of solid CO_2 at 1 atm, $-78.5°C$. The corresponding entries in Table 1–1 are based on a uniform division into 78.5 parts of the distance between the levels of the thermometer liquid at the ice point and the sublimation point of CO_2. The two gas scales are for a gas pressure of 1000 torr and are not corrected for nonideal behavior.

In practice, accurate liquid-in-glass thermometers are calibrated in centigrades; the degree marks are not exactly equidistant, to correct for the deviations shown in Table 1–1. Mercury (mp, $-38.9°C$; normal bp, $357°C$) thermometers may be used from about -39 to about $357°C$, and to $500°C$ and even higher when made of quartz tubing and filled with N_2 of sufficient pressure to keep the Hg liquid. For low temperatures, ethyl alcohol (mp, $-115°C$; bp, $78.3°C$), pentane, and toluene are popular thermometer liquids. The temperature dependence of electrical phenomena is also employed to measure temperature, with thermocouples, electrical-

---

[1] The torr is defined in Section 1–9.

Table 1–1
Comparison of Temperature Scales[a]

t, °C	Hg in glass 1	Hg in glass 2	Pentane	Toluene	He at 1000 torr	H$_2$ at 1000 torr
−200.0	—	—	−25.8	—	0.02	0.3
−100.0	—	—	−3.4	—	0.005	0.04
−78.5	—	—	0.0	0.0	. . .	. . .
−50.0	—	—	2.6	1.1	0.002	0.02
−30.0	0.28	0.13	2.9	1.2	. . .	. . .
0.0	0.0	0.0	0.0	0.0	0.0	0.0
30.0	−0.11	−0.04	−0.04	−7.6	. . .	. . .
50.0	−0.12	−0.03	—	. . .	0.000	−0.004
70.0	−0.08	−0.01	—	. . .	. . .	. . .
100.0	0.0	0.0	—	−24.4	0.0	0.0
200.0	−0.29	−0.84	—	—	0.001	0.02
300.0	−2.7	−4.4	—	—	0.003	0.04

[a] Entries are deviations $(t - t_{th})$ of the various thermometer temperatures t_{th} from the centigrade temperature t defined by $(1 - 1)$; the various thermometers are based on the fix points described in the text. . . ., no data available; —, outside range of thermometer.

resistance thermometers, and thermistors. Gas thermometers are cumbersome and are mainly used for calibrating purposes. They usually contain He and are used not at constant pressure, but at *constant volume*, with temperature changes proportional to *pressure changes*. Such gas thermometers are easier to handle and give more accurate results than the constant-pressure variety.

As is usually shown in the discussion of the properties of ideal gases, it is convenient to introduce an absolute or **Kelvin temperature** $T(°K)$ that is directly proportional to the volume V of an ideal gas at constant pressure,

$$T = \text{const} \cdot V \qquad (1-2)$$

The **degree Kelvin** is *defined* by the statement that the **triple point** of pure water, at which ice, liquid water, and vapor are at equilibrium, is at 273.1600°K. Because the zero of the Kelvin scale is fixed, only one fix point is required for this definition. The ice point is 0.010°K below the triple point of water, and therefore at 273.150°K.

It should be noted that the simple form of the ideal gas law, $PV = nRT$, is a consequence of the definition of T by (1–2). There is, however, no circular argument involved here, because the identical behavior of equimolar quantities of all gases at sufficiently low pressures can be established by using *any* temperature scale. The universal aspect of the absolute scale defined by (1–2) is not only that it makes possible a particularly simple formulation of the ideal gas law, but that many other laws of nature assume a similarly simple form through its use. An important example is the second law of thermodynamics, as will be seen, and the Boltzmann factor defined in Fig. 4–4.

It should also be noted that the triple point of water, to which the present definition of the Kelvin scale refers, is an invariant fix point that has no manmade aspects such as the freezing and boiling points of water have—the boiling point being related to atmospheric pressure, and the freezing point related to the amount of air dissolved in water. Furthermore, in this Kelvin scale the difference between the freezing and boiling points of water is no longer exactly 100 deg by definition, even though the assignment of 273.1600°K to the triple point of water makes this difference close to 100 deg. In other words, the temperature $t' = T - 273.150°$ is not identical with the centigrade temperature, even though it is very close to it. To recognize this fine point, the scale t' is called the **Celsius scale.** No distinction between degree centigrade and degree Celsius will be made in this book, and the approximation

$$T \approx t + 273.150 \qquad (1\text{–}3)$$

is completely acceptable.

The only aspect of the absolute Kelvin scale that is not universal is that the size of the degree is related to the properties of water. Any other size of the degree would, of course, do just as well, and indeed the Rankine scale[1] is just as absolute as the Kelvin

---

[1] The Rankine and Fahrenheit scales are related in the same way as are the Kelvin and Celsius scales. The value of the Rankine degree is $\frac{5}{9}$ that of the Kelvin.

scale.   The ratio of the temperatures on any two absolute scales must, however, be constant.

When T reaches zero, the corresponding volume V of an *ideal* gas becomes zero also.   This is, of course, an extrapolation, and there is no substance known that behaves as an ideal gas near 0°K. This has no bearing on the concept of an absolute zero of the temperature scale, but temperature measurements near 0°K would be difficult or impossible if ideal gas behavior were the only basis of the absolute scale.

1–4   SYSTEM AND SURROUNDINGS

It is often convenient to divide the physical universe into the **system,** the part under particular scrutiny, and the **surroundings.** The system may be complex and contain all kinds of substances, machinery, electrical equipment, etc.   Or it may be very simple and consist only of a homogeneous piece of matter, such as a certain volume of air.   What is included in the system is a matter of convenience that depends on the questions at issue.   The *boundaries* of the system may be real, such as the walls of a box, or they may exist in thought only.   Physical boundaries may be part of the system and their properties important, or they may not; they may be movable or fixed.

A system is **open** if a flow of matter across the boundaries is possible; otherwise it is **closed.**   If the boundaries do not permit the passage of *heat* into or out of the system, the system is **heat insulated** or **adiabatic** (Greek: *adiabatos*, not passable; *a*, not; *dia*, through; *bainein*, to go).   However, heat insulation need not exclude other interactions between system and surroundings: Mechanical or electrical work may be performed on the system through heat-insulated walls, even if only in an idealized situation.   If there is no interaction whatever between a system and its surroundings, the system is said to be **isolated.**

It is important to specify the system.   For example, it may be a liquid inside a vessel, bounded by the surface of the liquid and by the walls that may, but need not, be part of the system.   This system is open, because liquid may escape into the atmosphere as vapor, or further substance may be added from the surroundings. In another situation a vessel may be provided with a tight cover, with a liquid and a gas phase inside considered to be the system. This system would be closed. If heat is evolved during a process, the walls may take up some of the heat and might be counted as part of the system. Or the walls may be of heat-insulating material and the system adiabatic.

1–5 STATES AND STATE FUNCTIONS

The **state** of a system is described by specifying the values of all pertinent macroscopic variables, so that the system could be precisely duplicated from this information. Different arrangements of molecules and their velocities leading to the same macroscopic properties are thermodynamically indistinguishable. Description on the molecular level is therefore neither pertinent nor necessary to define the state of the system. If there is violent motion in a system it may be impossible to define its state.

Quantities that depend on the state of the system *only* and not, for example, on its history, are called **state variables** or **state functions.** For example, the volume, temperature, pressure, and density are state variables for a homogeneous system. It will be seen shortly that work and heat are *not* state functions.

State variables are not necessarily independent of each other. For example, in a specified amount of gas, volume and density are determined by the pressure and temperature. The relationship among temperature, pressure, and volume of a given amount of a substance is called the **equation of state,** which depends, of course, on the nature of the substance. The ideal gas equation is an example of an (idealized) equation of state.

When a system undergoes a change it is sometimes important to specify the **process** or the **path** along which such a change occurs. For example, an increase in the temperature of 1 liter of H_2O from 20 to 30°C may be achieved by supplying heat, by performing friction work, or by other means.

In an **isothermal** process or path the temperature remains fixed. This is often achieved by placing the system in a **thermostat**

—for example, a tank filled with a liquid of constant temperature. A temperature sensor puts into operation heating or cooling coils, as needed, and the liquid is stirred rapidly to maintain constant and uniform temperature everywhere.   In an **adiabatic** process the system is thermally insulated, so that no heat can flow into or out of the system.   An **isobaric** (Greek: *baros*, weight) process is a constant pressure process; in an **isochoric** (Greek: *chora*, place) process the volume remains constant.

When the state of a system is altered, the *change* of any *state function* depends, by definition, only on the initial and final states. It *must* therefore *be independent of the path* along which the change in state has taken place.   This fact may appear obvious at this point, but is sometimes overlooked by the beginner in more involved situations.   If, as is often done, the *initial state* is designated by 1 and the *final state* by 2, the increase ΔX of a state function X is defined by

$$\Delta X = X_2 - X_1 \qquad\qquad (1\text{--}4)$$

and ΔX is independent of the path along which the change of state has been effected.   Note that the definition of a Δ quantity is always analogous to that given in (1–4); that is, the initial value is subtracted from the final value.   Or, stated another way, the Δ quantity is what has to be added to the initial value to reach the final value; in the case of X, $X_2 = X_1 + \Delta X$.

It may even be impossible to define the *path* along which a change in state takes place, because conditions of violent internal motion may be involved along the way.   This does not affect the existence of state functions and (1–4) remains valid.

If states 1 and 2 coincide, one speaks of a **cyclic process** or a **cycle,** which thus leads from a given state through a sequence of changes back to the original state.   For example, the temperature of an isobaric (constant-pressure) system may be increased by performing frictional work, and then lowered to the original value by the removal of heat.   For any *cycle* and any state function X,

$$\Delta X = 0 \qquad\qquad (1\text{--}5)$$

A definition of state functions equivalent to that given earlier can be based on this property.

1–6   REVERSIBLE AND IRREVERSIBLE PATHS

Changes of state may be brought about along reversible or irreversible paths. A **reversible path** is one that may be followed in either direction. At any point the direction may be reversed by a small change in a variable such as the temperature or pressure.

Two examples will clarify what is meant. In the first, a cylinder containing a gas is equipped with a piston that exerts pressure on the gas. If this external pressure equals the internal pressure of the gas, there is equilibrium. By a slight decrease of the piston pressure the gas can be made to expand; by a slight increase, to contract. Suppose the gas is expanded by slowly decreasing the piston pressure so that at all times it is very slightly smaller than the pressure the gas exerts on the piston. Figure 1–1 shows the pressure P_{int} the gas exerts on the piston and the pressure P_{ext} the piston exerts on the gas, as the gas expands from state 1 to state 2. The smaller the pressure difference between piston and gas, the closer

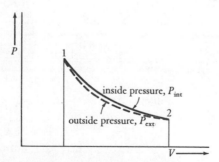

Figure 1–1   Pressure as a function of volume during the expansion of a gas. The gas expands only if there is a net force on the piston, requiring that the outside pressure is slightly below the inside pressure all along. This makes the expansion irreversible. The expansion is reversible only in the limit that the dashed curve matches the solid curve. Reversible expansion would require an infinite time and is therefore an idealized concept. For reversible expansion equilibrium would exist at every point of the expansion.

the lower curve lies to the upper curve and the slower the rate at which the gas expands. In the idealized case where the two curves coincide, expansion takes an infinite time, because there is no pressure difference left to act on the piston. In fact, in this limiting case, expansion can be changed into compression by an *infinitesimal* increase of the outside pressure, compression into expansion by an infinitesimal decrease of the outside pressure. Only under these circumstances is the expansion of the gas reversible. Reversible expansion of a gas is thus an idealized concept that can be carried out in thought only. *Any actual expansion is irreversible.*

The second example concerns an electrochemical cell of a certain potential υ that is opposed by an outside potential. There is no chemical reaction in the cell and no current flow when the two potentials match. When the magnitude of the outside potential is smaller than that of the cell by an infinitesimal amount, the cell acts as a galvanic cell; an infinitesimal current flows, and the electrochemical reaction of the cell proceeds infinitesimally slowly in the appropriate direction. In the opposite case, the cell acts as an electrolytic cell; the current flow is reversed and the reaction proceeds in the opposite direction. To make the cell reaction proceed *reversibly*, cell potential and outside potential would have to be equal to each other at all times. The cell would be held precisely in check by the outside potential at all times and the reaction would proceed infinitely slowly.

A reversible process is quite generally an idealized concept that represents the limit of a sequence of irreversible processes for which the parameter changes required to reverse the direction become smaller and smaller. At the limit it proceeds infinitely slowly through a *sequence of equilibrium states*. It is usually taken for granted that the external and internal values of a variable have to differ by a small amount to make the processes actually occur.

Reversible processes are very important in thermodynamic arguments. They represent idealizations that can be carried out in thought only, which is one reason why many thermodynamic arguments are based on the analysis of thought experiments.

Typical **irreversible processes** are (1) the flow of heat from a hot to a cold body, (2) the expansion of a gas into a vacuum, (3) the temperature increase of a system by the performance of friction work, and (4) the dissolving of sugar in water.

Irreversibility does not imply that it is impossible to force a process in the reverse direction, but rather that such a reversal cannot be achieved simply by changing parameters by infinitesimal amounts. Irreversible processes are also called **spontaneous,** even though they may proceed infinitely slowly. Other names are **actual** or **natural** processes, and the direction in which such processes occur or tend to occur is called the **natural direction.** *All actually occurring processes are irreversible.*

1–7 WORK

A system frequently performs **work** on the surroundings, or the surroundings may perform work on a system. This work may be mechanical, electrical, magnetic, etc. Work exists, however, only at the time it is performed, and thus is a *form of energy transfer.* As always in thermodynamics, it is only *macroscopic work* that is considered, not work on an atomic level. Thus, while work is performed when a fast-moving molecule is slowed by collision with a second molecule that is thereby sped up this does not constitute macroscopic work and is not counted. Work is denoted by w and is counted positive when performed by the surroundings on the system and negative otherwise. As will be seen, work is not a state function, and to emphasize this we use w rather than Δw for the work involved in a change of state. Similarly, Dw rather than dw is used to denote an infinitesimal quantity of work. The symbols Δ and d (as in ΔX and dX) are reserved for state functions, so that state functions and nonstate functions can be kept clearly distinct.

An important type of work is **expansion work,** work performed when a system expands against an outside pressure P_{ext}. It is always assumed here that such expansion does not impart kinetic energy to the movable parts of the boundary. Expansion work is considered negative, because it is performed on the surroundings.

As a special case, consider the system to be a substance contained in a cylinder of cross section A with a movable (frictionless) piston (Figure 1–2). The piston is to be moved a distance dl against an external pressure P_{ext}. The work Dw performed by the system is Fdl, where $F = P_{ext}A$ is the force exerted by the piston on the system. Thus $Dw = -P_{ext}A \, dl$. The important minus sign arises from the fact that for a positive dl (that is, an expansion) the system performs work on the surroundings which by our convention represents negative work. Since $A \, dl$ is the volume increase dV of the system,

$$Dw = -P_{ext} \, dV \qquad (1\text{–}6)$$

For a finite change in volume the external pressure P_{ext} need not remain constant during the change in volume. It is, however, supposed to be known for each point of the path along which the system expands. It may be given as a function of the temperatures T and volumes V that the system is to assume, $P = P(V, T)$. Thus for a finite change in volume,

$$w = -\int_{1}^{2} P_{ext}(V, T) \, dV \qquad (1\text{–}7)$$

The limits of the integral denote the initial and final states of the system.

As suggested by their general form, the expressions for Dw and w just given are not restricted to the simple cylinder and piston

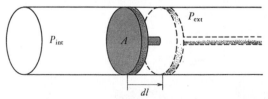

Figure 1–2 Expansion work. When the gas expands and moves the piston of area A by a distance dl, it performs the work $F \, dl$, where $F = AP_{ext}$. The volume increase of the gas is $dV = A \, dl$ and the work is thus $P_{ext}A \, dl = P_{ext} \, dV$. This is equal to $-Dw$, because work is performed on the surroundings when dV is positive.

arrangement for which they were derived.   They apply to any
expansion work.   In other words, changing the volume of any
system of completely irregular shape by dV against an external
pressure P_{ext} entails the work $Dw = -P_{ext}\, dV$.

In the important special case in which the outside pressure remains constant during a finite expansion of the system, P_{ext} may be
moved in front of the integral sign in (1–7), so that

$$w = -P_{ext}\int_1^2 dV = -P(V_2 - V_1) = -P\,\Delta V \qquad (1\text{–}8)$$

The subscript "ext" has been dropped in the latter half of
(1–8) because the context should imply that it is P_{ext} that is meant.
The subscripts "int" and "ext" will be used sparingly.   In their
absence it is always important to reflect whether a given P indicates
the internal or the external pressure.

A particular case of expansion against a constant pressure is
that of zero outside pressure, when $w = 0$.   *A system that expands into
a vacuum therefore performs no work.*

As a further important example, consider the *reversible* expansion of an *ideal gas* at constant temperature T, in which the
external pressure P_{ext} is successively reduced so that it always
balances the internal pressure P_{int} (Figure 1–3).   By the ideal gas
equation,

$$P_{ext} = P_{int} = \frac{nRT}{V} \qquad (1\text{–}9)$$

and thus

$$w = -\int_1^2 P_{ext}\, dV = -nRT\int_1^2 \frac{dV}{V} = -nRT \ln\left(\frac{V_2}{V_1}\right) \qquad (1\text{–}10)$$

Figure 1–4 is a pressure-volume diagram of this process; the colored
area represents the work performed by the system and is therefore
equal to $-w$.   As will be seen later, heat has to be supplied to the
system to keep the temperature of the expanding gas constant.

When a system contracts, w is positive, because the surroundings

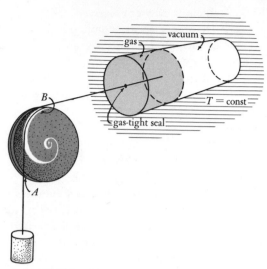

Figure 1–3   Machine for the reversible expansion of a perfect gas. In this idealized machine the right boundary of the gas is formed by a weightless disk that exerts a torque on a wheel, the disk being connected by a string to the rim of the wheel at point *A*. An opposite torque is supplied by a weight pulling on a second string. This string, attached to the wheel at *B*, runs in a groove that forms a helical spiral on the side of the wheel. As the gas expands, the pressure on the weightless disk is reduced and so is the torque that tends to turn the wheel clockwise. At the same time the torque in the opposite direction is decreased because the lever arm by which the weight is able to turn the wheel becomes shorter as the wheel rotates clockwise. The shape of the spiraling groove is such that the two torques exactly balance at all times.

now perform work on the system. This can be seen explicitly in (1–8) and (1–10) for the special cases considered there. In both equations the right side becomes positive when V_2 is smaller than V_1. The area in Figure 1–4 has to be counted negative, when the direction of the path is in the direction of the arrow shown, and positive when in the other direction. There is no need to discuss expansion and contraction work separately, since the formulas take the sign into account automatically.

For a cyclic process involving pressure-volume work only, w is the area enclosed by the path in a PV diagram (Fig. 1–5) when the path corresponds to counterclockwise rotation, to the negative of the area for clockwise rotation.

The work w that is transferred in a given process is an **extensive** quantity; if the system is increased to twice its size by doubling the amounts of all substances involved, etc., w also increases by a factor of 2.

For a given change in state, the work transferred depends on the path. A particularly interesting example is the isothermal expansion of a gas into a chamber that is originally completely evacuated (Fig. 1–6). The system consists of the contents of the entire apparatus of volume V_2, with a gas of volume V_1 and pressure P_1 on the left, and vacuum on the right. It is surrounded by a constant-temperature bath of temperature T. A hole in the center wall is at first closed by a frictionless valve that can be operated

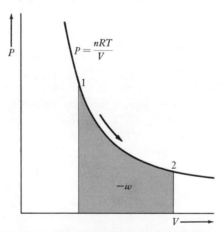

Figure 1–4   Reversible expansion of an ideal gas. When a gas is expanded the work performed is $\int_1^2 P\ dV$, which is equal to $-w$ because the work is performed on the surroundings. The integral is equal to the colored area. For an ideal gas at a constant temperature T and reversible expansion, the external pressure must be equal to the ideal gas pressure $P = nRT/V$.

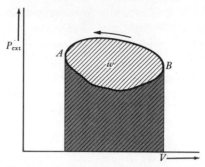

Figure 1–5 Pressure-volume work for a cyclic process. When
the path is traversed in the direction of the arrow, the area enclosed by the path is equal to w, being the difference between the
hatched and the colored areas: The hatched area is the work performed *on the system* during the compressive phase of the cycle, as
P_{ext} and V move from B to A on the upper part of the curve. The
colored area is the work performed *by the system* during the expan-
sive phase, as the lower part of the curve is traversed from A to B.

     When the path is traversed in the direction opposite to that
of the arrow, the area enclosed by the path equals $-w$.

without performing work on the system. When the hole is opened
the gas expands, and eventually fills the total volume V_2 at a uniform
equilibrium pressure P_2 that is determined by the values of V_2 and T.
No work is performed on the surroundings *and w is zero.*

     A given change in state of the gas, from V_1 and P_1 to V_2 and P_2,
at constant T, may, of course, be achieved in many other ways, and
w may be different for any two of them. The gas may be expanded
along a reversible path, as described earlier for the special case of
an ideal gas, Eq. (1–10). This is indeed the path for which the
integral $\int_1^2 P_{ext}\, dV$ for the change of state considered is a *maximum.*
All along this path P_{ext} equals P_{int} (except for an infinitesimal
amount), and at no point could P_{ext} be increased (thus increasing
the integral) without changing the expansion into a compression
[Figure 1–7(a)]. The outside pressure may, however, be made
smaller than P_{int} for any portion of the path. For this changed
portion of the path the contribution to the integral would be decreased, and in addition the expansion would not be reversible,

because it could not be changed into a compression by an infinitesimal increase of P_{ext}. It is apparent that the reversible path is the *only* path for which the integral considered has its *maximum* value. For any *actual* path, this integral, the work $-w$ performed by the system on the surroundings, is less than this maximum value. Therefore,

$$-w_{\text{act}} \leqslant -w_{\text{rev}} \qquad (1\text{--}11)$$

Consider now the opposite case, the compression of a perfect gas. In any actual case, P_{ext} must be larger than P_{int}, to overcome friction and to make the piston move [Fig. 1–7(b)]. The work performed on the system, w_{act}, is therefore larger than the work that would be necessary for compression along the idealized path of a continuous chain of equilibrium states. Therefore, in this case,

$$w_{\text{act}} \geqslant w_{\text{rev}} \qquad (1\text{--}12)$$

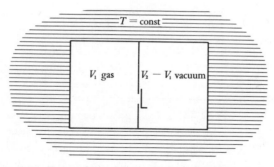

Figure 1–6 Expansion of a gas into an evacuated chamber. When the valve is opened, gas from the left chamber streams into the vacuum until the pressures on both sides of the opening have become equal. An intelligent choice of the system makes a thermodynamic analysis possible, even though the flow of the gas is highly turbulent, particularly at the beginning, so that the path the expansion follows is not defined: Let the system include the contents of both chambers, so that the work performed on the surroundings is zero (overlooking any work used to move the valve). The temperatures at the beginning and end are the same because of the constant-temperature bath.

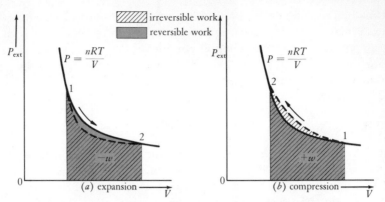

Figure 1–7 Reversible and irreversible work. During an actual *expansion* (a) the external pressure (dashed line) is always below the internal pressure (solid line), reaching the solid line only in the limiting case of a reversible expansion. The hatched area represents thus the irreversible, actual work and the colored area the reversible work; the areas represent $-w$ because work is done on the surroundings. The hatched area is smaller than the colored area.

During an actual *compression* (b) the external pressure is always above the internal pressure, except in the idealized limit of reversible compression. The hatched area (irreversible work) is now larger than the colored area (reversible work), but the areas now represent $+w$, because work is done on the system.

Note, however, that (1–11) and (1–12) have the same content when the signs are taken into consideration.[1] It is true for both compression and expansion that for a given change in state the work performed *by the system* is a maximum for a reversible path

$$-w_{\text{act}} \leqslant -w_{\text{rev}} = (-w)_{\text{max}} \tag{1–13}$$

A proposition analogous to the one that led to (1–11) holds for the electrical work performed by an electrochemical cell against an outside potential. As we shall see in Section 1–9, when an electric charge Q is moved against a potential $\mathcal{V}$ the work involved is the

---

[1] The handling of inequalities is discussed in Appendix 2.

product v_Q. This work reaches its maximum value when the outside potential is as large as possible; that is, when v is adjusted at all times to be only infinitesimally smaller than the cell potential. The maximum electrical work performed is thus achieved for a reversible path only, $-w_{act} \leqslant -w_{rev}$. For the opposite case, when work is performed on the cell by an outside potential, the relationship $w_{act} \geqslant w_{rev}$ obtains for a given change of state. Again the relationship (1–13) applies to both cases. As will be seen later, it is a consequence of the second law of thermodynamics that the maximum amount of work *any* system may perform on the surroundings, at constant temperature, is achieved for a reversible path only.

The discussion of the preceding pages shows that the work transferred during a change of state depends on the path. Work is not a state function.

1–8 HEAT AND HEAT CAPACITIES

The state of a system may be changed by permitting heat to flow into or out of it. Heat flow is a method of energy transfer analogous to the transfer of work. It is important for clarity to speak of heat only in connection with heat transfer. It is as meaningless to say a system contains heat as to say it contains work. A system may only contain *energy*, and this is discussed in more detail shortly. To give an analogous example from mechanics, a wound spring contains potential energy that may be used to perform work, but it does not therefore contain work. A hot body may transfer heat to a colder body, but it does not therefore contain heat.

The erroneous idea that a system may contain heat has historical origins, because heat was for a long time considered to be a fluid called the **caloric.** A body was thought to contain more caloric when hot than when cold. This notion must be guarded against, particularly since it is still implied by many customary expressions such as "heat flow." Another illustration is the constant-temperature bath referred to earlier, which is often called a **heat reservoir.** The constant-temperature bath does not contain heat, only energy. It may, however, supply or take up heat, and in *this* sense it is a heat reservoir.

In this book the same **sign convention** is used for heat as for work. That is, heat that is introduced into a system from the surroundings is counted positive, heat flowing from the system into the surroundings, negative.[1] Heat is an extensive quantity, as is work.

Heat always flows from a body of higher temperature to a body of lower temperature. Any *actual* heat transfer requires a temperature inequality, however small. It is an irreversible process like all actual processes. The transfer of heat is *reversible* only at temperature equality, when system and surroundings are at equilibrium. It is, as are all reversible processes, an idealized process, the limit of actual heat transfer at ever-smaller temperature differences.

The quantity of heat q that is necessary to change the state of a system depends on the path and is not a state function. Again q, rather than Δq, is used to emphasize this, and Dq rather than dq. For example, 1 liter of $H_2O(l)$ may be heated from 20 to 30°C by introducing heat, by operating a stirrer, by doing both, or by still other means. The heat q required is completely indefinite unless the path is known. It may even be negative (heat may have to be removed from the system), when an excessive amount of work is performed on the system; conversely it may be indefinitely large, because the system may be made to perform work on the surroundings.

The heat required to raise the temperature of 1 mole of a system by 1°C is called its **heat capacity** C. If the system is 1 mole of a pure substance, one speaks of the **molar heat capacity** of the substance. The analogous quantity for 1 g of substance is called the **specific heat capacity,** so that the molar heat capacity is the specific heat capacity multiplied by the molecular weight. For substances not consisting of molecules such as NaCl, one may be interested in the "formal" heat capacity, the specific heat capacity multiplied by

---

[1] In many texts work transferred to the system is counted negative, heat positive. It is particularly natural in the discussion of heat engines to do this, to count the heat introduced and the work performed positive. Unfortunately, there is no uniformity in the usage of these signs, but many recent texts treat work and heat the same way and count them positive when transferred from the surroundings to the system.

the formula weight. This is also usually referred to as molar heat capacity.

Frequently, other extensive quantities are transformed into **intensive** quantities—independent of amounts—by dividing them by the number of moles or gram-formula weights involved, so that they apply to 1 mole or 1 formula weight of substance. All such intensive quantities are given the attribute "molar." Examples are the molar volume, the molar energy, and the molar entropy. They are all denoted by symbols with a *tilde*, such as $\tilde{V}$, $\tilde{U}$, and $\tilde{S}$. The molar heat capacity is given the symbol C.

The molar heat capacity depends on the conditions under which the temperature increase is to occur, or, in other words, on the path. Two frequent situations are heating at constant pressure and heating at constant volume. The corresponding molar heat capacities are denoted by $\tilde{C}_P$ and $\tilde{C}_V$, the subscript indicating the quantity that is kept constant during heating. For gases the difference between $\tilde{C}_P$ and $\tilde{C}_V$ is considerable, as is explained in Section 2–2, while it is much smaller for liquids or solids.

The molar heat capacity of a substance depends on its temperature. It takes 17.98 cal/mole-deg to raise the temperature of 1 mole of water from 25 to 26°C and 18.12 cal/mole-deg to raise it from 95 to 96°C. (Units are discussed in the next section.) It is therefore more precise to define the molar heat capacity $\tilde{C}_X$ by the differential relationship

$$Dq_X = C_X \, dT = n\tilde{C}_X \, dT \qquad (1\text{--}14)$$

where Dq_X is the heat required to raise the temperature of n moles of substance from T to $T + dT$ along the path X.

The change of C_P and $\tilde{C}_V$ with temperature, in a range of some ten or even hundred °C, is usually small and will be neglected unless indicated otherwise. Thus, if n moles of substance are to be heated (or cooled) isobarically from T_1 to T_2, the amount of heat involved is

$$q \approx n\tilde{C}_P(T_2 - T_1) = n\tilde{C}_P \, \Delta T \qquad (1\text{--}15)$$

If q is positive, the heat has to be supplied; if negative, it is liberated.

1–9 UNITS OF WORK AND HEAT

Several units of *work* are useful in thermodynamics.   Among them are the joule, the erg, and the liter-atmosphere.   The joule is the unit appropriate to the mks (meter-kilogram-second) system and is closely related to common electrical units, as will be seen.   The erg belongs in the cgs (centimeter-gram-second) system, and the liter-atmosphere is commonly used for pressure-volume work, as explained below.

The unit of force in the mks system is the **newton,** the force that accelerates a mass of 1 kg by 1 m/sec^2; it is thus also 1 kg-m/sec^2. The unit of work, the **joule** is the work performed by 1 newton along a path of 1 m.   One joule is thus also 1 kg-m^2/sec^2.

In the cgs system the force unit is the **dyne,** the force that accelerates 1 gram by 1 cm/sec^2.   The unit of work is the **erg,** equal to the work performed by 1 dyne acting for 1 cm.   One erg is thus 1 g-cm^2/sec^2 so that

$$1 \text{ joule} = (1 \text{ kg-m}^2/\text{sec}^2) \times (10^3 \text{ g/kg}) \times (10^4 \text{ cm}^2/\text{m}^2) = 10^7 \text{ ergs}$$

$$(1\text{–}16)$$

The joule can also be related to electrical quantities.   It is the work performed when 1 coulomb of electricity flows through a potential of 1 volt: 1 joule = 1 volt-coulomb.   In other words, the product of electrical potential and charge represents work.   This may be made more plausible by the following argument.   We start with the fact that the watt-second is an energy unit.   This should be familiar to anyone who has paid an electricity bill, because the kilowatt-hour (kwhr), equal to 1000 watt-hours, is the customary unit of energy on the bill.   The watt is thus a unit of power, of energy per unit time, and the energy represented by a current flowing for a certain time is the product of its power and this time. Next, we note that the wattage of a current is the product of its voltage and amperage, 1 watt = 1 volt-amp.   The energy unit of 1 watt-sec is thus also 1 volt-amp-sec.   Finally, 1 amp flowing for 1 sec represents the electric charge of 1 coulomb, so that 1 amp-sec equals 1 coulomb and thus 1 watt-sec = 1 volt-amp-sec = 1 volt-coulomb. The volt-coulomb is thus an energy unit, and happens to be identical with the joule, as already mentioned. Thus

$$1 \text{ joule} = 1 \text{ volt-coulomb} = 1 \text{ watt-sec} \qquad (1-17)$$

and corresponding power units are

$$1 \text{ joule/sec} = 1 \text{ volt-amp} = 1 \text{ watt} \qquad (1-18)$$

You should remember that the product of charge and electrical potential represents work, just as does the product of force and distance.

Before discussing the units convenient for pressure-volume work we need a word on *pressure units*. The units used in this book are the atmosphere and the torr. The **torr** is identical with the **mm Hg,** the pressure exerted by a column of mercury 1 mm high. It is named after the noted Italian scientist Torricelli, inventor of the barometer. The **standard atmosphere (atm)** is the average pressure of the atmosphere at sea level and equals 760 torr. Pressure is force per area and 1 atm happens to be very close to the pressure exerted by a weight of 1 kg on an area of 1 cm² at the earth's surface; more exactly, 1 atm = 1.0332 kg/cm².[1] The pressure unit in the mks system is the newton per square meter, and 1 atm equals 101,325 newtons/m². This is, in fact, the present *definition* of the atmosphere. It corresponds to 1.01325×10^6 dynes/cm² in the cgs system:

$$1 \text{ atm} = 760 \text{ torr} = 1.0332 \text{ kg/cm}^2 = 101,325 \text{ newtons/m}^2$$
$$= 1.01325 \times 10^6 \text{ dynes/cm}^2$$

The unit frequently used for volume-pressure work is the **liter-atmosphere** (liter-atm), obtained when the volume is expressed in liters and the pressure in atmospheres. To convert liter-atmospheres to joules we remember that 1 joule is 1 newton-m and that 1 liter is 1000.028 cm³ or 1.000028×10^{-3} m³:

---

[1] This is the *weight* unit, or the kilopoise as it is sometimes called, not the mass unit.

$$1 \text{ liter-atm} = 101{,}325 \text{ (newtons/m}^2\text{)} \times 1.000028 \times 10^{-3} \text{ m}^3$$
$$= 101.328 \text{ joules} \qquad (1\text{-}19)$$

Units of heat that are commonly used by scientists are the **calorie** (cal) and the **kilocalorie** (kcal), the latter equal to 1000 cal. The calorie was for many years defined as the amount of heat required to raise the temperature of 1 g of water from 14.5 to 15.5°C. By international agreement it is now associated with the joule, and the calorie, or, more precisely, the **thermochemical calorie** is *defined* to be 4.1840 joules:

$$1 \text{ cal} = 4.1840 \text{ joules} = 4.1840 \times 10^7 \text{ ergs} \qquad (1\text{-}20)$$

Conversion factors between units of work and heat are contained in Table 1–2 and facing page 1.

The units given the *gas constant R* are often liter-atm/mole-deg, but it is useful to know R in other energy units per mole-degree as well:

$$R = 0.082053 \text{ liter-atm/mole-deg}$$
$$= 8.3143 \text{ joules/mole-deg} = 1.9872 \text{ cal/mole-deg} \qquad (1\text{-}21)$$

Note that RT is always an energy per mole.

In terms of work the calorie is a large unit. This will be apparent from several examples.

EXAMPLE 1

How many meters can 1 kg be lifted by the energy represented by 1 cal? How many feet can 1 lb be lifted? The work needed to lift 1 kg by 1 m is 9.80 kg-m²/sec² or 9.80 joules, because the earth acceleration is 9.80 m/sec². Thus 1 kg can be lifted by 4.1840 joules/9.80 (joule/m) = **0.427 m.** Next, 1 kg equals 2.20 lb and 1 ft equals 0.305 m. Thus 1 lb can be lifted by a 2.20-times larger distance than the kilogram, or by 2.20 × 0.427 m/0.305 (m/ft) = **3.08 ft.** We may thus say that 1 cal = 0.427 m-kg = 3.08 ft-lb, keeping in mind that the last two units are weight units and not mass units.

For chemical reactions the kilocalorie is more useful than the calorie. For example, the heat of combustion of 1 g of wood is about 4 kcal, and since the weight of a kitchen match is about 0.5 g, the heat liberated by burning half a kitchen match is roughly 1 kcal. The heat of combustion of 1 g of sugar or of 1 g of starch is also about 4 kcal. This is not surprising, since sugar, wood, and starch are closely related chemically.

EXAMPLE 2

How high can a person weighing 123 lb be lifted by fully utilizing the energy in 10 g of sugar? Using the result of Example 1, 40×10^3 cal would suffice to lift 1 lb by $40 \times 10^3 \times 0.308$ ft = 12,300 ft, or 123 lb by $(12,300/123)$ ft = **1000 ft.**

Thus to work off the energy in a well-sugared cup of tea a climb of 1000 ft would be about right, if all sugar were to go into climbing energy, which is far from true. Even when resting, an adult human uses up some 70 to 80 kcal/hour. Moderate exercise may triple this quantity, and heavy work may raise the energy requirement by a factor of 5 or 10. In these terms, 10 g of sugar would keep a resting adult going for some 30 minutes, but he would need considerably more when working.

Confusion may arise because the calorie of nutritionists is the kilocalorie of chemists. Sometimes the abbreviation Cal with a capital C is used to designate kilocalories.

Table 1–2
Conversion Factors

		cal	joules	liter-atm
1 cal	=	1	4.1840	0.041291
1 joule	=	0.23901	1	0.0098689
1 liter-atm	=	24.218	101.328	1

EXAMPLE 3

The heat of combustion of 1 g of gasoline is 11.5 kcal, which comes to about 29,400 kcal/gal. If it were possible to convert this energy completely into work, how high could 1 metric ton (1000 kg or 2200 lb) be lifted? Again referring to Example 1, 1 cal would suffice to lift 1 kg by 0.427 m. Thus, 1 gal of gasoline could lift 1 kg by $29,400 \times 10^3 \times 0.427$ m $= 12.6 \times 10^6$ m, or 1000 kg by **12.6 km.** Since 1 mile equals 16.1 m, this corresponds to **7.8 miles.**

The following examples illustrate calculations of pressure-volume work.

EXAMPLE 4

Suppose that 1 mole of perfect gas at 25°C and 5.00 atm is expanded *irreversibly* against the constant outside pressure of 1 atm until the internal pressure has been lowered to 1 atm. The expansion is to be at constant T, by addition of heat energy as required. What is w for this case?

The initial volume is

$$V_1 = RT/P = 1 \text{ mole} \times 0.0821 \text{ (liter-atm/mole-deg)}$$
$$\times 298 \text{ deg}/5.00 \text{ atm} = 4.893 \text{ liters}$$

The final volume is five times larger, or $V_2 = 24.47$ liters.

The work performed on the system is, by (1–8),

$$w = -P \, \Delta V = -P(V_2 - V_1) = -1 \text{ atm} (24.47 - 4.89) \text{ liters}$$
$$= -19.58 \text{ liter-atm}$$

Converted to calories this is $w =$ **−473.9 cal.**

EXAMPLE 5

The same gas considered in Example 4 is expanded *reversibly* from 5.00 to 1.00 atm at 25°C. What is w for this second path? The volumes V_1 and V_2 are the same as in Example 4.

The work performed on the system is, by (1–10),

$$w = -RT \ln \frac{V_2}{V_1} = 1 \text{mole} \times 1.987 \text{ (cal/mole-deg)}$$
$$\times 298 \text{ deg} \times \ln 5$$

Using $\ln 5 = 2.303 \log 5 = 2.303 \times 0.69897$ and multiplying all factors, $w = -953.1$ **cal.**

The work performed on the surroundings along the irreversible path of Example 4 is smaller than along the reversible path of Example 5, as it must be. It may be asked how the irreversible expansion that constitutes the path of Example 4 might actually be performed. One possible method is shown in Fig. 1–8. The container holding the gas is connected to a cylinder with a piston that moves up slowly so as to maintain a pressure of just 1 atm in the space underneath it. A porous plug prevents the expanding gas that is at a pressure above 1 atm from acting directly on the frictionless piston and imparting kinetic energy to it, which would represent work other than the pressure-volume work performed by the gas.

PROBLEMS

1–1. *The Rankine scale*. The Rankine scale is proportional to the Kelvin scale and the temperature difference between the boiling

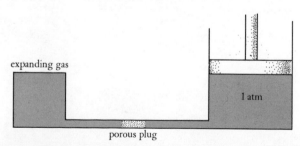

Figure 1–8 Expansion of a gas against a constant outside pressure. The gas to be expanded has an initial pressure of 5 atm. As it expands the piston is permitted to rise so that the pressure in the compartment on the right stays at 1 atm. The porous plug impedes the expansion sufficiently to keep it orderly.

point of water at 1 atm pressure and the freezing point of water when saturated with air of 1 atm pressure (273.15°K) is 180° Rankine. From the information given, find the temperatures of these two fix points on the Rankine scale.

1–2. *Absolute zero temperature.* The densities of air at 0°C and 100°C are, respectively, 1.293 and 0.946 g/liter. Find a value of absolute zero in degree Celsius, assuming that air obeys the perfect gas law.

1–3. *Thermal interaction.* A penny weighing 3.1 g is heated to 500°C and dropped into a beaker containing 100 ml of water at 20°C. What is the temperature when thermal interaction has ceased? Assume that the specific heat capacities are 1.00 cal/g-deg for water and 0.094 cal/g-deg for the penny.

1–4. *Heating water.* One liter of water at 20°C is heated by a 110-volt 1-amp current for 10 min. What is the final temperature? (Note that if alternating current is used, voltage and amperage given represent average values, because of their sinusoidal oscillations. The averages given are appropriate to give average watts when multiplied together.) The specific heat capacity C_P for H_2O is 1 cal/g-deg.

1–5. *Gas constant.* Express the gas constant R in joules per mole-degree, where the degree refers to the Rankine rather than the Kelvin scale.

1–6. *Expansion of a gas.* Four moles of a perfect gas are expanded reversibly at 25°C from 80 to 120 liters. Find w in calories and liter-atmospheres.

2 The First Law of Thermodynamics

*T*he state functions energy and enthalpy are the subjects of this chapter, with particular emphasis on enthalpy. *Enthalpies of reaction and standard enthalpies are defined, and the temperature dependence of enthalpy is developed and used to estimate flame and explosion temperatures. Further topics are bond enthalpies and resonance energy.*

2–1 STATEMENT OF THE LAW

When the state of a system is changed, transfer of the heat q and of the work w may be involved. As discussed, both q and w depend on the path. However—and this is the content of the first law—*the sum $q + w$ is independent of the path.* This combination can therefore be associated with the increase ΔU of a *function of state U,*

$$\Delta U = q + w \tag{2–1}$$

which is called the **internal energy** (Greek: *en*, in; *ergon*, work) of the system.

The adjective "internal" implies that other kinds of energy may be associated with the system. For example, the whole system may be in motion and therefore possess kinetic energy. The attribute "internal" is often omitted, because there are usually no grounds for confusion.

To give an example of a change in the internal energy of a substance, we consider the heating of 1 mole of liquid water from 0 to 100°C. The change in energy is 1.8 kcal, and is the same regardless of the form in which this energy is transferred to the water—by heating, by performing work as by swirling an eggbeater, by electrical means, or in any other way.

Because q and w are always zero for an *isolated system*, it follows

34

that ΔU is always zero for such a system. *The energy of an isolated system is constant.* Clausius concluded that the energy of the universe is therefore constant, but this statement rests on cosmological assumptions that may be incorrect.

It also follows from the first law that

$$\Delta U_{\text{system}} = -\Delta U_{\text{surroundings}}$$

The first law stated in this form prohibits the existence of a machine that creates work without compensating changes elsewhere in the universe. The forbidden machine is called a **perpetuum mobile,** or more precisely, a perpetuum mobile of the first kind, because it would violate the first law (Figure 2–1). The restriction is needed because the second law of thermodynamics prohibits a more subtle kind of perpetuum mobile, said to be of the second kind.

Equation (2–1) defines only *changes* of the internal energy, and not the internal energy itself. The *absolute internal energy* of a system remains undefined in thermodynamics, and an arbitrary additive constant may be chosen as is convenient. Microscopically, the inter-

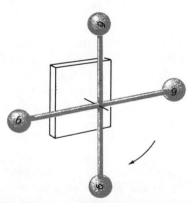

Figure 2–1 Tolman's perpetual motion machine. In his lectures on thermodynamics Professor R. C. Tolman used to delight in presenting this tongue-in-cheek example of a perpetuum mobile of the first kind. The numbers indicate weights, in arbitrary units.

nal energy of a substance is the entire energy of its atoms or molecules, kinetic and potential. This energy can be changed only by
interactions with the outside, and the total change is independent of
the detailed path. For thermodynamic considerations a detailed
analysis of the many interactions on the molecular level is not needed.

The energy of a given amount of a phase depends on the temperature T and the volume V: $U = U(T,V)$. The independent
variables may be replaced by other pairs, such as P and T, or U
itself may be chosen as one of the independent variables.

2–2 MOLAR HEAT CAPACITIES AND THE FIRST LAW

To change the temperature of a substance from T to $T + dT$
by heat transfer alone, the heat $Dq_X = C_X \, dT$ is required, where
X specifies the path along which the temperature change is to occur.
For the case of pressure-volume work only, $Dw = -P \, dV$. Thus
$Dq = dU + P \, dV$, and if, in addition, the volume is kept constant,
$dV = 0$ and $Dq_V = dU$. Therefore, $Dq_V = C_V \, dT = dU$, and
finally,

$$C_V = \left(\frac{dU}{dT}\right)_V \qquad\qquad (2\text{–}2)$$

This equation may be taken as the thermodynamic definition of C_V.
The restriction to pressure-volume work can be dropped, because
U is a state function, so that dU is independent of the details of the
path. The subscript V of the term on the right is a reminder that
U depends in general not only on T but also on V, and that in the
differentiation V is to be treated as a constant.[1]

---

[1] This derivative is usually written $(\partial U/\partial T)_V$ and called a partial
derivative. The symbol ∂ implies that U may depend on other variables
also, variables that are treated as constant when forming the derivative.
If you are familiar with partial derivatives, you may feel that the subscript
V is redundant, as it is understood that all variables other than the one considered are kept constant. However, the independent variables are frequently changed in thermodynamics, and the subscripts are used to keep
tabs. For example, $(\partial U/\partial T)_V$ implies that the independent variables are

It is an important property of the **perfect gas** that U is a function of T only, $U = U(T)$. In this particular case no subscript is needed on the right side of (2–2),

$$C_V = \frac{dU(T)}{dT} \tag{2–3}$$

It is easy to understand that for a perfect gas U is independent of the volume, because a perfect gas corresponds to the limiting case of zero intermolecular forces. Upon isothermal expansion there are thus no intermolecular attractions to overcome that could store potential energy, and the internal energy does not change. This fact—that for a perfect gas U is independent of V—can also be derived from the perfect gas equation by using the second law of thermodynamics (Section 5–7).

When a substance is heated at *constant pressure*, the volume is no longer constant and $P\,dV$ is no longer zero. If there is pressure-volume work only,

$$Dq_P = C_P\,dT = dU - Dw = dU + P\,dV$$

and therefore

$$C_P = \left(\frac{dU}{dT}\right)_P + P\left(\frac{dV}{dT}\right)_P \tag{2–4}$$

The subscripts P on the right are a reminder that P must be kept constant in the differentiation. As was true for (2–2), this expression is valid generally, and the restriction to pressure-volume work may be dropped.

Again, for a perfect gas U is a function of T only, and the first term on the right of (2–4) equals C_V by (2–3). The second term can be found by treating P as a constant in the differentiation of $V = nRT/P$:

T and V, while $(\partial U/\partial T)_P$ implies that they are T and P. The two derivatives are different. Partial derivatives are important in any deeper development of thermodynamics, and an indication of their usefulness is given in Section 5–7.

$$P\left[\frac{d}{dT}\left(\frac{nRT}{P}\right)\right]_P = P\frac{nR}{P}\frac{dT}{dT} = nR$$

Finally, for 1 mole of a perfect gas

$$\tilde{C}_P = \tilde{C}_V + R \tag{2-5}$$

The difference between $\tilde{C}_P$ and $\tilde{C}_V$ is thus just the gas constant. For real gases (2–5) remains approximately true, because intermolecular attractions are small enough so that the work performed against them upon expansion is insignificant compared to the work performed against the outside pressure. This is, of course, not a thermodynamic consideration.

The magnitude of $\tilde{C}_P$ for gases ranges from about 5 to 8 cal/mole-deg and higher (see Appendix 4), while R is about 2 cal/mole-deg. The difference between $\tilde{C}_P$ and $\tilde{C}_V$ for gases is thus sizeable.

When a solid or a liquid expands, the work done against internal forces is some 10,000 times that done against the atmospheric pressure. The situation is just the reverse of that for gases. However, the volume expansion caused by heating is small, and the difference between $\tilde{C}_P$ and $\tilde{C}_V$ for the condensed phases is much smaller than it is for gases. In the special case in which there is no volume expansion upon heating (for example, for water at 4°C), $\tilde{C}_P$ equals $\tilde{C}_V$. Appendix 4 contains $\tilde{C}_P$ values at 25°C for a number of elements and compounds.

Chemists are often interested in the heat that is required or must be removed to keep the temperature constant when a chemical reaction proceeds. For *reactions* at *constant volume* there is no pressure-volume work and $w = 0$ in the absence of frictional work, expenditure of electrical energy, etc. Therefore, the heat q_V that has to be supplied to keep T constant equals the increase in internal energy,

$$q_V = \Delta U = U_{\text{prod}} - U_{\text{reac}} \tag{2-6}$$

It is customary to impose the restriction of constant temperature, but in fact (2–6) also holds when the temperature is permitted to change, being simply a statement of the first law when w is zero.

The **heat of reaction** at constant volume is defined as the heat liberated—that is, as $-q_V$. Thus when ΔU is negative, $(-q_V) = -\Delta U$ is positive, so that heat is liberated by the reaction; the reaction is **exothermic.** When ΔU is positive, heat is required and the reaction is **endothermic** (Greek: *endon*, within). Chemical processes are usually run in open vessels at atmospheric pressure, so that they take place at constant pressure rather than constant volume. For this reason it is not the heats of reaction at constant volume that are of primary interest but the heats of reaction at constant pressure. In fact, unspecified "heats of reaction" imply constant pressure. Such heats of reaction are considered at the end of Section 2–3.

2–3 ENTHALPY

When the volume is not kept constant, pressure-volume work must be taken into account. Although pressure-volume work may be of great importance, as it is for heat engines, it may also just be incidental, and this is the usual situation in chemistry. Chemical reactions are usually performed in vessels open to the atmosphere, so that the pressure during a reaction remains essentially constant. If gases are evolved or used up, or the volume of the system changes in any other way during the reaction, the resulting reversible pressure-volume work done on the system is, by (1–8),

$$-\int_1^2 P\,dV = -P(V_2 - V_1) = -P\,\Delta V \qquad (2\text{–}7)$$

For a reaction with volume increase or positive ΔV, the work $P\,\Delta V$ done on the surroundings is of no particular interest, but must nevertheless be taken into account, because the energy for it has to come from somewhere. Conversely, for a reaction with volume loss, or negative ΔV, the surroundings perform the work $-P\,\Delta V$ on the system automatically.

It would be handy to have a method to deal with this $P\,\Delta V$ work implicitly. Let the total work performed on the system be separated into two terms, the pressure-volume work $-P\,\Delta V$ and the remainder w', called the **net work:** $w = w' - P \, \Delta V$. What is thus needed is a formulation in which only the net work w' performed on the system,

$$w' = w + P \, \Delta V \qquad (2\text{-}8)$$

appears explicitly. This can be accomplished for isobaric processes by introducing a new function, the **enthalpy** H (Greek: *enthalpein*, to warm), defined by the equation

$$H = U + PV \qquad (2\text{-}9)$$

Because U, P, and V are functions of state, the enthalpy is one also. The enthalpy was introduced into thermodynamics by the American physicist and physical chemist J. Willard Gibbs, who was one of the founders of modern chemical thermodynamics. It will now be shown that for constant-pressure processes the use of H indeed takes pressure-volume work into account automatically.

Consider a particular change of state for which initial and final pressures are identical. This is often referred to as a change along a constant-pressure or isobaric path, but all that is really required here is that $P_{\text{initial}} = P_{\text{final}}$ so that $\Delta P = 0$. With these conditions,[1]

$$\Delta H = \Delta U + \Delta PV = \Delta U + P \, \Delta V \qquad (2\text{-}10)$$

We use (2–8) to introduce the net work w' into the first law, and obtain

$$\Delta U = q + w = q + w' - P \, \Delta V \qquad (2\text{-}11)$$
$$\Delta H = \Delta U + P \, \Delta V = q + w' \qquad (2\text{-}12)$$

It is seen that for an isobaric path only the net work w' appears in ΔH.

---

[1] Note that while $\Delta(PV) = P \, \Delta V$ when $P = \text{const}$, in general the expanded form of $\Delta(PV)$ is more complicated. By definition $\Delta(PV) = P_2 V_2 - P_1 V_1 = (P_1 + \Delta P)(V_1 + \Delta V) - P_1 V_1$; expanded, $\Delta(PV) = V_1 \, \Delta P + P_1 \, \Delta V + \Delta P \, \Delta V$. The last term must not be overlooked, even though the equation $d(PV) = P \, dV + V \, dP$ may tempt one to do so.

For a particular constant-pressure path for which the *net work* (but not necessarily the pressure-volume work) is *zero*,

$$\Delta H = H_{\text{prod}} - H_{\text{reac}} = q_P \qquad (2\text{--}13)$$

The enthalpy increase during an isobaric reaction is thus the heat q_P that has to be supplied in the absence of any but expansion work to satisfy the first law. Again the **heat of reaction** is defined as the heat liberated—that is, as $-q_P$. In this text we shall speak of the **enthalpy of reaction** rather than the heat of reaction. Constant-pressure processes are endothermic when ΔH is positive, exothermic when negative. The temperature is usually presumed to stay constant, but (2–13) is valid also when final and initial temperatures are different.

The heat capacity C_P is closely related to H. To increase the temperature of any substance from T to $T + dT$ at constant pressure involving only pressure-volume work, the heat

$$dq_P = dH = C_P \, dT$$

must be transferred to the system, and therefore

$$C_P = \left(\frac{dH}{dT}\right)_P \qquad (2\text{--}14)$$

This or the equivalent equation (2–4) may indeed serve as thermodynamic definitions of C_P. The limitation to pressure-volume work may be dropped, because all variables involved in (2–14) are state functions. For a perfect gas, $U = U(T)$ and $PV = nRT$, so that $H = U + nRT$ is a function of T only. Thus, with (2–3), and for 1 mole,

$$\tilde{C}_P = \frac{d\tilde{H}}{dT} = \frac{d\tilde{U}}{dT} + \frac{d(RT)}{dT} = \tilde{C}_V + R \qquad (2\text{--}15)$$

a result derived earlier by a more lengthy argument. This last development illustrates the usefulness of H.

Both C_P and C_V are always positive, and U and H always increase with temperature (V or P being kept unchanged).

When a solid substance melts, the increase in its enthalpy is called the **heat of fusion** or **enthalpy of fusion**. Similarly the increases in enthalpy that accompany the vaporization of a liquid or of a solid are called the **heats** or **enthalpies of vaporization and sublimation**. Constant pressure is, of course, implied. Table 2–1 gives examples that refer to 1 atm, to normal melting, boiling, or sublimation temperatures, as the case may be, and to 1 mole of substance. The table also contains examples of the enthalpy changes that accompany chemical reactions. Note that reversing a reaction implies a change in sign of the value of ΔH. The units of ΔH are usually **kilocalories**, and ΔH refers, as it always will in this book, to as many moles of reactants and products as are indicated by the coefficients of the over-all chemical equation given. Confusion may arise because of the following sign differences. Because of historical development, the terms heat of fusion, evaporation, and sublimation stand for the heat that is *required* to fuse, evaporate, or sublimate a substance; the heat of reaction is the heat *liberated* by a chemical reaction. This is the reason why it is best *not* to speak of *heats* of reaction, but rather of *the* ΔH, *the enthalpy change*, or just *the enthalpy of a reaction*.

Table 2–1
Enthalpy Changes for Some Phase Changes and Chemical Reactions

	Phase change or reaction	ΔH, kcal	t, °C
(1)	$H_2O(s) = H_2O(l)$	1.44	0
(2)	$H_2O(l) = H_2O(g)$	9.71	100
(3)	$Br_2(l) = Br_2(g)$	7.68	59
(4)	$I_2(s) = I_2(g)$	14.88	25[a]
(5)	$C(graphite) = C(g)$	171.70	25[a]
(6)	$C(graphite) + O_2(g) = CO_2(g)$	−94.05	25[a]
(7)	$CO(g) + \frac{1}{2}O_2(g) = CO_2(g)$	−67.63	25[a]
(8)	$H_2(g) + \frac{1}{2}O_2(g) = H_2O(l)$	−68.32	25[a]

[a] Not the equilibrium temperature at 1 atm.

In many texts the heat of reaction $-q_P$ is indicated in combination with the chemical equation, as shown by the following example:

$$H_2(g) + \tfrac{1}{2}O_2(g) = H_2O(l) + 68.32 \text{ kcal} \qquad (2\text{–}16)$$

It is important to realize that the 68.32 kcal on the right represent $-\Delta H$ of the reaction. The practice exemplified by (2–16) is not followed in this book.

It must be noted that for all the reactions in Table 2–1 values of ΔU could be listed also, as they could for any changes of state, whether or not they are at constant volume or pressure. The usefulness of ΔH is that for reactions at constant pressure the enthalpy decrease ΔH directly measures the heat used up by the reaction if there is pressure-volume work only. It equally indicates the net work w', the work other than pressure-volume work, that the reaction is capable of producing in the absence of heat evolution.

2–4 COMBINING ENTHALPIES OF REACTION

Being a function of state, the enthalpy increase for any change of state is independent of the path. This has important implications for the enthalpy changes of chemical reactions: When the chemical equations describing such reactions are added or otherwise combined into an equation describing a new reaction, the corresponding ΔH values, combined in the same way, yield the ΔH for the new reactions. This is because this ΔH does not depend on the actual course of the reaction. This important result is called the **Hess law of constant heat sums.**

The application of this law is illustrated by the two examples that follow:

EXAMPLE 1

The enthalpy increase that accompanies the combustion of graphite to carbon monoxide at 25°C can be obtained by noting that the equation of this reaction,

$$C(\text{graphite}) + \tfrac{1}{2}O_2(g) = CO(g)$$

may be obtained by subtracting reaction (7) of Table 2–1 from (6). The enthalpy change for the new reaction may therefore be obtained by subtracting ΔH of (7) from that of (6), $\Delta H = -94.05 - (-67.63) = $ **−26.42 kcal.** It is possible to combine graphite and oxygen to form CO not only directly, or as a sequence of (6) and (7), but along many other paths involving any number of steps. For all these paths the total of the ΔH values is -26.42 kcal.

Many reaction enthalpies have to be measured indirectly, by following a roundabout path leading from the reactants to the products, or from the products to the reactants. An experimental procedure that is often followed is to burn separately, in oxygen, all reactants and products that are combustible, to measure the **enthalpies of combustion,** and to combine the results. An example of this follows.

EXAMPLE 2

The enthalpy ΔH for the reaction

$$2C(graphite) + 2H_2(g) + H_2O(g) = C_2H_5OH(l) \quad (2\text{–}17)$$

can be found by measuring the enthalpies or heats of combustion of ethanol, graphite, and hydrogen:

$$C_2H_5OH(l) + 3O_2(g) = 2CO_2(g) + 3H_2O(g) \quad \Delta H_{18} = -258.39 \text{ kcal} \quad (2\text{–}18)$$

$$2C(graphite) + 2O_2(g) = 2CO_2(g) \quad \Delta H_{19} = -188.10 \text{ kcal} \quad (2\text{–}19)$$

$$2H_2(g) + O_2(g) = 2H_2O(g) \quad \Delta H_{20} = -136.64 \text{ kcal} \quad (2\text{–}20)$$

Inspection shows that the chemical equation in (2–17) is symbolically equal to (2–19) + (2–20) − (2–18) and thus $\Delta H_{17} = \Delta H_{19} + \Delta H_{20} - \Delta H_{18} = (-136.64 - 188.10 + 258.39)$ kcal = **−66.35 kcal.**

Enthalpies of reaction for simple gas molecules may often be obtained from spectroscopic data that yield their dissociation energy. The $P \Delta V$ term has to be supplied from other measurements, or from the perfect gas equation if the substances involved behave sufficiently as perfect gases.

2–5 STANDARD ENTHALPIES

Within the framework of thermodynamics, only relative values of $H = U + PV$ are defined, because only relative values for U are defined. If the framework is widened, absolute energies may be defined. For example, if a system has the mass m, its absolute energy is, by the Einstein formula, $U = mc^2$. Changes in the internal energy caused by heating, chemical reactions, etc., affect the mass of a system, and the absolute energy of any state may be determined by weighing with sufficient accuracy. However, this is not feasible experimentally, and—of even greater importance—the absolute energy and enthalpy values obtained would be enormous and extremely cumbersome to use.

Consider, for example, the absolute energy of 1 mole of liquid H_2O at 25°C. It is, to the best accuracy known, 18.0153 (g/mole) $\times$ $(2.997925)^2 \times 10^{20}$ cm^2/sec$^{2(1)}$ = 161.9135 $\times 10^{20}$ erg/mole = $(161.9135 \times 10^{13}$ joules/mole$)/4184.00$ (joules/kcal) = 3.86983×10^{11} kcal/mole. This is an exceedingly large quantity compared to the energies involved in thermal interactions, chemical reactions, and the like. For example, to heat the same water by 1°C would take 0.018 kcal, and to electrolyze it to form hydrogen and oxygen gas at 1 atm and 298°K would take 68.32 kcal/mole. These energy changes affect the absolute energies only at a place many digits past those known. The weights of substances are thus not measurably changed by chemical reactions. Even if absolute energies were known with the accuracy needed, they would be entirely impractical here because of their unwieldy magnitudes.

Although the use of absolute energies and thus enthalpies in chemical thermodynamics is out of the question, it is possible to

---

[1] $c = 2.997925 \times 10^{10}$ cm/sec.

assign zero enthalpy to suitable reference states *by convention*. This is of great value, because it permits the assignment and tabulation of a standard enthalpy for each substance. These standard enthalpies are useful in many computations, as will be seen.

On first sight it might be sensible to assign the energy zero to the isolated atoms of all elements, at 0°K. The enthalpy of any substance would then be the change in $U + PV$ incurred when the substance is formed from free atoms, and heat removed or furnished to reach the temperature desired. This is not very practical, however, because the state of reference chosen is not readily accessible by experiment, and it would therefore be difficult to measure the quantities of interest with any accuracy. The conventions actually chosen fulfill the experimental requirement that a reference state be realized easily and reproducibly.

The conventions may be separated into two parts, the definition of standard states for all substances, and that of reference states on which tabulated enthalpy values are based:

(1) A substance is in its **standard state** when under a pressure of 1 atm and at a standard temperature usually chosen to be 25°C or 298°K (more accurately 298.15°K, but the difference of 0.15° is insignificant and will be neglected). For dissolved molecular or ionic species a concentration (or more accurately, an "effective" concentration or activity) of 1 mole/liter is implied. Quantities referring to standard states are designated by a superscript zero (such as X^0 for a quantity X); if the standard state is chosen to be at a temperature T that differs from 298°K, as is sometimes useful, this is indicated by using T in parentheses, $X^0(T)$. Thus X^0 specifies a standard state of 1 atm, 1 mole/liter for dissolved species, and 298°K, whereas $X^0(1000)$ refers to the same pressure and concentration but at 1000°K. In other words, the temperature of a standard state is flexible and may need special mention, whereas pressure and concentration are fixed. Note that at conditions other than standard the superscript zero has no meaning. Furthermore, the standard states discussed here must not be confused with the standard conditions customarily abbreviated by STP (standard temperature and pressure) that are often used when specifying quantities of a gas and that imply 1 atm and 0°C.

(2) The **reference states** for tabulated enthalpies are the *chemical*

elements in their most stable states at standard conditions. Under these conditions a value of *zero enthalpy* is assigned to each element. To all compounds are assigned **standard molar enthalpies of formation** $\tilde{H}_f^0$ that represent the enthalpy gain, positive or negative, when 1 mole of the compound is formed at standard conditions from the elements in their most stable forms. In some texts this quantity is also given, among others, the symbol $\Delta \tilde{H}_f^0$ or $\Delta H f^0$. Often we shall call it more briefly the **standard molar enthalpy.** For the chemical elements in their most stable states, $\tilde{H}_f^0$ is thus zero. At a temperature T other than 298°K the reference state for the enthalpy of formation $\tilde{H}_f^0(T)$ of a compound is again the elements at 1 atm in their most stable form, but now at the temperature T. Thus $\tilde{H}_f^0(T)$ for the elements in their most stable form at T is zero. Most of the discussion in this text concerns the temperature of 298°K, but sight must not be lost of the way the reference states are defined at T other than 298°K.

The conventions about zero enthalpy are just as arbitrary as the choice of the zero for terrestrial altitudes and just as important and useful. Indeed, to use absolute heights measured from the earth's center for terrestrial purposes would be comparable to using absolute enthalpies here, even though not as extreme.

EXAMPLE 3

What is the standard enthalpy (of formation) $\tilde{H}_f^0$ of liquid water? For the reaction

$$H_2(g) + \tfrac{1}{2}O_2(g) = H_2O(l) \qquad (2\text{-}21)$$

the enthalpy gain at standard conditions is -68.32 kcal. The standard molar enthalpy $\tilde{H}_f^0$ of liquid water is thus **-68.32 kcal/mole;** that of $H_2(g)$ and $O_2(g)$ is zero.

Some substances or modifications of substances are not stable at standard conditions, as for example, water vapor at 25°C and 1 atm. In such cases standard enthalpies may be assigned by extrapolation, as exemplified in the next section. Enthalpies of transformation may also be measured indirectly as described in Section 4–11. For elements that are not in their most stable forms at standard conditions, $\tilde{H}_f^0$ is the enthalpy gain when these forms are produced from the most stable modification. Standard enthalpies of free atoms are equal to the enthalpy increase that attends the formation of 1 mole of atoms from the element in its most stable state, all at 25°C and 1 atm. The dissolving of a substance is accompanied by an enthalpy change called **enthalpy of solution,** ΔH_{soln}. The heat liberated upon dissolving the substances is $-\Delta H_{\text{soln}}$. Its value may depend on the solute concentration achieved, so that there may also be enthalpy changes when a solution is diluted.

For aqueous solutions of salts it is possible to apportion the enthalpy of solution to the ions concerned. Because it is impossible to prepare solutions of just one ionic species, the apportionment is not unique and the enthalpy of one particular species has to be assigned arbitrarily. By convention the standard enthalpy of H^+ is chosen to be zero. As already mentioned, **standard enthalpies of ions** refer to concentrations (more precisely, activities) of 1 mole/liter. To specify that ions are at standard conditions, the term aq is sometimes used, as in $Cl^-(aq)$, $H^+(aq)$. Examples follow shortly. Appendix 4 contains the standard molar enthalpies $\tilde{H}_f^0$ for a number of elements, compounds, atoms, and aqueous ions, some in forms that are not those most stable at standard conditions.

When the values of $\tilde{H}_f^0$ for the reactants and products of a reaction are known, it is possible to compute the standard enthalpy change ΔH^0 for the reaction. This is extremely useful. Illustrations follow, with $\tilde{H}_f^0$ values shown in kilocalories per mole beneath the chemical symbols.

EXAMPLE 4

By the important reaction

$$H_2O(g) + C(\text{graphite}) = CO(g) + H_2(g) \qquad (2\text{--}22)$$

$$-57.80 \qquad\qquad 0 \qquad\qquad -26.42 \qquad\quad 0$$

water gas, an equimolar mixture of CO and H_2, is made from carbon and water. What is ΔH^0 for this reaction? The change in standard enthalpies is

$$\Delta H^0 = (-26.42 + 57.80) \text{ kcal} = \textbf{31.38 kcal}$$

The reaction is actually carried out at around 600°C by passing steam over hot coal. The $\Delta H°$ just given applies to 25°C and shows the reaction to be endothermic at that temperature. It turns out to be endothermic at 600°C also, and to maintain this temperature the steam is turned off every few minutes and replaced by a brief blast of air.

The enthalpy change when forming molecules in the gas phase from atoms is frequently of interest. A case in point is the following example.

EXAMPLE 5

What is the enthalpy change when benzene vapor is made from carbon and hydrogen atoms?

$$6C(g) + 6H(g) = C_6H_6(g) \qquad (2–23)$$

$$171.70 \qquad 52.09 \qquad 19.82$$

The enthalpy increase under standard conditions is

$$\Delta H^0 = (19.82 - 6 \times 171.70 - 6 \times 52.09) \text{ kcal}$$

$$= -1322.92 \text{ kcal}$$

This example is taken up again in Section 2–11.

EXAMPLE 6

What is ΔH^0 for the dissolving of NaCl in water to form a 1-M solution of Na^+ and Cl^-? The process is represented by the equation

$$NaCl(s) = Na^+(aq) + Cl^-(aq) \qquad (2–24)$$

$$-98.23 \qquad -57.28 \qquad -40.02$$

and therefore

$$\Delta H^0 = (-57.28 - 40.02 + 98.23) \text{ kcal} = 0.93 \text{ kcal}$$

This is the enthalpy of solution of NaCl. The reaction is slightly endothermic.

EXAMPLE 7

What is the enthalpy increase associated with the neutralization of H$^+$ with OH$^-$ to form water, by reacting a strong
acid with a strong base? The reaction is

$$H^+(aq) + OH^-(aq) = H_2O(l) \qquad (2\text{--}25)$$

$$0 \qquad\quad -54.96 \qquad -68.32$$

and the enthalpy increase is

$$\Delta H^0 = (-68.32 + 54.96) \text{ kcal} = \mathbf{-13.36 \text{ kcal}}$$

The reaction is exothermic; and ΔH_0 is called the **enthalpy of
neutralization.**

The standard enthalpy change ΔH^0 for any reaction is given by
the equation

$$\Delta H^0 = \sum H_f^0{}_{\text{ prod}} - \sum H_f^0{}_{\text{ react}} \qquad (2\text{--}26)$$

Extensive tabulations of H_f^0 values going far beyond the list given
in Appendix 4 are available. Remember that ΔH^0 always refers to
a specific way of writing a chemical reaction, that is, to as many
moles of reactants as is indicated by the coefficients of the chemical
equation describing the over-all reaction being changed to the
proper numbers of moles of products. Only if the chemical equation
is stated does ΔH^0 have meaning.

2–6   ENTHALPY CHANGES AT TEMPERATURES
OTHER THAN 298°K

The values of ΔH at temperatures other than 298°K can be
found from ΔH^0 and the heat capacities $\tilde{C}_P$ of the substances concerned, by using the fact that ΔH is independent of the path. Figure
2–2 illustrates the method for reaction (2–21), the combination of

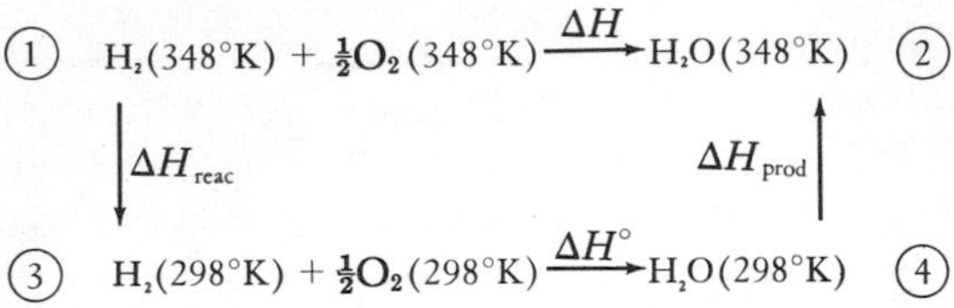

Figure 2–2 **Example of a computation of** ΔH. The value of ΔH that applies when going from state 1 to state 2 may be found by choosing a roundabout path that goes through states 3 and 4; ΔH is the sum of the enthalpy changes for the three portions of this path: $\Delta H = \Delta H_{reac} + \Delta H^0 + \Delta H_{prod}$.

hydrogen and oxygen to form liquid water at 348°K or 75°C. The four different states are designated by the numbers 1 through 4, as follows: (1) reactants at 348°K; (2) products at 348°K; (3) reactants at 298°K; and (4) products at 298°K; all at 1 atm. The ΔH sought is the change in enthalpy when going from (1) to (2). Instead of proceeding from (1) to (2) directly, the reactants may first be cooled to 298°K, reacted at 298°K, and the products heated back to 348°K. The respective enthalpy changes are denoted by ΔH_{reac}, ΔH^0, and ΔH_{prod}, so that

$$\Delta H = \Delta H_{reac} + \Delta H^0 + \Delta H_{prod} \tag{2–27}$$

To find ΔH_{reac}, the molar heat capacities for H_2 and O_2 must be known (Appendix 4); they are assumed to be constant:

$$\Delta H_{reac} \approx (298 - 348) \, [\tilde{C}_P(H_2) + \tfrac{1}{2}\tilde{C}_P(O_2)]$$
$$= -50[6.89 + \tfrac{1}{2}(7.02)] \, cal = -0.52 \, kcal \tag{2–28}$$

Similarly, for ΔH_{prod},

$$\Delta H_{prod} \approx (348 - 298)[\tilde{C}_P(H_2O)] = 50 \times 18.00 \, cal$$
$$= 0.90 \, kcal \tag{2–29}$$

Therefore, and because $\Delta H^0 = -68.32$ kcal (Appendix 4),

$$\Delta H = (-0.52 - 68.32 + 0.90) \, kcal = -67.94 \, kcal \tag{2–30}$$

In a similar way ΔH may be calculated for reactions in which the temperatures of the reactants and products are not equal (Problem 2–15).

This result is not exact, because the assumed temperature independence of the various $\tilde{C}_P$'s is only approximate. In more accurate computations, integrals such as

$$\Delta H_{\text{reac}} = \int_{298}^{348} [\tilde{C}_P(\text{H}_2) + \tfrac{1}{2}\tilde{C}_P(\text{O}_2)]\, dT$$

replace (2–28) and (2–29). We shall not concern ourselves with this refinement.

EXAMPLE 8

Given is $\tilde{H}_f^0$ for liquid water. Find $\tilde{H}_f^0$ for water vapor at standard conditions. What is needed is ΔH^0 for the transformation

$$\text{H}_2\text{O}(l,\ 298°\text{K},\ 1\ \text{atm}) = \text{H}_2\text{O}(g,\ 298°\text{K},\ 1\ \text{atm}) \qquad (2\text{–}31)$$

To calculate it a three-step process is carried out: (1) heating the water to 373°K, (2) vaporization to steam of 1 atm and 373°K, and (3) hypothetical cooling of the steam at 1 atm, without condensation, to 298°K. For steps (1) and (3) constant $\tilde{C}_P$'s are assumed, of values 18.00 and 8.02 (Appendix 4), the second value to apply to the hypothetical steam. The values of ΔH for the three steps are (1) $75 \times 18.00 = 1350$ cal/mole, (2) 9.71 kcal/mole (Table 2–1), and (3) $-75 \times 8.02 = -602$ cal/mole. The sum is $(1.35 + 9.71 - 0.602)$ kcal/mole $= 10.46$ kcal/mole. This must be added to $\tilde{H}_f^0$ for liquid water, -68.32, to obtain H_f^0 for the vapor, $(-68.32 + 10.46)$ kcal/mole $= \mathbf{-57.86\ kcal/mole}$. The value given in Appendix 4 is -57.80 kcal/mole. The difference is caused by the approximation in our computations, which are seen to be quite good.

2–7   MAXIMUM FLAME AND EXPLOSION TEMPERATURES

A much more ambitious undertaking, particularly on first sight, is the computation of temperatures that may be reached by an

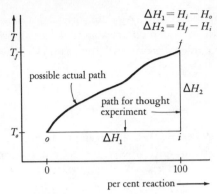

$$\Delta H_1 = H_i - H_o$$
$$\Delta H_2 = H_f - H_i$$

Figure 2–3 Maximum flame temperature. To calculate the maximum possible flame temperature the actual path that leads from the original state o to the final state f is replaced in thought by a two-step procedure. First, the flame reaction is performed at room temperature leading to the intermediate state i. Second, the enthalpy liberated is used to heat the reaction products. The maximum final temperature T_f is that for which this enthalpy is exactly used up.

exothermic reaction like the burning of hydrogen in chlorine, in the ideal case that no heat is lost to the surroundings. On the face of it, this is impossibly involved. As the reaction proceeds, the temperature rises. But ΔH depends on the temperature and thus changes continually; this change, in turn, affects the temperature rise.

However, these difficulties disappear once it is realized that ΔH must be zero, because the process is run so that q and w' are zero: No heat is transferred to the surroundings, and there is only pressure-volume work. This represents an idealization, of course, but if we accept it, we see that all heat produced is used to increase the temperature of the system. What is sought is a final temperature T_f, such that ΔH is zero when going from the reactants at the original temperature T_0 to the products at T_f. The next important realization is that the actual path does not matter, because H is a function of state. It can therefore be replaced in thought by one that is more suitable for computation. A convenient path is the following two-step procedure (Fig. 2–3).

1. The reaction is run from the original state, designated by the subscript o, to an intermediary state i, where the reaction is completed but the temperature is still the original T_o. The enthalpy change is

$$\Delta H_1 = H_i - H_o \qquad (2\text{--}32)$$

2. The products are heated from T_o to that temperature T_f that corresponds to an enthalpy change equal and opposite to ΔH_1,

$$\Delta H_2 = H_f - H_i = -\Delta H_1 \qquad (2\text{--}33)$$

For the total of both steps,

$$\Delta H = \Delta H_1 + \Delta H_2 = 0$$

as required. The temperature calculated in step (2) is the final temperature T_f that is reached along *any* isobaric path for which there is no heat loss to the surroundings and along which only pressure-volume work is performed. If there is heat loss to the surroundings, or if non-pressure-volume work is performed on the surroundings, the final temperature is less than T_f. The maximum temperature that a flame based on the reaction considered may reach is therefore T_f.

EXAMPLE 9

What is the maximum temperature that can be obtained by burning hydrogen in chlorine with an initial temperature of 298°K? The enthalpy change ΔH_1 is just $\tilde{H}_f^0(\text{HCl})$ (Appendix 4):

$$\tfrac{1}{2}H_2(g) + \tfrac{1}{2}Cl_2(g) = HCl(g) \qquad \Delta H_1 = -22.06 \text{ kcal}$$

When the resultant HCl gas is heated from 298°K to T_f°K its enthalpy increase is approximately

$$\Delta H_2 = \tilde{C}_P(T_f - 298) = 7.0(T_f - 298) \, 10^{-3} \text{ kcal}$$

where $\tilde{C}_P$ has been assumed constant and equal to 7.0 cal/mole-deg. Since $\Delta H_2 = -\Delta H_1 = 22.06$ kcal,

$$7.0(T_f - 298) = 22,060$$

$$T_f = 298 + 22,060/7.0 = \mathbf{3450°K}$$

The highest temperature that can be reached is thus about 3400°K or 3100°C. It must be understood that these values are only rough estimates. Not only has the heat loss to the surroundings been neglected, but HCl is slightly dissociated into Cl_2 and H_2 at this high temperature, so that the reaction does not quite go to completion. In addition, $\tilde{C}_P$ increases considerably with temperature and, most important of all, Cl_2 is almost completely dissociated into atoms at 3400°K and H_2 is dissociated to some extent also. However, more accurate results can be easily obtained by taking these details into account.

For reactions that are confined to a closed space such as explosions in a bomb (before bursting), ΔU and C_V must be used instead of ΔH and $\tilde{C}_P$, but otherwise the basic idea is the same. In addition, the maximum pressure can be calculated. The values computed are, of course, theoretical maximum values, and to reach them the bomb must hold together long enough for the reaction to reach completion. This method of computing maximum flame and explosion temperatures is a particularly good illustration of the value of the state-function concept.

2–8   PRESSURE DEPENDENCE OF U AND H

Both U and H are functions of the pressure P and the temperature T. However, at moderate pressures the change of $\tilde{H}$ and $\tilde{U}$ with pressure is only a few calories per mole-atmosphere. The reason for this is different in the case of condensed phases (solids and liquids) from that for the case of gases. For condensed phases the volume change caused by a pressure increase is small, so that the isothermal compression work and the increase in U and H upon compression are small.   For gases the volume change upon compression is large, but the intermolecular forces are small because the average intermolecular distances in gases are much larger than in condensed phases.   As mentioned earlier, for *perfect* gases both U and H are functions of T alone and are thus independent of pressure.   For real gases, U and H are *almost* independent of P and the isothermal compression work is converted almost entirely into heat that is absorbed by the constant-temperature bath.

The pressure dependence of U and H is important only when high accuracy is required, or when the pressure change amounts to many atmospheres.

2–9   THE DIFFERENCE BETWEEN ΔU AND ΔH

For any constant-pressure process,

$$\Delta H = \Delta U + P \, \Delta V \qquad (2\text{–}34)$$

However, for reactions and transformations between condensed phases, ΔV is so small that the term $P \, \Delta V$ becomes negligible and can be neglected in (2–34).   This is not necessarily true when gases are involved.   Suppose that among the reactants are n_1 total moles of gases that disappear while n_2 total moles of gases appear among the products.   Assuming perfect gas behavior and neglecting the volume change of the condensed reactants and products,

$$P \, \Delta V = P(V_2 - V_1) \approx P[(n_2 RT/P) - (n_1 RT/P)]$$
$$= RT(n_2 - n_1)$$

Therefore,

$$\Delta H \approx \Delta U + RT \, \Delta n_{\text{gas}} \qquad (2\text{–}35)$$

where Δn_{gas} represents the *increase* in the moles of gas caused by the reaction, that is, the total number of moles of gas appearing in the reaction or transformation, diminished by the total number of moles of gas that are used up.

EXAMPLE 10

What is ΔU for the vaporization of 1 mole of water at 25°C? The value of ΔH is $\tilde{H}_f^0$ (H_2O, g) $-$ $\tilde{H}_f^0$ (H_2O, l) $= (68.32 - 57.80)$ kcal $= 10.52$ kcal (Appendix 4) and Δn_{gas} is 1. Thus $\Delta U \approx (10.52 - 1.99 \times 298 \times 10^{-3})$ kcal $= (10.52 - 0.593)$ kcal $= $ **9.93 kcal.** In contrast, when ice is melted at 0°C, $P\,\Delta V$ is so small as to be negligible, to wit: The density of ice at 0°C is 0.915 g/ml, that of liquid water 0.99987 g/ml, so that for the melting of 1 mole of ice $\Delta V = 18.0(1/1.000 - 1/0.915)$ ml $\approx 18.0\ (1.000 - 1.085)$ ml $= -1.53$ ml. Thus $P\ \Delta V = -1.53 \times 10^{-3}$ liter-atm $\times$ (1 cal/0.0413 liter-atm) $= -0.037$ cal $= -4 \times 10^{-5}$ kcal, and $\Delta U \approx \Delta H = 1.44$ kcal.

EXAMPLE 11

What is ΔU for the chemical reaction

$$2NO_2(g) + \quad KCl(s) \quad = \quad KNO_3(s) + ONCl(g)$$

$$8.09 \qquad -104.18 \qquad -117.76 \qquad 12.57$$

This remarkable reaction takes place at room temperature and permits the preparation of nitrosyl chloride. Here $\Delta n_{gas} = 1 - 2 = -1$, and $(\Delta n_{gas}\,RT) = -0.59$ kcal. From the $\tilde{H}_f^0$ values given beneath the chemical symbols, $\Delta H = (-117.76 + 12.57 - 2 \times 8.09 + 104.18)$ kcal $= -17.19$ kcal, so that $\Delta U \approx (-17.19 + 0.59)$ kcal $= $ **−16.60 kcal.**

2–10   BOND ENTHALPIES

When a molecular compound, for example C_2H_6, is decomposed into atoms, the bonds holding the atoms together are broken and the enthalpy of the system is increased. It is found that **bond enthalpies** may be assigned to the different kinds of bonds like C—C and H—H, so that for many compounds the sum of these bond enthalpies is approximately equal to the total enthalpy that has to be supplied to break the bonds. The compounds considered must, however, be in the gas state, so that intermolecular interactions may be neglected. The contribution of volume changes to the enthalpy is, of course, automatically included. It is usually small.

On first thought, it would be expected that average **bond energies** rather than bond enthalpies, and in fact values extrapolated to $0°K$, would be additive. However, within the approximation that the additivity is found to hold, the differences between energy and enthalpy and between $0°K$ and room temperature can be neglected. Because enthalpies are more useful, the average values for the different bonds have been selected to represent enthalpies rather than energies of forming compounds from atoms.

Table 2–2 contains a number of representative bond enthalpies for reactions at 1 atm and $25°C$. If liquid or solid compounds are considered, the enthalpies of evaporation or sublimation must be corrected for. Two examples of the use of these values follow.

EXAMPLE 12

Estimate the enthalpy required for the decomposition of ethane into atoms. The bond enthalpies needed in this calculation are, in kilocalories per mole, 98.8 for C—H and 83.1 for C—C. In the reaction

$$\begin{array}{cc} H & H \\ | & | \\ H\!-\!C\!-\!C\!-\!H(g) = 2C(g) + 6H(g) \\ | & | \\ H & H \end{array}$$

six C—H bonds and one C—C bond are broken, so that

$$\Delta H \approx (6 \times 98.8 + 1 \times 83.1)\ \text{kcal} = \textbf{675.9 kcal}$$

The experimental value is 676 kcal and is related to the standard enthalpy of ethane, $\tilde{H}_f^0 = -20.24$ kcal/mole (Appendix 4), as follows.

Decomposition of ethane to the elements in standard states:

$$C_2H_6(g) = 2C(\text{graphite}) + 3H_2(g) \qquad \Delta H = 20.24\ \text{kcal}$$

Table 2–2
Representative Bond Enthalpies[a]
(in kcal/mole)

H—H	104.2	C—Cl	78.5
H—C	98.8	C—Br	65.9
H—Si	70.4	C—I	57.4
H—N	93.4	Si—Si	42.2
H—P	76.4	Si—O	88.2
H—O	110.6	N—N	38.4
H—S	81.1	N=N	100
H—F	134.6	N≡N	226.2
H—Cl	103.2	N—F	64.5
H—Br	87.5	N—Cl	47.7
H—I	71.4	P—P	51.3
C—C	83.1	O—O	33.2
C=C	147	O—F	44.2
C≡C	194	O—Cl	48.5
C—Si	69.3	S—S	50.9
C—N	69.7	F—F	36.6
C=N	147	F—Cl	60.6
C≡N	213	Cl—Cl	58.0
C—O	84.0	Cl—Br	52.3
C=O	172	Cl—I	50.3
C—S	62.0	Br—Br	46.1
C≡S	114	Br—I	42.5
C—F	115.8	I—I	36.1

[a] Data from L. Pauling, *College Chemistry*, 3rd ed., Freeman, San Francisco, 1964.

Sublimation of graphite (171.70 kcal/mole):

$$2C(\text{graphite}) = 2C(g) \qquad \Delta H = 2 \times 171.70 \text{ kcal}$$
$$= 343.40 \text{ kcal}$$

Formation of H atoms (52.09 kcal/mole):

$$3H_2(g) = 6H(g) \qquad \Delta H = 6 \times 52.09 \text{ kcal}$$
$$= 312.54 \text{ kcal}$$

The sum is $\Delta H = (20.24 + 343.40 + 312.54)$ kcal = 676.18 kcal.

EXAMPLE 13

Estimate the enthalpy change for the hydrogenation of acetylene, that is, for the reaction

$$
\begin{array}{c}
\ \text{H}\quad\text{H} \\
\ |\qquad| \\
\text{H--C}\equiv\text{C--H} + 2\text{H--H} = \text{H--C--C--H} \\
\ |\qquad| \\
\ \text{H}\quad\text{H}
\end{array}
$$

where all substances are in the gas phase. Because ΔH for this reaction is independent of the path, any path that is convenient for computation may be chosen, whether or not it bears any resemblance to the actual path. Thus we consider that the bonds broken and formed are as follows, with bond enthalpies (in kcal/mole) in parentheses: broken [gain of enthalpy], one $C\equiv C$ (194) and two H—H (104.2); formed [loss of enthalpy], four C—H (98.8) and one C—C (83.1). Therefore,

$$\Delta H \approx (194 + 2 \times 104.2 - 4 \times 98.8 - 83.1)\,\text{kcal} = \mathbf{-75.9\,kcal}$$

This estimated value may be compared with the actual value, which is equal to the difference between the standard enthalpies of acetylene (54.19) and ethane (-20.24), because the standard enthalpy of H_2 is zero:

$$\Delta H = (-20.24 - 54.19)\,\text{kcal} = -74.43\,\text{kcal}$$

In both examples the agreement between the estimated and actual ΔH is quite good. However, estimated values should be resorted to only when standard enthalpies or other experimental data are not available, for example, when considering hypothetical compounds that have not yet been synthesized.

An important point is that bond enthalpies are *average* values and must not be confused with the enthalpies required to break specific bonds. For example, to break the first of the two O—H bonds in H_2O requires the enthalpy 119.95 kcal/mole,

$$\underset{H}{\overset{O}{\diagup}}\overset{}{\underset{H}{\diagdown}} = H + O—H \qquad \Delta H = 119.95 \text{ kcal}$$

and breakage of the O—H bond in the remaining OH radical takes 101.19 kcal/mole,

$$O—H = H + O \qquad \Delta H = 101.19 \text{ kcal}$$

It is thus harder to break the first bond in H_2O than the second. In the first step the relatively unstable OH radical is formed, in the second the more stable O atom. The O—H bond enthalpy in Table 2–2 (110.6 kcal/mole) is the *average* of the values for the two individual steps.

It should also be understood that different authors may prefer slightly different bond enthalpies or bond energies. In calculations it is important to use the same source for all values.

The possibility of estimating enthalpies of compounds by the method discussed is of course a fact of molecular structure and has nothing to do with thermodynamics. For certain types of compounds there are large deviations between estimated and actual enthalpies. These deviations are of great structural interest. An important class of such deviations is considered next.

2–11 BOND ENTHALPIES AND RESONANCE

An important group of compounds for which the discrepancy between estimated and actual enthalpies is large and structurally significant is that of aromatic compounds, such as benzene and naphthalene. For example, the experimental value of the enthalpy required to dissociate benzene molecules in the vapor state into atoms is 1322.92 kcal [Eq. (2–23)]. Suppose the bonding in benzene is that of Kekulé structure I (Fig. 2–4), which contains three C=C, three C—C, and six C—H. The estimated value for the same

62   *Basic Chemical Thermodynamics*

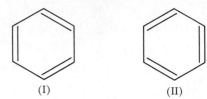

(I)   (II)

Figure 2–4 The two Kekulé structures for benzene. The
corners of the hexagons shown represent carbon atoms to which
hydrogen atoms are attached. Neither of the two formulas shown
represents the chemical properties of benzene adequately, but a
kind of superposition attesting to the simultaneous presence of
features of both formulas is more satisfactory. Compounds for which
this type of description is possible are always stabilized by resonance
energy, and resonance is said to exist between the formulas concerned.

enthalpy change would be $(3 \times 147 + 3 \times 83.1 + 6 \times 98.8)$ kcal
$= 1283.1$ kcal. Benzene is thus more stable by 40 kcal/mole than
would correspond to Kekulé structure I. As discussed in many
chemistry texts, the behavior of benzene is different from what would
be expected for a compound of formula I. It can be described as a
superposition of, or a hybrid between, the two Kekulé structures I
and II, stabilized by a resonance energy. This resonance energy is
thus estimated to be 40 kcal/mole.

There are many other aromatic compounds, and many non-
aromatic and nonorganic compounds that are similarly stabilized
by resonance.

PROBLEMS

2–1. *Waterfall.* Estimate the maximum temperature difference
of water before and after having dropped through the entire height
of a 100-m waterfall.

2–2. *Heating of bullet.* A lead bullet weighing 10 g and having
a velocity of 1000 m/sec strikes an unyielding obstacle. Assume that
5 per cent of the kinetic energy of the bullet goes into increasing its
temperature, and that the specific heat capacity of Pb is constant
and 0.032 cal/deg-g. What is the temperature increase?

2–3. *Stirring water.* A mass of 10 kg moves through a height of 3 m, causing a paddle wheel to stir 500 g water initially at 25°C. What is the final temperature of the (liquid) water? $C_P = 1.00$ cal/g-deg.

2–4. *Isothermal expansion of a gas.* Three moles of an ideal gas are expanded at 300°K so that the volume is increased by a factor four and work against a constant outside pressure of 2 atm is performed. Find w, q, ΔU, and ΔH. Initial pressure = 8 atm.

2–5. *Adiabatic expansion of a gas.* One mole of a perfect gas at 27°C and 10 atm is expanded adiabatically against a constant pressure of 1 atm. What is the final temperature? Assume R to be 2 cal/mole-deg and a molar heat capacity C_V of 3 cal/mole-deg. (*Hint:* Consider that $\Delta U = w = C_V \Delta T$, because the process is adiabatic and U is a function of T only.)

2–6. *Implications of the first law.* Indicate whether each of the following statements is true or false as it stands. If the statement is not true, indicate in what way it is false and whether it could be made into a true statement by a slight change in wording. State if the statement is true but unnecessarily restricted, and indicate what qualifying words or phrases can be omitted:

(*a*) The work done by the system on the surroundings during a change in state is never greater than the decrease in the energy of the system.

(*b*) The enthalpy of a system cannot change during an adiabatic process.

(*c*) When a system undergoes a given isothermal change in state, its change in enthalpy does not depend upon the process involved.

(*d*) When a change in state occurs, the increase in the enthalpy of the system must equal the decrease in the enthalpy of the surroundings.

(*e*) A spontaneous change is always accompanied by a decrease in the energy of the system.

(*f*) The equation $\Delta U = q + w$ is applicable to any macroscopic process, provided no electrical work is done by the system on the surroundings.

(*g*) No change in state occurring within an isolated system can cause a change in its energy or its enthalpy.

(*h*) For any constant pressure process, the increase in enthalpy equals the heat absorbed whether electrical work is done during the process or not.

(*i*) A reversible process is one in which the amount of energy lost by the system is just sufficient to restore the system to its initial state.

(*j*) When an imperfect gas expands into a vacuum it does work because the molecules of the gas have been separated from one another against an attractive (van der Waals) force.

2–7. *Change of state.* State, for each of the following processes, which of the quantities w, q, ΔU, and ΔH is equal to zero. In each case the system is the material described:

(*a*) Liquid water and liquid sulfuric acid are mixed adiabatically at constant pressure.

(*b*) Liquid water at 100°C and 1 atm is injected into an evacuated bulb whose walls are maintained at 100°C and allowed to come to equilibrium. Enough water is injected so not all of it evaporates. The initial state is that existing the instant after injection.

(*c*) Two imperfect gases mix adiabatically, the total volume remaining constant.

(*d*) A perfect gas undergoes a reversible, isothermal expansion.

2–8. *Enthalpy of solution.* When 40.0 g of NaCl is dissolved in 200 ml of H_2O at 20°C, the temperature is lowered by 1.5°C; a similar experiment for KCl leads to a temperature decrease of 9.1°. For 50 g of a mixture of NaCl and KCl a temperature lowering of 7.9°C is observed. What is the weight percentage of NaCl in the mixture?

2–9. *Enthalpy of formation.* (*a*) The enthalpy of combustion of benzoic acid, C_6H_5COOH, at 25°C, is -771.31 kcal/mole. What is the enthalpy of formation? Use values of standard enthalpies of formation listed in Appendix 4 as needed. (*b*) What is the enthalpy of formation of succinic acid, $HOOCCH_2CH_2COOH$, for which the enthalpy of combustion is -356.99 kcal/mole?

2–10. *Enthalpy of reaction.* From the values of $\tilde{H}_f^0$ given in Appendix 4, find ΔH for the following reactions: (*a*) $KCl(s) = K^+(aq) + Cl^-(aq)$; (*b*) $C_2H_5OH(l) + \frac{1}{2}O_2(g) = CH_3COOH(l) + H_2(g)$; (*c*) $Na_2CO_3(s) + 2H^+(aq) = 2Na^+(aq) + CO_2(g) + H_2O(l)$.

2–11. *Energy and enthalpy of combustion.* The combustion of 1 mole of acetylene to liquid water and gaseous CO_2 yields 311.5 kcal at constant volume and at 20°C. What is the enthalpy of combustion of acetylene under the same conditions except that the pressure is kept constant at 1 atm? Consider all gases involved in the reaction to be perfect and neglect the volume of the liquid water produced.

2–12. *Energy of reaction.* From the values of $\tilde{H}_f^0$ in Appendix 4, find ΔH at 25°C for the reaction $CH_4(g) + 2O_2(g) = CO_2(g) + 2H_2O(l)$. Estimate ΔU for the same process.

2–13. *Enthalpy of combustion.* Calculate the enthalpy of combustion to $H_2O(l)$ and $CO_2(g)$ of ethyl alcohol, $C_2H_5OH(l)$ in kilocalories per mole, at 25°C. Use the enthalpies of formation given in Appendix 4.

2–14. *Enthalpy of reaction.* Calculate ΔH for the reaction

$$H_2O_2(l) = H_2O(g) + \tfrac{1}{2}O_2(g)$$

at 140°C from data given in Appendix 4 (assuming the values of C_P given to remain constant). Note that the normal boiling point of H_2O_2 is 152°C and assume that C_P for $H_2O_2(l)$ is 1.00 cal/g-deg.

2–15. *Enthalpy change for different initial and final temperatures.* The reaction $CO(g) + \tfrac{1}{2}O_2(g) = CO_2(g)$ corresponds to an enthalpy increase of -67.63 kcal at 25°. What is the enthalpy increase if the temperature of the reactants is 0°C and that of the product 125°C. Assume that the molar heat capacities $\tilde{C}_P$ are constant and have the following values, in calories per mole-degree: O_2 and CO, 7.0; CO_2, 8.9.

2–16. *Enthalpy of reaction.* At 25°C, ΔH for the reaction $C(s) + \tfrac{1}{2}O_2(g) = CO(g)$ is -26.42 kcal. What is it at 125°C? Assume that the molar heat capacities are constant and have the values (in cal/mole-deg): $C(s)$, 2; $O_2(g)$, 7; $CO(g)$, 7.

2–17. *Resonance energy of phenanthrene.* The enthalpy of combustion of gaseous phenanthrene to $CO_2(g)$ and $H_2O(l)$ is -1705 kcal/mole at 25°C. The compound may be represented as resonance hybrid between the formulas

Find the resonance energy of phenanthrene. Use the values of Appendix 4 and Table 2–2.

2–18. *Adiabatic heating of air.* An evacuated and sealed flask is surrounded by air of 1 atm and 20°C. The seal is broken and air rushes into the flask. What is the final temperature of this air, assuming that no heat is transferred to the flask and that the final pressure is 1 atm? The air may be treated as a perfect gas with $\tilde{C}_V = 5.00$ cal/mole-deg. (*Hint:* Imagine the air rushing into the flask as being bounded by a film and choose the system to be the contents of the film and the flask. Consider the work the outside atmosphere performs on this system.)

2–19. *Heating water.* Exactly 1 kg of H_2O (25°C) is heated in a beaker by burning under it 1 liter of C_3H_8 (measured at 25°C and 1 atm pressure). Assume that 60 per cent of the heat evolved goes into the water in the beaker, while the remainder is lost in vaporizing the H_2O formed in the combustion, in heating gases, and in radiation. What is the final temperature of the H_2O? The enthalpy of combustion of C_3H_8 at 1 atm and 25°C is -530.4 kcal/mole.

2–20. *Maximum flame temperature.* The enthalpy of combustion of 1 mole of $CO(g)$ to $CO_2(g)$ at 25°C and a constant pressure of 1 atm is -67.6 kcal. What is the maximum possible temperature that may be reached by burning $CO(g)$ in air (20 per cent O_2, 80 per cent N_2 by volume) if any heat loss by radiation, etc., may be neglected? Molar heat capacities (in cal/mole-deg) are: $CO(g)$, 7.0; $CO_2(g)$, 9.0; $O_2(g)$, 7.0; $N_2(g)$, 7.0.

2–21. *Determination of CO concentration.* Dry air containing a small amount of CO was passed through a container in which was placed a catalyst for the oxidation of CO to CO_2. Because of the heat evolved in this oxidation the temperature of the air increased by 3.2°C. Calculate the weight per cent of CO in the sample of air. Use the enthalpies of formation listed in Appendix 4 and assume that C_P of air is 0.241 cal/g-deg. Neglect the heating of the CO_2.

2–22. *Decomposition of hydrogen peroxide.* An aqueous solution containing 75 weight per cent H_2O_2 is forced at 25°C and 1 atm through a tube containing a catalyst so that the reaction

$$H_2O_2(l) = H_2O(g) + \tfrac{1}{2}O_2(g)$$

occurs. What is the final temperature of the products? *Data:* Enthalpy of reaction at 25°C; -12.96 kcal. Molar heat capacities (assumed constant) in calories per mole-degree: $H_2O(l)$, 18.0; $H_2O(g)$, 9.0; $O_2(g)$, 7.0. Enthalpy of vaporization of $H_2O(l)$ at 100°C; 9.71 kcal/mole.

2–23. *Maximum flame temperature.* Propane, C_3H_8, is burned completely to $CO_2(g)$ and $H_2O(g)$ in an excess of 100 per cent air (20 per cent O_2, 80 per cent N_2 by volume). What is the maximum possible temperature that may be achieved in a perfectly insulated system starting at 25°C and maintaining 1 atm pressure? Use the values of $\tilde{H}_f^0$ given in Appendix 4. Assume $\tilde{C}_P$ to be independent of temperature and to have the following values (in cal/mole-deg): $H_2O(g)$ and $CO_2(g)$, 9.0; $O_2(g)$ and $N_2(g)$, 7.0.

2–24. *Maximum temperature.* Find the maximum possible temperature that may be reached by reacting 1 mole of $Ca(OH)_2(s)$ with 1 liter of a 2-M HCl solution, both at 25°C and 1 atm. Assume that the standard molar enthalpies of formation given in Appendix 4 apply. Assume that the final volume of the solution is 1 liter and that C_P of the solution is constant and the same as that of H_2O, 1.00 cal/ml-deg.

2–25. *Explosion in closed bomb.* A closed bomb, immersed in a water bath at 25°C, contains 0.1 mole $CO(g)$ and 0.05 mole $O_2(g)$. The gases explode and yield 0.1 mole $CO_2(g)$. The heat capacity of the system (water bath, bomb, and CO_2) is 10^4 cal/deg. Assume the gases to be perfect and use the standard enthalpies of formation given in Appendix 4. Calculate (*a*) the change in the energy of the system, (*b*) the change in the temperature of the system, and (*c*) the change in the enthalpy of the system, neglecting the expansion of the bomb and the water bath.

2–26. *Cooling by vaporization.* Water of 35°C is sprayed into dry air at 35°C until the resulting air contains just one volume per cent of water vapor. What is the temperature of the humidified air? The molar enthalpy of vaporization of water at 35°C is 10.42 kcal/mole. Assume that $\tilde{C}_P$ for the humid air is 7.0 cal/mole-deg. (One mole of air is that quantity that occupies 22.4 liters at 1 atm and 0°C.)

2–27. *Exploding nitroglycerine.* One-tenth mole of nitroglycerine is exploded in a confined space of 10 ml. The reaction equation is approximately

$$C_3H_5N_3O_9(l) = 3CO_2(g) + \tfrac{5}{2}H_2O(g) + \tfrac{3}{2}N_2(g) + \tfrac{1}{4}O_2(g)$$

with an enthalpy of reaction of -337.4 kcal/mole at 20°C. What are the expected maximum temperature and pressure reached by the reaction? Assume constant molar heat capacities $\tilde{C}_V$ and the following values (in calories per mole-degree): CO_2, 7.0; $H_2O(g)$, 7.0; N_2, 5.0; O_2, 5.0. Neglect the air present originally in the container.

2–28. *Mixing of gases.* A box with walls of a thermally non-conducting material is divided into two compartments by a partition of the same material. One compartment contains 0.4 mole of He at 20° and 1 atm; the other contains 0.6 mole of N_2 at 100° and 2 atm. The partition is removed so that the two gases mix. What is the final temperature and pressure? The molar heat capacities of He and of N_2 at constant volume are 2.98 and 4.95 cal/mole-deg, respectively. The gases may be assumed to be perfect gases, and to behave as such on mixing.

2–29. *Compression of a liquid.* One mole of liquid CCl_4 ($M = 153.8$) is compressed reversibly and isothermally at 20°C from 1 to 5 atm. The density at 1 atm and 20°C is 1.595 g/cm³ and the isothermal compressibility coefficient is $(1/V)(dV/dP) \approx 90.7 \times 10^{-6}$ atm⁻¹. Assume that this coefficient is constant and find w in liter-atmospheres and in calories. Compare this with w for the reversible compression of 1 mole of an ideal gas (for example, Example 5, Chapter 1). Do you expect the difference between $\tilde{C}_P$ and $\tilde{C}_V$ for liquid CCl_4 to be small or large?

2–30. *Adiabate for a perfect gas.* (a) Derive the following equation, which relates T and V when a perfect gas is expanded or compressed adiabatically:

$$TV^{(\gamma-1)} = \text{const}$$

where $\gamma = C_P/C_V$ and where C_V is assumed to be constant. (*Hint:* Note that because $q = 0$ and $U = U(T)$, $dU = -P \, dV = C_V \, dT$.) Use the perfect gas equation and $C_P = C_V + nR$. (b) Use the perfect gas equation to transform the foregoing equation of the adiabate into the equivalent forms $PV^\gamma = \text{const}$ and $T^\gamma P^{1-\gamma} = \text{const}$.

3 The Second Law of Thermodynamics

The second law and entropy are considered, the difference between reversible and irreversible paths pointed out, and the thermo-dynamic temperature scale presented. Application to adiabatic changes is followed by discussion of nonadiabatic paths. Two irreversible processes are discussed in detail; the flow of heat between unequal temperatures, and the expansion of a perfect gas into a vacuum.

3–1   ENTROPY AND THE SECOND LAW

The quantity that plays a major role in the second law of thermodynamics is an integral that has no obvious, immediate meaning.   It is the integral, along the path taken by a system as it undergoes a change of state, over the heat increments Dq transferred to the system, each Dq divided by the outside temperature T at which it is transferred.   In formulas, it is the integral

$$\int_1^2 \frac{Dq}{T} \tag{3–1}$$

taken along the path in question, from the starting point 1 to the final point 2, with T the continually changing temperature *of the surroundings* (rather than of the system, in case they are different). The nature of this integral turns out to depend upon whether the path is reversible or irreversible.   This gives the second law its importance and its very special character, because it permits the formulation of criteria for the reversibility of a process and, since reversibility is related to equilibrium, of criteria for the existence of equilibrium.   In addition, it gives a direction to time by stating in which direction an irreversible process may occur spontaneously.

In detail, the second law may be expressed by the following related statements:

(1) For any change of state *along a reversible path, the integral* (3–1) *is independent of the path.* It thus defines the change ΔS of a *function of state S,*

$$\int_1^2 \frac{Dq_{\text{rev}}}{T} = S_2 - S_1 = \Delta S \tag{3–2}$$

This function of state is called the **entropy,** a name introduced by Clausius.

(2) *Along an irreversible* path in the direction actually traversed, *the integral* (3–1) *is* path-dependent and *always smaller* than the same integral over a reversible path,

$$\int_1^2 \frac{Dq_{\text{act}}}{T} < \int_1^2 \frac{Dq_{\text{rev}}}{T} \tag{3–3}$$

The second integral in (3–3) is by definition the change ΔS of the entropy, so that also

$$\int_1^2 \frac{Dq_{\text{act}}}{T} < \Delta S \tag{3–4}$$

for any irreversible or spontaneous process in the direction in which it may proceed. The inequality (3–4) applies thus to all actual or natural processes. If the path of an irreversible process could be pursued in the opposite direction, which is by definition of irreversibility forbidden, the limits and thus the sign of the value of the integral in (3–4) would change, and the integral would therefore be larger than ΔS. It follows that

(3) Processes for which

$$\int_1^2 \frac{Dq_{\text{act}}}{T} > \Delta S \tag{3–5}$$

are prohibited. Such processes are also called **unnatural.** Because the proper handling of inequalities is important in applications of the second law, some of the contingencies that may arise are explained in Appendix 2.

As stated earlier, thermodynamic arguments have no bearing on the speed with which reactions may proceed. For example, although the word spontaneous commonly implies a time element, in thermodynamics a process is called spontaneous when it obeys (3–4), and is thus permitted, even though its rate may be zero and its completion may take an infinite time.

The procedure for finding ΔS for an irreversible process depends on the fact that S is a function of state: All details of the actual process except the initial and final states are ignored, because the details of the path are irrelevant in the calculation of ΔS. The path is replaced by a reversible path that connects the two states and that is specifically invented for the convenient evaluation of the integral (3–1); this reversible path can strictly exist in thought only, because any actual path is irreversible. The integral is evaluated along this reversible path and the resulting ΔS is independent of the path, as mentioned before. The only general statement that can be made for the integral (3–1) along the actual path is that it is smaller than ΔS.

For infinitesimal *reversible* processes,

$$dS = \frac{Dq}{T} \qquad \text{and} \qquad Dq = T\,dS$$

while for infinitesimal *actual* processes

$$dS > \frac{Dq}{T} \qquad \text{and} \qquad Dq < T\,dS$$

Several points are important: (1) Only entropy *differences* are defined by thermodynamics. An additive constant in the entropy is therefore still free for disposal. This constant is fixed by the third law of thermodynamics and by the statistical interpretation of entropy. These matters are taken up later. (2) The entropy difference between two states can be defined thermodynamically only if it is possible to invent a reversible path that connects the two states, at least in thought. (3) The temperature scale denoted by T is the only one for which the earlier statements about the integral (3–1) are true and may therefore be defined entirely on thermodynamic grounds, without recourse to the behavior of perfect gases. This is the real basis of its absolute nature, and it is called the **thermodynamic temperature scale** for this reason. There is, however, no compelling reason to choose a particular size of the degree, and this is the only aspect of the Kelvin or the Rankine scale that is not absolute. (4) Entropy is an extensive quantity. When the total amounts of substances undergoing a given change of state are multiplied by a certain factor, the amounts of heat transferred during the change, and therefore the total entropy change, are multiplied by the same factor. Similarly, the entropies of two independent systems are additive, just as are their energies and enthalpies.

There are many other ways to state the second law of thermodynamics, all of them equivalent. Some are nonmathematical, such as the statement that no *cyclic* process exists that can produce work in constant-temperature surroundings, but that the simultaneous transfer of heat to surroundings of lower temperature is required. A machine that would produce work without such transfer of heat is called a **perpetuum mobile of the second kind** because it would violate the second law (Fig. 3–1). An equivalent statement is that no device can be made that solely transfers heat from a body of lower temperature to a body of higher temperature without expenditure of work or net changes in other bodies. Although these statements are lucid and intuitively easy to understand, equivalent mathematical statements like those given earlier are more powerful in their application to different situations.

As previously stated, there is no immediately obvious meaning of entropy. However, the next three sections will show how the second law is used, and will demonstrate that it leads to sensible results in spite of its abstractness.

3–2   ENTROPY CHANGE IN ADIABATIC AND IN ISOLATED SYSTEMS

For any process in an adiabatic system, Dq remains zero by definition. Therefore, for any process in such a system,

$$\int_1^2 \frac{Dq}{T} = 0 \qquad (3\text{–}6)$$

any adia-
batic path

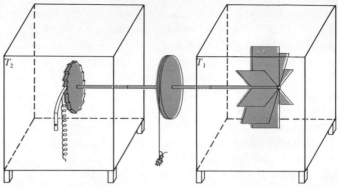

Figure 3–1 Feynman's perpetual motion machine. Random bombardment by air molecules would make the windmill twist now this way, now the other, were it not for the ratchet-and-pawl arrangement that permits rotation in one direction only. The windmill is thus expected to turn slowly in one direction thereby lifting, perhaps, a bug. The air molecules responsible for the rotation are slowed down and the air surrounding the windmill cools. This is a perpetuum mobile of the second kind. In a simple but brilliant analysis Feynman[1] points out that the pawl is subject to random temperature motion also, which may lift it sufficiently to permit the ratchet to turn backward every so often. Furthermore, the pawl acts not just as a stopping device preventing rotation in one direction, but also as a mechanism able to *drive* the axle in this "forbidden" direction, being pressed against the inclined-plane-profile of the teeth of the ratchet by a spring. Feynman's analysis shows that work is performed only if the temperature of the air surrounding the windmill differs from that of the pawl and its environment, and that the second law of thermodynamics is quantitatively obeyed.

If the process is reversible, the integral represents ΔS, which is therefore zero for the adiabatic process considered.   Reversible adiabatic processes may thus also be called **isentropic.**   If the process is irreversible, the integral, while still zero, no longer represents ΔS, but we deduce from (3–4) that

---

[1] R. P. Feynman, R. B. Leighton, and M. Sands, *The Feynman Lectures on Physics*, Addison-Wesley, Reading, Mass., 1964, Volume 1, Chapter 46.

$$\Delta S > 0 \qquad\qquad (3\text{–}7)$$

In other words, ΔS must be positive for any actual adiabatic process. To find ΔS for such a process a new path must be invented that leads from the same initial to the same final states and is reversible. It need not be adiabatic, because it is just an auxiliary path, used to calculate ΔS. In fact, an adiabatic reversible path *need not exist*.

Consider, for example, a system that consists initially of two quantities of water at different temperatures. The two quantities are mixed adiabatically, and it is desired to find the change in entropy of the system. The process considered is certainly irreversible. To reach the same final state reversibly, the two portions of water must be brought to the common final temperature separately and *reversibly*, before being mixed. The mixing will then no longer correspond to a change of state. Reversible heating entails transfer of heat from a source of a temperature that is kept adjusted to match the temperature of the body being heated. The reversible path used is certainly not adiabatic. The details of the calculations involved are given in Example 1.

It follows then from the second law that *the entropy of an adiabatic system can never decrease*. It remains constant for reversible processes and increases for irreversible ones. For unnatural adiabatic processes, the entropy of the system would decrease.

All processes that actually occur are irreversible and thus increase the entropy of an adiabatic system. Once the entropy has attained a value beyond which it cannot increase, all processes must cease. **Equilibrium** in an adiabatic system is characterized by the *maximum* possible value of the *entropy*. The tendency toward increase in entropy represents an important driving force for chemical and physical processes.

If the direction of an irreversible adiabatic process were to be reversed the entropy would decrease. This is prohibited, as implied by the word "irreversible." The second law thus tells in which direction irreversible processes may proceed. It gives a direction, an arrow to time.

All these considerations apply also to *isolated systems*, which are by necessity adiabatic. In particular, the universe may be considered to be an isolated system, whence the famous statement of Clausius': "The entropy of the world strives toward a maximum." Once this maximum has been reached, there is no driving force left to make anything happen. This has been called "*Wärmetod* of the universe" by Clausius. It has been translated as "heat death" but must be imagined not as a death of flame and fire, but rather as a prosaic end of completely uniform, uninteresting temperature, and monotonous randomness in everything else. The assumption that the universe is closed and isolated is, of course, outside of thermodynamics and hard to verify.

3–3   NONADIABATIC SYSTEMS

In nonadiabatic systems a decrease of the entropy is perfectly possible, provided it is at least balanced by an entropy increase of the surroundings. This can be seen by combining the system considered and its surroundings into a new isolated system. The entropy change in the new system, ΔS_{tot}, is the sum of the entropy change of the original system, ΔS_{syst}, and that of the surroundings, ΔS_{surr}. Because the total system is isolated,

$$\Delta S_{tot} = \Delta S_{syst} + \Delta S_{surr} \geqslant 0 \qquad \text{or} \qquad \Delta S_{surr} \geqslant -\Delta S_{syst}$$

Therefore, if the entropy of the system decreases, this must be compensated by *at least* an equal entropy increase of the surroundings.

EXAMPLE 1

Through an electric resistor of 10 ohms that is kept at a constant temperature of 25°C by a stream of water a current of 5 amp is passed. What are the entropy changes of the resistor and of the surroundings in 1 sec? The entropy change of the resistor is zero, because entropy is a function of state and the state of the resistor remains unchanged. However, the resistor transfers energy in the form of heat to the surroundings. The voltage across the resistor is the product of current and resistance, which is $5 \times 10 = 50$ volts. The power is $50 \times 5 = 250$ volt-amp or watts (see p. 26), which comes to an energy of 250 joules or

$250/4.184 = 59.74$ cal dissipated in 1 sec. The entropy gain of the surroundings during the second is

$$\Delta S = \int_1^2 \frac{Dq}{T} = \frac{1}{T} \int_1^2 Dq = 59.7 \text{ cal}/298 \text{ deg} = \mathbf{0.200 \text{ cal/deg}}$$

This causes an entropy gain of the universe by 0.200 cal/deg during the second considered—a positive quantity, as it must be.

3–4   TWO IRREVERSIBLE PROCESSES

Entropy principles are now applied to two simple irreversible processes, the first concerning transfer of heat, the second expansion of a gas into a vacuum.

We consider first the transfer of the (positive) heat Dq from a body of temperature T_1 to one of temperature T_2. This is not necessarily a reversible process, but the same final state may be reached reversibly by transferring the positive heat Dq from body 1 to a constant-temperature bath at T_1 and an equal Dq from a bath at T_2 to body 2. Taking signs into account, the entropy changes of bodies 1 and 2 are

$$dS_1 = -\frac{Dq}{T_1} \qquad dS_2 = +\frac{Dq}{T_2}$$

In the actual transfer of Dq from body 1 to body 2 there are no interactions between the two bodies and the surroundings. The total entropy change, $dS_1 + dS_2$, therefore, cannot be negative. It follows that

$$\frac{Dq}{T_2} - \frac{Dq}{T_1} = Dq \left(\frac{1}{T_2} - \frac{1}{T_1} \right) \geqslant 0 \qquad \text{or} \qquad T_1 \geqslant T_2$$

When T_1 equals T_2 the heat Dq may flow in either direction: There is equilibrium. For spontaneous, irreversible heat flow, T_1 must be larger than T_2. Both results are in such complete agreement with experience as to appear almost trivial. In fact, the first of them is our original criterion for temperature equality of two bodies and has also just been used to devise a reversible path to find the entropy change. Our example is thus of circular nature, but it is instructive and at least has not led to internal contradictions.

The second example deals with the isothermal expansion of a perfect gas into a vacuum, which was considered earlier (Section 1–7). Initial and final volumes are V_1 and V_2. To find ΔS, the irreversible process is replaced by an isothermal reversible expansion of the gas, in which the pressure on the gas is reduced gradually so as to be always equal to nRT/V. Because the temperature remains constant and $U = U(T)$, $dU = 0$ and therefore $Dq_{rev} = -Dw = P\,dV$. Furthermore, $Dq_{rev}/T = (nRT/VT)dV = nR\,dV/V$, so that

$$\Delta S = \int_1^2 \frac{Dq_{rev}}{T} = nR \int_1^2 \frac{dV}{V} = nR\ln V\big|_1^2 = nR(\ln V_2 - \ln V_1)$$

Finally,

$$\Delta S = nR \ln \left(\frac{V_2}{V_1}\right) \tag{3–8}$$

This is the entropy change for the isothermal expansion of a perfect gas no matter what the path, whether it be the reversible one chosen or any irreversible path, like expansion into a vacuum. On the other hand, for the actual path

$$\int_1^2 \frac{Dq}{T} = 0$$

because $w = 0$ as discussed earlier, and since $\Delta U = 0$, q and Dq remain zero also. In this special case isothermal and adiabatic paths coincide. Applying the second law, we have

$$\Delta S = nR \ln \left(\frac{V_2}{V_1}\right) \geqslant 0 \tag{3–9}$$

The process considered is thus spontaneous provided V_2 is larger than V_1, as has been tacitly assumed. If V_2 were smaller than V_1, ΔS would be negative; the process, a spontaneous contraction, is hence against the second law. Equilibrium exists only if V_2 is equal to V_1, or if there is no vacuum for the gas to expand into.

In a similar way, other irreversible processes, such as heating a system by frictional work and dissolving sugar in water, are paralleled by an increase in entropy.

EXAMPLE 2

The pressure on 1 mole of helium is reduced from 1 atm to 0.1 atm at 50°C. Assume the gas to be perfect and to have a constant molar heat capacity $\tilde{C}_V$ of 2.97 cal/mole-deg. What are ΔU, ΔH, and ΔS? For a perfect gas U and H depend on the temperature only, and therefore $\Delta U = \Delta H = 0$, and $Dq = -Dw$. If the expansion is carried our reversibly, $Dw = -P\,dV = -Pd(RT/P)_T = -PRT(-dP/P^2) = RT\,dP/P$, so that $Dq_{\text{rev}}/T = -R\,dP/P$. Thus, $\Delta S = -R \int_1^{0.1} dP/P = -R \ln(0.1/1) = R \ln 10 = 1.987 \times 2.303$ cal/mole-deg = **4.58 cal/mole-deg.**

4 The Microscopic Interpretation of Entropy, the Third Law, and Applications

"What, never? Well, hardly ever."
—W. S. Gilbert

Boltzmann's statistical interpretation of entropy is developed and examples are provided. The change of entropy with temperature is analyzed in some detail, and entropy changes caused by phase transformations are considered. The rules of Pictet-Trouton and of Hildebrand are discussed and their meaning explored. This is followed by a statement of the third law of thermodynamics and an exposition of its molecular basis. Some of the consequences of this law are indicated, the evaluation of entropies from thermal measurements considered, and the difference between absolute and standard entropies explained. Finally, the efficiency of heat engines and refrigerators is examined and the Clausius-Clapeyron equation derived.

4–1 STATISTICAL INTERPRETATION OF THE ENTROPY

Although not part of thermodynamics proper, the microscopic interpretation is particularly helpful in imparting an intuitive feeling for entropy and in permitting the development of plausibility arguments for its behavior.

The macroscopic state of an isolated system may be described by stating chemical compositions and the values of volume, pressure, total energy, and similar macroscopic quantities. It is not necessary to describe the locations and velocities of all atoms and molecules involved. For example, in a gas the *pressure* is the result of momentum transfer to the wall in many collisions. No details need be specified —only the average momentum transferred needs be known to account for the pressure on the wall. A given *temperature* is characterized by a certain velocity distribution, and the question of which particular molecules have velocities in a certain range is left open.

A state in which all details that can be known about atoms and

molecules are specified is called a microscopic state or **microstate.**
Usually, a huge number of possible microstates corresponds to a
given macroscopic state or **macrostate.** They are indistinguishable
at the macroscopic level and are called **realizations** of the macrostate. To illustrate, there are many different microstates in which
the velocities of individual molecules differ but for which the *average* velocity is unchanged, so that all these microstates correspond to
the same macroscopic quantity, called temperature. The number
of microscopic realizations of a macroscopic state of fixed energy is
denoted by Ω.

Suppose that an isolated system is in a certain macroscopic
state 1 with Ω_1 microscopic realizations, and that there is accessible
to it a macrostate 2 with Ω_2 microscopic realizations. If Ω_2 is larger
than Ω_1, it stands to reason that the system tends to assume state 2
under the randomizing influence of temperature motion. The state
of a system tends to move in the direction of increasing numbers of
realizations until Ω has reached the highest value possible.

An example designed to illustrate this behavior concerns a box
containing many red and blue spheres of equal size and mass. At
the beginning all red spheres are placed in layers at the bottom of
the box, and the blue spheres on top. The box is then shaken vigor-
ously. At the end the distribution of the colored spheres is random.
The microscopic realizations of the initial state are obtained by interchanging all the red spheres and, separately, all the blue spheres
among themselves. The microstates that correspond to the final
macrostate are obtained by interchanging *all* spheres with each
other, regardless of their color. Clearly, the final state has more
microscopic realizations than the initial state. There are parallels
between this example and the dissolving of a substance. Starting
with pure solvent and solute the temperature motion will eventually
cause the solute molecules to be distributed evenly throughout the
solvent, just as continued shaking of the box results eventually in a
completely random distribution of the colored spheres. It is extremely unlikely that a solution will ever become unmixed into pure
solvent and solute, just as it is unlikely that shaking of the box will
ever substantially decrease the randomness of the distribution of the
colored spheres.

In another example, the first state is the initial state of the expansion of a gas into a vacuum, with all gas at volume V_1. State 2 corresponds to the complete expansion of the gas to the final volume V_2. Because V_2 is larger than V_1, the number of microscopic realizations of the final state is larger than that of the initial state. This example is treated more quantitatively in Section 4–2.

It is apparent that Ω and S behave in a similar way. Both increase during spontaneous processes in isolated systems and assume their maximum values when equilibrium has been reached. The same behavior is shared by any function that increases steadily (or monotonically) with Ω, and the question is whether it is possible to equate any such function with S. It was shown by Boltzmann that this is indeed the case for the natural logarithm of Ω. He showed that for an isolated system the entropy must be proportional to $\ln \Omega$, and he set

$$S = k \ln \Omega \qquad (4\text{–}1)$$

The proportionality factor is the Boltzmann constant or the gas constant R divided by Avogadro's number N, $k = R/N = (1.9872$ cal/mole-deg$)/0.602252 \times 10^{24}$ mole$^{-1} = 3.2996 \times 10^{-24}$ cal/deg $= 1.38054 \times 10^{-23}$ joule/deg. Note that (4–1) refers not to an entropy *difference* but to absolute entropy. However, more of this in Section 4–6.

The appropriateness of setting $k \ln \Omega$ equal to the entropy can be seen as follows: Consider two isolated, and therefore independent, systems 1 and 2. Associated with them are the quantities S_1, S_2, Ω_1, and Ω_2. Without disturbing the independence of the two systems they may be joined in thought into one total system. Now *each* of the Ω_1 microscopic realizations of the state of system 1 may be combined with *any one* of the Ω_2 realizations of the state of system 2 into a possible realization of the state of the total system. The number Ω of such realizations is thus equal to the product $\Omega_1\Omega_2$,

$$\Omega = \Omega_1\Omega_2 \qquad (4\text{–}2)$$

On the other hand, the entropy of the total system is the *sum* of the entropies of the separate and independent systems,

$$S = S_1 + S_2 \qquad (4\text{–}3)$$

It is seen that (4–2) and (4–3) are compatible with (4–1):

$$S_1 + S_2 = k \ln \Omega_1 + k \ln \Omega_2 = k \ln(\Omega_1\Omega_2) = k \ln \Omega = S$$

It can be shown that the logarithm is the only function that shows the behavior just discussed (see Appendix 3).

The evaluation of Ω for a given situation usually requires quantum mechanics. Boltzmann's relationship (4–1) will therefore be used mainly in a qualitative way to understand the nature of entropy. It is seen that *entropy is a measure of molecular disorder*, and the increase in entropy parallels increase in this disorder. The second law is thus a matter of probability: Under the influence of temperature motion a system tends to assume the state of maximum probability. The arrow of time is in the direction of spreading the total energy of a system over as many energy levels as are accessible.

If increase of entropy is a probability matter, there is always the chance that the second law might be broken. The path along which a system moves may at rare times veer to less likely states rather than proceeding along to more and more likely states. To illustrate, the usually random temperature motions of the molecules of an object may all happen to be directed upward, so that the whole object moves upward in apparent defiance of gravity. Such a phenomenon would not violate the first law, because the source of the kinetic energy for this motion would be the internal energy of the object. The object would be cooler than it was, because temperature is a measure of the part of molecular motions that is random. The chance that the second law is broken in such fashion can be calculated and is so incredibly small for any macroscopic object that the possibility of its observation can be ruled out. Minute objects do, however, exhibit randomness in their behavior. Examples are the Brownian motion, and the fluctuations in the density of air that are responsible for the blue color of the sky.

4–2 A QUANTITATIVE EXAMPLE

There are cases where quantitative considerations using Ω are possible at an elementary level. One of them is the adiabatic expansion of n moles of a perfect gas considered earlier. It is not necessary to find the value of Ω itself, but only to establish how it depends on the gas volume V. To this end we imagine this volume divided into a huge number of very small cells, and the $N' = nN$ molecules distributed over these cells. The cells are all to have equal and constant volume, so that the total number of cells is proportional to V. The total number of microstates is proportional to the number of different distributions over the cells. Because there is no interaction among the molecules of a perfect gas, each molecule may occupy any of these cells independently of all other molecules. For each molecule the number of possibilities is proportional to V, and for N' molecules therefore to $V^{N'}$, so that

$$\Omega = \text{const} \cdot V^{N'} \tag{4–4}$$

The constant contains the number of possibilities of apportioning the molecules to the different velocity ranges, which are independent of V or the size of the cells chosen.

The foregoing count includes microstates where a majority of the molecules are crowded into one or just a few cells—microstates that are by intuition very unlikely. Closer examination shows, however, that the number of such microstates is exceedingly small compared to those of approximately uniform distributions, provided N' is very large. The contribution to Ω from such realizations is negligible. There are, of course, continuous *small* fluctuations from the average occupancy of the cells, and the density of the gas is never exactly uniform.

If the gas expands from the volume V_1 to V_2, the ratio of the corresponding Ω's is

$$\frac{\Omega_1}{\Omega_2} = \frac{\text{const } V_1^{N'}}{\text{const } V_2^{N'}} = \left(\frac{V_1}{V_2}\right)^{N'}$$

The constants cancel, and use of (4–1) gives the result for ΔS:

$$\Delta S = k \ln \Omega_2 - k \ln \Omega_1 = k \ln \frac{\Omega_2}{\Omega_1} = k \ln \left(\frac{V_2}{V_1}\right)^{nN}$$

$$= nNk \ln \left(\frac{V_2}{V_1}\right) = nR \ln \left(\frac{V_2}{V_1}\right) \tag{4–5}$$

This is identical with the thermodynamic result (3–8).

The same result may be obtained by the argument that the ratio Ω_1/Ω_2 must equal the ratio of the chance of finding all molecules spread over the original volume V_1 to that of finding them distributed over the final volume V_2. Now the ratio of the chance of finding *a particular* molecule in V_1 to finding it in V_2 is simply V_1/V_2. Because all $\mathcal{N}'$ molecules are independent of each other, the chance ratio for all molecules is the product of all the ratios for each of them, or $\Omega_1/\Omega_2 = (V_1/V_2)^{\mathcal{N}'}$, as before.

4–3   TEMPERATURE DEPENDENCE OF THE ENTROPY

To investigate the dependence of entropy on temperature, we begin with the entropy change for an infinitesimal reversible process, $dS = Dq_{rev}/T$, and set $Dq_{rev} = C_X\, dT$. As explained earlier, the heat capacity C_X depends on the details of the reversible path X.

For example, at constant pressure, $Dq_{rev} = C_P\, dT$, so that $dS = (C_P/T)\, dT$. For a finite reversible change at constant pressure, the entropy change is therefore

$$\Delta S = \int_{T_1}^{T_2} \left(\frac{C_P}{T}\right) dT \tag{4–6}$$

Because dT/T is just equal to $d \ln T$, $(C_P/T)\, dT$ may also be written $C_P\, d \ln T$, and thus

$$\Delta S = \int_{T_1}^{T_2} C_P\, d \ln T \tag{4–7}$$

EXAMPLE 1

What is the entropy increase when 100 g of H_2O at 0°C are mixed adiabatically with 100 g of H_2O at 100°C, both in liquid form? This is an example of an irreversible adiabatic process discussed earlier (p. 75). Assuming a constant specific-heat capacity C_P of 1.00 cal/g-deg, the final temperature is seen to be 50°C, because for this final temperature the enthalpy gain of the water being heated is just compensated by the enthalpy loss of the water being cooled. To reach the same final state reversibly, we heat the cold water from 273 to 323°K by placing it in contact with a temperature bath that is kept adjusted to be only by an infinitesimal amount warmer than the water. The hot water is cooled from 373 to 323°K in a similar way. The entropy change is

$$\Delta S = \int_{273}^{323} C_P \, d \ln T + \int_{373}^{323} C_P \, d \ln T$$

$$= C_P \ln \frac{323}{273} + C_P \ln \frac{323}{373} = C_P \ln [(323)^2/273 \times 373]$$

where C_P is the heat capacity of 100 g of water, or 100 cal/deg. In numbers,

$$\Delta S = (100 \times 2.30 \log 1.0246) \text{ cal/deg} = \mathbf{2.43 \ cal/degree}$$

When C_P is not constant, its dependence on the temperature may be handled graphically. To give an example, Fig. 4–1 shows

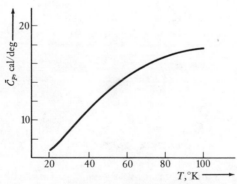

Figure 4–1   The molar heat capacity $\tilde{C}_P$ of crystalline PbI₂. The heat capacity may be determined by measuring the energy δU required to increase the temperature of the substance investigated from T to $T + \delta T$, where both δT and δU are small quantities. The molar heat capacity—$\tilde{C}_P$ for constant-pressure measurements—is the limit of the ratio $\delta U/\delta T$ as δT goes to zero. The heating is usually accomplished by electrical means.

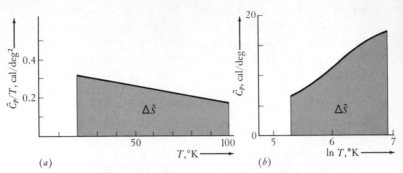

Figure 4–2 Two calculations of the entropy increase caused by a temperature increase. In (*a*), $\tilde{C}_P/T$ is plotted against the temperature. By (4–6) the area shown equals $\Delta\tilde{S}$ when $PbI_2(s)$ is heated from 20 to 100°K. In (*b*), $\tilde{C}_P$ is plotted against $\ln T$ and by (4–7) the area shown is again equal to $\Delta\tilde{S}$.

the molar heat capacity of $PbI_2(s)$ between 20 and 100°K. In Fig. 4–2(*a*) $\tilde{C}_P/T$ is plotted versus T, and in Fig. 4–2(*b*) C_P versus $\ln T$. By (4–6) and (4–7) the areas shown both represent $\Delta\tilde{S}$ for heating $PbI_2(s)$ from 20 to 100°K.

Similarly, for heating at constant volume, we have

$$\Delta S = \int_{T_1}^{T_2} \left(\frac{C_V}{T}\right) dT = \int_{T_1}^{T_2} C_V \, d\ln T \qquad (4\text{–}8)$$

It is seen from (4–6) and (4–8) that the entropy of a substance *increases* when the temperature is increased along a reversible *constant-pressure* or *constant-volume* path.

When the heating occurs at *constant volume*, the entropy increase is due exclusively to an increase in randomness of molecular motion. For gases the spread of atomic or molecular velocities is larger at higher temperatures, as seen for example in Fig. 4–3, where the velocity distributions for O_2 at 273 and 373°K are shown. The same is true for rotational and vibrational motions of molecules. For example, Fig. 4–4 refers to idealized molecules with evenly

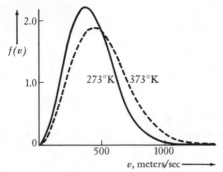

Figure 4–3 Maxwell-Boltzmann distribution for O₂. The fraction of molecules with speeds in the range extending from v to $v + dv$ is given by $f(v)\ dv$. The total area under either curve is thus equal to unity. At the higher temperature the energy is seen to be spread over a wider total range of velocities, corresponding to a higher entropy.

spaced energy levels and the increase in the spread of the level occupancies caused by doubling the temperature. Generally, increase of entropy means spreading of the total energy over more energy levels.

For heating at *constant pressure* there is an additional increase in randomness, connected with the volume increase. This corresponds, of course, to the larger heat input required in constant-*pressure* heating over heating at constant *volume*. Isolated exceptions exist in which the volume decreases upon temperature increase. An example is water at temperatures below the density maximum. However, C_P is never smaller than C_V, and even when the volume decreases as the temperature is raised at constant P, the increase in the randomness of molecular arrangement is still larger than it would be at constant V. Only when there is no volume change with temperature (water at density maximum) are C_P and C_V equal.

It is important to see that the entropy *need* not increase with temperature. For example, when a gas is compressed adiabatically and reversibly, there is *no* entropy change. The randomness on the molecular level remains constant. However, the decrease in

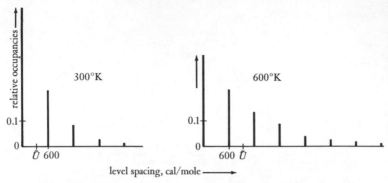

Figure 4–4 Fractional occupancies for idealized molecules with evenly spaced energy levels. The lengths of the vertical lines are proportional to the relative occupancies of the levels. The sum of the lengths is 1.0 in both diagrams. The level separation is indicated in calories per mole, so that, for example, 1 mole of molecules at the 600 cal/mole level would contain an energy of 600 cal. The values of $\bar{U}$ shown represent the total energy of 1 mole of molecules distributed over the different levels as indicated. At 600°K the spread over the levels is larger than at 300°K and the entropy is also larger. The energy $\bar{U}$ of the system is larger at 600°K because of the larger number of molecules in high energy levels.

The exponential decrease of the lengths of the vertical lines that is evident upon inspection is characteristic of what is known as the Boltzmann factor. This factor, $\exp(-\epsilon/kT)$, gives the ratio of the occupancies at temperature T of any two energy levels separated by the energy ϵ; k is the same Boltzmann constant that appears in (4–1). If the level separation is given in terms of $N\epsilon$, that is, of the energy of Avogadro's number or 1 mole of molecules, ϵ/kT is replaced by $N\epsilon/RT$ because $R = kN$. One mole of molecules at T contains an energy comparable with the energy RT; per molecule this energy is kT.

volume corresponds to a decrease in randomness of the spatial distribution of the molecule. To compensate for this loss, there must be an equal increase in randomness of molecular motion. This implies an increase in temperature, which is indeed observed. The increase in temperature is, of course, required by the first law also, because the performance of the work required in the adiabatic compression increases the energy of the gas. Higher energy implies higher temperature, since the energy of a gas is a monotonic or steadily increasing function of the temperature.

Conversely the temperature of a gas may be lowered by reversible adiabatic expansion, called therefore **adiabatic cooling.** The expansion by itself increases the randomness, and because $\Delta S = 0$, the randomness of the temperature motion and thus the temperature itself must decrease. This is discussed further in Section 8–3.

Although the discussion of adiabatic expansion in the two preceding paragraphs always holds for gases, it more generally applies only to substances that expand upon temperature increase. For a contrary example, when water below its density maximum is compressed adiabatically and reversibly, there is slight cooling, because to a smaller volume there corresponds *more* randomness in this case. Since $\Delta S = 0$, a smaller volume leads to a lower temperature.

The entropy of a system may even decrease upon temperature increase, provided the volume is decreased sufficiently. This is illustrated by the next example. All that can be said unequivocally is that the entropy always increases upon reversible input of heat. When Dq_{rev} is positive, so is $dS = Dq_{rev}/T$. This formula also shows that the increase of randomness caused by a given Dq_{rev} is larger at low than at high temperatures, on account of the factor $1/T$.

EXAMPLE 2

What is ΔS for the following change of state: He(g, 22.4 liters, 273°K) = He(g, 2.24 liters, 546°K) assuming He to be a perfect gas and to have a constant molar heat capacity $\tilde{C}_P$ of 2.97 cal/mole-deg? We carry out the following two steps reversibly: First we raise the temperature isochorically to 546°K.

For this step $\Delta S_1 = \int_{273}^{546} \tilde{C}_V \, d \ln T = \tilde{C}_V \ln(546/273) =$ 2.97 × 0.693 cal/mole-deg = 2.06 cal/mole-deg. Next we decrease the volume isothermally from 22.4 to 2.24 liters. Since $U = U(T)$, $dU = 0$ and $Dq = -Dw$. For a reversible compression $Dw = -P \, dV = -RT \, dV/V$, so that $Dq_{rev}/T =$

$R \ dV/V$.   Thus, $\Delta S_2 = R \displaystyle\int_{22.4}^{2.24} d \ln V = R \ln(2.24/22.4) =$
$-R \ln 10 = -1.99 \times 2.30$ cal/mole-deg $= -4.58$ cal/mole-deg.   Finally, $\Delta S = \Delta S_1 + \Delta S_2 = -2.52$ **cal/mole-deg.**   This is a decrease in entropy, in spite of the increase in temperature.

4–4   ENTROPY CHANGES IN PHASE TRANSFORMATIONS

During a reversible phase transformation such as melting or evaporation, the transformation temperature T_{tr} remains constant and may thus be placed in front of the integral in the formula for the entropy change.   Consider, for example, the vaporization of a liquid at its normal boiling point T_b and at 1 atm.   This can readily be done reversibly in a bath of constant temperature T_b (Fig. 4–5)

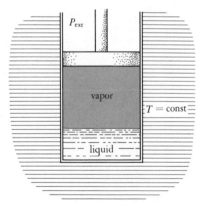

Figure 4–5   Reversible vaporization of a liquid at T_b and 1 atm.   The constant-temperature bath supplies the enthalpy of vaporization at the equilibrium temperature T_b.   The vaporization is reversible because it can be changed into a condensation by an infinitesimal increase in the external pressure P_{ext}: As long as P_{ext} is smaller than the vapor pressure of 1 atm by an infinitesimal amount, the piston slowly moves outward and the liquid is vaporized.   If the external pressure exceeds the vapor pressure the piston moves slowly inward and vapor condenses.

that supplies the enthalpy of vaporization ΔH_{vap}. The entropy of vaporization ΔS_{vap} is then

$$\Delta S_{vap} = \int_1^2 \frac{Dq_{rev}}{T_b} = \frac{1}{T_b} \int_1^2 Dq_{rev} = \frac{\Delta H_{vap}}{T_b}$$

where ΔH_{vap} is the enthalpy of vaporization and T_b is the boiling point. Quite generally, for any phase transformation the entropy change ΔS_{tr} is

$$\Delta S_{tr} = \frac{\Delta H_{tr}}{T_{tr}} \qquad (4\text{--}9)$$

with ΔH_{tr} the enthalpy change for the transformation and T_{tr} the transformation temperature at which the two phases are at equilibrium. For example, two solid phases may be involved, such as orthorhombic and monoclinic sulfur.

The entropy increases when a solid is melted or sublimated, or when a liquid is vaporized, because ΔH_{tr} is positive in all these cases. This is readily understood on the microscopic plane, because the state of disorder increases in all three cases considered.

Caution must, however, be used in arguments that relate entropy increase to loss of order. A good example of apparent contradictions that may arise in this connection is due to Bridgman and concerns a supercooled melt that suddenly crystallizes. This is a spontaneous process, so that the entropy must increase. Yet, how can it, since crystallization of the liquid results in a more orderly state? The answer is that if the system is adiabatic, the heat of fusion liberated increases the temperature, and thus the thermal motion, sufficiently so that there is a net increase in disorder. If the system is kept at constant temperature, the heat liberated increases the entropy of the surroundings sufficiently to cause a net gain of the total entropy of system and surroundings. An example is worked out in Problem 4–10.

Table 4–1 contains a number of entropies of fusion and of vaporization. It will be noted that the entropy of fusion is generally smaller than the entropy of vaporization. This indicates that the increase in randomness is smaller when going from the solid to the

Table 4–1
Molar Entropies of Fusion and Vaporization

	$\Delta \tilde{S}_{melt}$, cal/mole-deg	$\Delta \tilde{S}_{vap}$, cal/mole-deg
N_2	2.73	17.2
O_2	1.95	18.1
Cl_2	8.89	20.4
CO	2.93	17.7
CH_4	2.47	17.8
CCl_4	2.31	20.5
NH_3	6.92	23.3
PH_3	1.94	18.8
Hg	2.38	22.0

liquid than when going from the liquid to the vapor. Note also the orders of magnitudes of these molar entropy changes, a few tenths to some 10 cal/mole-deg. It is *small* calories per mole-degree that are involved, while the corresponding molar enthalpy changes are best expressed in kilocalories per mole. Furthermore, the dimensionality of entropy differs from that of energy and enthalpy by the factor *degree*$^{-1}$.

4–5   THE RULES OF PICTET–TROUTON AND OF HILDEBRAND

Inspection of Table 4–1 shows that the entropies of vaporization for many liquids are approximately the same, but that there is no similar regularity shown by the entropies of fusion. The approximate constancy of $\Delta \tilde{S}_{vap}$ is called the **rule of Pictet and Trouton,** according to which

$$\frac{\Delta \tilde{H}_{vap}}{T_b} = \Delta \tilde{S}_{vap} \approx 21 \text{ cal/mole-deg} \qquad (4\text{–}10)$$

where T_b is the boiling temperature at 1 atm. This rule holds fairly well for many liquids, but there are also exceptions, as seen in Table 4–1.

The quantities related by the rule of Pictet and Trouton are those at the normal boiling point. The change in state is that of 1 mole liquid to vapor at 1 atm, in equilibrium with the liquid at the normal boiling temperature. It was argued by Hildebrand that for comparison purposes it would be better to evaluate $\Delta \tilde{S}_{vap}$ for a change in state chosen so the molar volumes of the different vapors are always the same, rather than to make the comparison at a common pressure of 1 atm. Table 4–2 contains such ΔS_{vap} data, for which the vapor volume has been arbitrarily chosen to be 22.4

Table 4–2
Molar Entropies of Vaporization[a]

Substance	T_b, °K	T', °K	$\Delta \tilde{S}_{vap}(T_b)$, cal/deg-mole	$\Delta \tilde{S}_{vap}(T')$, cal/deg-mole
He	4.22	1.53	4.7	13.1
Ne	27.2	21.1	15.8	20.4
Ar	87.3	77.5	17.9	20.2
H_2	20.39	13.7	10.6	15.8
N_2	77.3	67.5	17.2	19.8
O_2	90.2	80.4	18.1	20.3
F_2	85.2	75.4	17.7	20.0
Cl_2	239	236	20.4	20.7
CH_4	111.7	101	17.5	19.4
C_2H_2	189	184	22.2	22.8
C_2N_2	252	250	22.1	22.3
CO	81.7	72.0	17.7	20.1
CCl_4	350	358	20.5	20.0
CH_3OH	338	344	24.9	24.5
NH_3	240	237	23.2	23.5
H_2O	373	383	26.1	25.4
H_2O_2	423	435	30.1	29.9
PH_3	185	178	18.9	19.6
Cu	2855	3500	25.5	20.8
Hg	630	680	22.1	20.4

[a] Data from L. Pauling, *College Chemistry*, 3rd ed., Freeman, San Francisco, 1964.

liters, the mole volume of a perfect gas at STP. For each liquid the boiling temperature T' at which the vapor occupies 22.4 liters can be found from the following two conditions: (1) the vapor pressure P' must satisfy the (known) vapor pressure equation $P' = P_{vap}(T')$; (2) assuming that the vapor behaves like a perfect gas (good enough for the present purpose), P' must satisfy the perfect gas equation $P' = RT'/22.4$. The two conditions combined, $P_{vap}(T') = RT'/22.4$ specify T'. The difference between ΔH_{vap} at T_b and at T' is small and can be neglected.

It is found that for many liquids

$$\Delta S_{vap}(T') = \frac{\Delta H_{vap}}{T'} \approx 20.3 \text{ cal/deg}$$

This improved version of the Pictet-Trouton rule is called Hildebrand's rule. Table 4–2 contains examples of some liquids that obey these rules and of others that do not (see also Problem 4–19).

Eyring and others have offered the structural explanation for this constancy of the entropy of vaporization, that in a liquid each molecule is inside a cage bounded by other molecules, in which it may execute unhindered motions that are interfered with only by collisions with the molecules bounding the cage. The molecules in the liquid thus behave similarly to gas molecules, except for the much smaller volume available to them. If the average volume in which the center of mass of a molecule in the liquid may move freely is $\tilde{V}_{liq}$ (per mole), the evaporation of the liquid to vapor of volume $\tilde{V}_{vap}$ may be roughly compared with the isothermal, reversible expansion of 1 mole of gas of volume $\tilde{V}_{liq}$ to $\tilde{V}_{vap}$. The molar entropy increase $\Delta \tilde{S}$ for this change of volume is, by (3–8),

$$\Delta \tilde{S} = R \ln \left(\frac{\tilde{V}_{vap}}{\tilde{V}_{liq}} \right)$$

The fact that the constancy of $\Delta \tilde{S}_{vap}$ is improved when insisting on a constant volume of the vapor lends support to this explanation, but requires that $\tilde{V}_{liq}$ also be approximately constant from liquid to liquid. The value of $\tilde{V}_{liq}$ is $\tilde{V}_{vap} \exp(-\Delta \tilde{S}/R) = [22{,}400 \exp (-20.3/1.99)]$ ml $= (22{,}400/27{,}200)$ ml $= 0.82$ ml.

The molecular theory of liquids is not sufficiently advanced to interpret this result completely. The cage theory is largely qualitative and has not found wide acceptance. The cages are, of course, not stationary, but move about, disappear, and reappear with great rapidity.

In all cases of large deviations from the Hildebrand or Pictet-Trouton rules there exist structural explanations. For example, when hydrogen bonds are formed in the liquid the liquid is more highly ordered than normal. The increase in randomness upon evaporation is therefore larger than normal, with a corresponding larger entropy of evaporation. This is the case for H_2O, H_2O_2, CH_3OH, and NH_3. There are also deviations when the molecules involved are elongated or differ in other ways from being roughly spherical. This decreases the randomness in the liquid phase, because neighboring molecules tend to line up in a complementary fashion when packed together closely, whereas there is no similar lining up required for roughly spherical molecules. Good examples are the linear molecules cyanogen, $N \equiv C — C \equiv N$, and acetylene, $H — C \equiv C — H$. Hydrogen and helium have abnormally small values of ΔS_{vap} because of quantum effects associated with the small masses of these molecules.

4–6   THIRD LAW OF THERMODYNAMICS

The content of the third law of thermodynamics is that the *entropy of a well-ordered crystalline phase tends toward zero as the absolute zero of temperature is approached*. The additive constant left disposable by the second-law definition of the entropy is thereby fixed. It is seen, however, that the qualification "well-ordered" in the statement of the third law cannot be defined on the macroscopic level but is borrowed from the microscopic description. It is impossible to state the third law without such a qualification, and in this regard the third law transcends the bounds of thermodynamics.

Turning to the statistical interpretation of entropy we see that to $S = 0$ corresponds $\Omega = 1$. Zero entropy thus corresponds to a state that has only one microscopic realization. Indeed, a perfectly ordered crystal at $0°K$ corresponds to exactly one microstate.

This is the ground state of the crystal, where each atom has a well-defined equilibrium position and is in its state of motion of lowest energy. It is important to realize and is part of the fundamentals of quantum mechanics that identical particles (like electrons, protons, and atoms of the same atomic number and mass number) are indistinguishable and that their interchange cannot be recognized and does not lead to new microstates (see also Appendix 3).

For phases in which not all randomness of arrangement or of motion is removed as the temperature approaches zero, a nonzero **residual entropy** remains. This happens, for example, with glasses, in which randomness of atomic arrangement persists. Furthermore, there are crystals known that have a disordered structure and it has been found experimentally that their entropies do not go to zero when the temperature zero is approached.

For example, it is found that at very low temperatures crystals of CO still have an entropy of 1.1 cal/mole-deg, whereas in the same temperature region the isoelectronic substance N_2 has zero entropy. The structural reason for the residual entropy of CO crystals is this: The two ends of the CO molecule are similar enough that upon packing into a crystal it does not greatly matter which of the two possible ways each molecule is oriented. If it did not matter at all, the number of microstates for 1 mole of crystalline CO at $0°K$ would therefore be $2 \cdot 2 \cdot 2 \cdots \cdots 2$, N times, or $\Omega_0 = 2^N$. This would correspond to the residual entropy $\tilde{S}_0$,

$$\tilde{S}_0 = k \ln 2^N = Nk \ln 2^N = R \ln 2 = 1.99 \times 0.693 \text{ cal/mole-deg}$$
$$= 1.4 \text{ cal/mole-deg}$$

The fact that the experimental value is somewhat smaller may be due to partial ordering in the crystal, or to experimental inaccuracy. Once a crystal with a certain arrangement of CO molecules has been formed, further lowering of the temperature is not expected to produce a more highly ordered structure. Even if such a structure were slightly more stable than the disordered structure, the enthalpy of activation needed for the required reorientation of the molecules would not be available. It is therefore not expected that the experimental value of the residual entropy would decrease further if the crystals were cooled to temperatures lower than those used to determine the value given, at least not in a finite time. The disorder is said to be **frozen in.** There are other cases of disordered crystals for which the residual entropy has been measured and found to be in agreement with expectations.

4–7 CONSEQUENCES OF THE THIRD LAW

The third law leads to a number of consequences, all of which have been verified experimentally. Some of them are that the heat capacities C_P and C_V must vanish as the absolute zero of temperature is approached, and that thermal expansion must approach zero. A further important consequence is that the absolute zero of temperature itself cannot be reached. The closer to zero the temperature of a system is, the more difficult further cooling becomes. It has been said that the effort required to cool a system near 0°K is represented better by a temperature scale ln T rather than T. At 1°K, ln T equals zero; below 1°K, ln T assumes negative values, and as T approaches zero, ln T approaches minus infinity. Decrease of ln T in equal steps $\Delta(\ln T)$ corresponds to lowering T in equal *relative* steps $(\Delta T/T)$, because $\Delta(\ln T) \approx \Delta T/T$ $(d \ln T = dT/T)$.

The lowest temperature reached to date is 2×10^{-5}°K. Low-temperature phenomena are the subject of the interesting and fruitful modern fields of low-temperature chemistry and physics, and of low-temperature engineering. The subject is discussed further in Section 8–3.

4–8 ENTROPIES FROM THERMAL MEASUREMENTS

An important result of the third law is that it permits the determination of entropies by thermal measurements, for substances that assume a well-ordered crystalline structure, so that their residual entropy is zero. Choosing $T_1 = 0$ and $T_2 = T$ in (4–6) and (4–7) leads to the two equivalent expressions

$$S(T) = \int_0^T \frac{C_P}{T} dT \qquad (4\text{–}11)$$

and

$$S(T) = \int_0^T C_P \, d \ln T \qquad (4\text{--}12)$$

The determination of $S(T)$ thus entails experimental measurement of C_P as function of T. Either C_P/T may then be plotted versus T, or C_P versus $\ln T$, and the corresponding areas evaluated graphically. Since it is not possible to reach the absolute zero experimentally, C_P cannot be measured all the way to 0°K. However, procedures of extrapolation are available which are based on the theory of heat capacities of solids.

This development gives the rather drab heat capacities a more interesting aspect: They provide an experimental approach to measuring entropies that are fundamental in determining the direction in which chemical reactions and other processes tend to proceed, and counter to which *no process* may proceed. A moment's reflection shows that this is not surprising. The energy of a system is spread over many possible modes of motion—translational, rotational, vibrational, etc.; in addition the forces acting between molecules claim a certain potential energy for storage. At a given temperature each of these categories contains a certain amount of energy, according to rules that have been worked out by statistical mechanics. When the temperature of the system is raised, the energy in the different modes has to be increased to the level that corresponds to the new temperature. This energy increase is measured by the heat capacity, and conversely, experimental determination of the heat capacity yields information about the energy soaked up by the system. A large heat capacity implies a large number of modes of motion that can be excited, and therefore a large increase in randomness and thus in entropy.

Yet another important aspect of heat capacities has already been discussed—they relate enthalpies of reaction at different temperatures (Section 2–6).

If there are phase transitions between 0 and T°K, such as melting or a transformation from the original solid to a new solid modification, the transformation temperatures and the enthalpies of transformation must be determined also. Consider, for example,

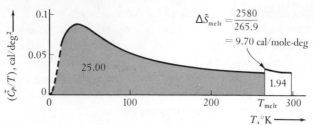

Figure 4–6   Computation of the molar entropy of bromine.
The graph shows C_P/T plotted against T for solid and for liquid
bromine.   Near $0°K$ the measured values for $Br_2(s)$ have been
supplemented by extrapolated values.   The colored area is the
entropy increase when crystalline bromine is heated to its melting
point.   Upon melting the entropy is increased by $\Delta H_m/T_m$, and
$\Delta \tilde{S}$ for heating liquid bromine from the melting point to $298°K$
is equal to the clear area.

liquid bromine at T (Fig. 4–6).   From measurements of the molar
heat capacities of solid and liquid Br_2 at different temperatures, of
the temperature and enthalpy of melting, T_{melt} and $\Delta \tilde{H}_{\text{melt}}$, $\tilde{S}(T)$
may be found:

$$\tilde{S}(T) = \int_0^{T_{\text{melt}}} \tilde{C}_P(s) \, d \ln T + \frac{\Delta \tilde{H}_{\text{melt}}}{T_{\text{melt}}} + \int_{T_{\text{melt}}}^{T} \tilde{C}_P(l) \, d \ln T \tag{4–13}$$

Thus

$$\tilde{S}(298) = (25.00 + 9.70 + 1.94) \text{ cal/mole-deg}$$
$$= 36.64 \text{ cal/mole-deg}$$

More terms are required in cases for which there are several phase
transitions between $0°K$ and T.

Other methods of calculating entropies are available.   For
gases consisting of simple molecules the entropy may be calculated
from spectroscopic information by formulas derived by statistical
mechanics.   Still other methods are mentioned in Chapters 5 and 7.

There has been good agreement in all cases where the entropy of a substance has been obtained by two or more methods.

Entropies of a number of substances at 298°K and 1 atm, obtained by the method described or by other methods are shown in Appendix 4. The magnitudes of these entropies range from about 0.5 to less than 100 cal/mole-deg. The unit calorie per mole-degree is often called the **entropy unit, eu.**

The following generalizations can be made: The entropies of condensed phases are in general smaller than those of gases, and solids tend to have lower entropies than liquids. The entropy of atomic gases is approximately constant, but there is some variation parallel to the masses of the atoms involved.

For gases with polyatomic molecules the molecular motions may often be considered to consist of translational, rotational, and vibrational parts, so that the entropy is the sum of translational, rotational, and vibrational terms. (There may be other terms, such as terms arising when different groups in a molecule are able to rotate against each other. Such refinements will not be considered.)

The translational entropy increases with the molecular mass, as was the case for monoatomic gases. The reason in both cases is that the translational energy levels are more densely spaced as the mass increases. The number of levels over which the energy may be spread is thus larger and the entropy is higher.

In a similar way the energy levels of molecular vibrations and rotations are more closely spaced when the masses of the atoms involved increase. Figure 4–7 shows, for example, some of the rotational levels for the hydrogen halides, and the rotational entropy that corresponds to the occupancies of these levels at 298°C. It is seen to rise from HF through HI. Total entropy values are also given. The main contribution to the total entropy is from translational motion, and increases in the same direction. Vibrational contributions are negligible for HF and small but increasing for HCl, HBr, and HI.

Another example of the operation of the same principles is that gases with molecules containing H atoms have slightly lower entropies than those with D atoms. The difference between the entropies of H_2 (31.2 cal/mole-deg) and D_2 (34.6 cal/mole-deg) is particularly striking.

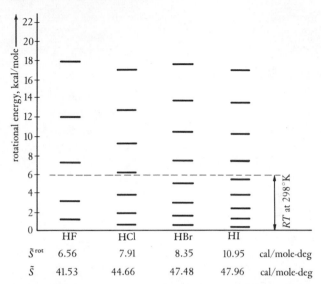

	HF	HCl	HBr	HI	
$\bar{S}^{rot}$	6.56	7.91	8.35	10.95	cal/mole-deg
$\bar{S}$	41.53	44.66	47.48	47.96	cal/mole-deg

Figure 4–7 Rotational energy levels, rotational and total entropies for hydrogen halides at 298°K. The spacings of the levels are shown in kilocalories per mole, referring thus to 1 mole or Avogadro's number of molecules. The energy RT is characteristic of the thermal energy of 1 mole of molecules at the temperature T. The levels are spaced more closely for the molecules with higher moments of inertia, going from HF to HI. The rotational entropy increases in the same direction, because the thermal energy may be spread over successively more levels.

An understanding of all these trends is valuable, but it is important to realize that, counted per total number of atoms rather than molecules, monoatomic gases have the highest entropy. It is, for example, 30.13 cal/mole-deg for Avogadro's number of H atoms and 15.61 cal/mole-deg for one-half Avogadro's number of H_2 molecules. The reason the entropy is cut almost in half in this case is, of course, that half the atoms become severely restricted in their motions when tied to the remaining atoms.

There exist a number of exact relationships between molecular structure and entropy and additional semiempirical rules that permit the calculation or estimation of the entropies of gases.

The entropy of solids is the higher the more dense the spacing of the energy levels for the vibrations of its atoms, ions, or molecules against each other (lattice vibrations). This level spacing becomes closer with softer substances and with heavier atoms. Thus soft heavy metals have the highest entropy (for example: Pb, 15.51 cal/deg). Hard substances of light atoms have low entropies. Diamond is the hardest substance and has the lowest entropy (0.58 cal/deg) of any room-temperature solid known. Graphite, although generally considered soft, is soft only because the layers slip over each other easily. Deformation of the layers themselves is more difficult, and graphite has a relatively low entropy at room temperature (1.36 cal/deg). Comparison must, of course, always be on the same level, that is, per mole of atoms. Thus the molar entropy of $I_2(s)$ is 27.9 cal/deg, but the value per mole of atoms is only 13.9 cal/deg. This value is still high because it relates to a soft solid and heavy atoms.

It is finally of interest to find the order of magnitude of Ω that corresponds to a representative entropy value such as 10 cal/deg. Since $k = 3.30 \times 10^{-24}$ cal/deg, we have

$$10 = k \ln \Omega = 3.30 \times 10^{-24} \times 2.30 \log \Omega$$
$$\log \Omega = 1.32 \times 10^{24}$$
$$\Omega = 10^{1.32 \times 10^{24}}$$

It is hard enough to imagine the magnitude of Avogadro's number $\mathcal{N}$, but the above number with a quantity of zeros almost equal to $\mathcal{N}$ strains the imagination further, by a factor of the order of $\mathcal{N}$ itself.

The statistical interpretation of the second law makes it the law of the probable rather than the law of the certain. However, improbabilities of the order of 10^{-N} are so exceedingly small that the statistical interpretation of the second law makes it the law of the *overwhelmingly* probable, and macroscopic violations of the second law are unthinkable. Examples of such essentially impossible violations are these: (1) The velocities of all molecules of the air in a flask become directed the same way by accident so that a vacuum is spontaneously created on one side of the flask. (2) A sufficient number of molecular velocities in a body become directed upward by accident, so that the body moves upward, a contingency mentioned earlier.   (3) The velocity distribution accidentally changes so that one part of a body becomes warmer, the other cooler.   There are, however, always minute local fluctuations in density, pressure, and temperature.

4–9   ABSOLUTE AND STANDARD ENTROPIES

Entropies that are based on the third law are often called *absolute* entropies.   It must be noted, however, that the term "absolute" is misleading to some extent.   Although it is consistent to say that a macrostate has the *absolute* entropy zero when there is *only one* microscopic representation for it, the definition of "microstate" is partly a matter of convention.   For example, most well-ordered crystals in their lowest quantum states of atomic motion do not *really* correspond to one microstate, if the different possible orientations of the nuclear spins of their atoms are taken into account.   The resulting **spin entropy** is zero only for substances in which the nuclei of all atoms happen to have zero spin (an example is He[4]).   As our understanding of the structure of nuclei increases, other "types" of entropy may turn up.   However, in chemical reactions the spin entropies and other entropies that may be connected with the details of the structure of nuclei do not change and may be disregarded.   It is thus permissible to agree on the *convention* to assign the value 1 to Ω for a well-ordered crystal in the ground state of atomic motion.

Another point to be made is that, in general, chemical elements are mixtures of different isotopes.   This implies randomness and thus residual entropy, because the interchange of atoms of the same atomic number but different mass numbers leads to new microstates.   However, this entropy changes only if the isotopic composition of the elements concerned is changed.   This is not usually the case to any significant extent in chemical reactions.   The entropy effect related to a change in isotopic composition is therefore ignored by convention, except in special cases.

To assign zero entropy to well-ordered crystals in their lowest states of internal motion is thus a convention that has absolute aspects but is by no means comparable to the absolute nature of the zero point of the thermodynamic temperature scale. Absolute entropies will be simply designated by S unless they refer to the standard state and 1 mole of the substance concerned; in this case $\tilde{S}^0$ is used when the temperature is 298.15°K and $\tilde{S}^0(T)$ when the temperature is T°K. Values of S^0 for many substances are given in Appendix 4.

The absolute entropy must not be confused with the **standard entropy of formation** $\tilde{S}_f^0$ of a compound, which is the entropy of forming it from the elements at standard states,

$$\tilde{S}_f^0 = \tilde{S}^0 \text{ (compound)}$$

$$- \sum \tilde{S}^0 \text{ (elements in most stable form at standard conditions)}$$

This is mentioned mainly to point up the difference between absolute entropy and entropy of formation, because with few exceptions we shall use absolute entropies.

To find the standard entropy *of a reaction*, one may use absolute entropies or entropies of formation of products and reactants, or any other kind, as long as the reference state for reactants and products is the same. Thus

$$\Delta S^0 = \sum S^0_{\text{prod}} - \sum S^0_{\text{reac}}$$

$$= \sum S_f^0{}_{\text{prod}} - \sum S_f^0{}_{\text{reac}} \tag{4-14}$$

because the entropies of any reference states cancel.

4–10   EFFICIENCY OF HEAT ENGINES AND REFRIGERATORS

The second law readily permits the derivation of the maximum efficiencies of thermal engines and of refrigerators. The standard heat engine is a cyclic device that operates between two constant-temperature baths [Fig. 4–8(a)]. During each cycle the heat $|q_h|$ is transferred from the bath at the higher temperature T_h to the device, the heat $|q_l|$ from the device to the bath at the lower temperature T_l, and the work $|w|$ is performed on the surroundings. Taking the directions of transfer of heat and work into account, $q_h = |q_h|$, $q_l = -|q_l|$, and $w = -|w|$. By the first law, ΔU is zero for a cyclic

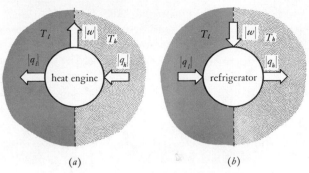

Figure 4–8 Heat engine (*a*) **and refrigerator** (*b*). The *heat engine* takes up the heat $|q_h|$ at a temperature T_h, performs the work $|w|$, and discards the heat $|q_l|$ at a temperature T_l that is lower than T_h. The **refrigerator** consumes the work $|w|$ and absorbs the heat $|q_l|$ at a temperature T_l. It delivers the heat $|q_h|$ at a temperature T_h that is above T_l.

process, so that $q_h + q_l + w = |q_h| - |q_l| - |w| = 0$ and therefore $|w| = |q_h| - |q_l|$. By the second law $\int Dq/T \leqslant \Delta S = 0$ for a cyclic process. The integral is simply $q_h/T_h + q_l/T_l$ because the transfer of heat occurs at the constant temperatures T_h and T_l. Therefore, $q_h/T_h + q_l/T_l = |q_h|/T_h - |q_l|/T_l \leqslant 0$, and by multiplication with the positive quantity $T_l/|q_h|$, $T_l/T_h - |q_l|/|q_h| \leqslant 0$.[1] Thus

$$\left|\frac{q_l}{q_h}\right| \geqslant \frac{T_l}{T_h}$$

The heat $|q_l|$ is that part of $|q_h|$ that cannot be converted into work under the circumstances, and is therefore lost. The efficiency of the engine is measured by the ratio of the work $|w|$ to the heat $|q_h|$ taken from the bath at the higher temperatures, $\text{eff} = |w|/|q_h| = (|q_h| - |q_l|)/|q_h| = 1 - |q_l|/|q_h| \leqslant 1 - T_l/T_h$. Then,

$$\text{eff} \equiv \left|\frac{w}{q_h}\right| \leqslant \frac{(T_h - T_l)}{T_h} \text{ for a heat engine} \tag{4–15}$$

---

[1] See Appendix 2 for the handling of inequalities.

The *equals* sign is valid for a reversible machine, the *smaller than* for an actual, irreversible machine. The result is independent of the materials used in the device, or the details of construction. All that matters are the temperatures of the two baths. The maximum efficiency reaches unity only when T_l is zero, and is zero when T_h and T_l are equal. It thus takes two baths of different temperatures to create work. For a given T_l, the maximum efficiency is higher as T_h increases.

In a refrigerator the cycle is run in the opposite direction [Fig. 4–8(b)]. The work $|w|$ is used to "pump" the heat $|q_l|$ from the low-temperature bath to the high-temperature bath, into which the heat $|q_h|$ is transferred. Therefore, $q_l = |q_l|$, $q_h = -|q_h|$, and $w = |w|$. By the first law $q_h + q_l + w = 0$, so that $|q_h| = |q_l| + |w|$. By the second law $\int Dq/T = q_l/T_l + q_h/T_h \leqslant 0$, or $|q_l|/T_l - |q_h|/T_h \leqslant 0$, so that $|q_h|/|q_l| \geqslant T_h/T_l$.

A refrigerator may be rated by the **performance coefficient** (perf. coeff.) $= |q_l|/|w|$, which is the ratio of the heat $|q_l|$ removed at T_l to the work $|w|$ needed to do this. In other words, when the work $|w|$ is multiplied by the performance coefficient, the heat $|q_l|$ is obtained that $|w|$ is able to pump. In contrast to the efficiency of a heat engine, the coefficient of performance of a refrigerator may be larger than 1. The larger this coefficient is, the better the refrigerator. Using the relationships just derived, $|w|/|q_l| = (|q_h| - |q_l|)/|q_l| = (|q_h|/|q_l|) - 1 \geqslant (T_h/T_l) - 1 = (T_h - T_l)/T_l$, and therefore

$$\text{perf. coeff.} = \left|\frac{q_l}{w}\right| \leqslant \frac{T_l}{T_h - T_l} \tag{4–16}$$

Again the *equals* sign refers to a reversible machine, and the *smaller than* to an actual, irreversible machine. The performance coefficient is zero when $T_l = 0$, because there is no heat to be pumped in this case. The other limit, an infinite performance coefficient, is the trivial case in which T_l and T_h are equal.

An important idealized cyclic heat engine that is reversible is the **Carnot cycle,** named after the discoverer of the second law. In it a perfect gas is carried through a cycle of reversible expansions and compressions, and a detailed analysis shows that the engine satisfies

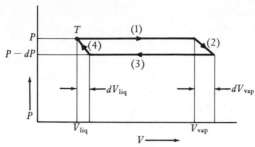

Figure 4–9 An evaporation-condensation cycle. A specified amount of liquid at T, P (black dot) is evaporated isothermally, the vapor cooled to $T - dT$ by adiabatic expansion, condensed at $T - dT$ and returned to the original temperature by adiabatic compression. The work w is the negative of the area enclosed by the path, because work is performed on the surroundings (see Fig. 1–5).

(4–15) when used as heat engine and (4–16) when used as a refrigerator, both expressions taken with the *equals* sign. Details of the Carnot cycle may be found in most thermodynamics and physical chemistry texts but are omitted here, because they have little bearing on applications to chemistry.

4–11 THE CLAUSIUS–CLAPEYRON EQUATION

The analysis of another idealized cycle permits the derivation of an important equation concerning the vapor pressure of a liquid or a solid. The engine undergoing the cyclic process is a cylinder fitted with a piston and filled with liquid and vapor at equilibrium. Heat baths of temperature T and $T - dT$ are available, and the vapor pressures of the liquid at these temperatures are P and $P - dP$. The cycle is as follows:

(1) The cylinder is brought into thermal contact with the bath at T, and n moles of liquid are vaporized reversibly against a constant outside pressure P (Fig. 4–9). (2) Thermal contact is broken, and temperature and pressure are decreased to $T - dT$ and $P - dP$ by a very small adiabatic expansion. (3) Thermal contact is estab-

lished with the bath at $T - dT$, and the vapor condensed reversibly by an outside pressure $P - dP$. (4) Return to the original state is achieved by adiabatic compression.

The work performed on the system is equal to minus the area of the figure described by the path (see Fig. 1–5), or approximately $-w = dP \Delta V$, where $\Delta V = V_{\text{vap}} - V_{\text{liq}}$ is the volume increase upon vaporization. The heat taken up at the higher temperature is the heat of vaporization, $q_h = \Delta H$. Applying (4–15),

$$\left| \frac{w}{q_h} \right| = -\frac{w}{q_h} = \frac{dT}{T} = \frac{dP \, \Delta V}{\Delta H}$$

Rearrangement leads to the **Clapeyron equation**

$$\left(\frac{dP}{dT} \right)_{\text{equil}} = \frac{\Delta H}{T \, \Delta V} \qquad (4–17)$$

which relates the temperature dependence of the vapor pressure to the enthalpy and volume changes in vaporization. The same relation also holds for the vaporization of a solid, because the liquid in the cylinder could be replaced by a solid without changing the results. Note that for use in (4–17), ΔH is most conveniently expressed in liter-atmospheres.

Often the following approximations are introduced into the Clapeyron equation: The volume of the liquid or solid is neglected, because it is small compared to that of the vapor. The vapor is assumed to behave as a perfect gas, so that its volume is nRT/P. Thus $\Delta V \approx V_{\text{vap}} \approx nRT/P$. Insertion in (4–17) and rearrangement leads to

$$\left[\left(\frac{1}{P} \right) \frac{dP}{dT} \right]_{\text{equil}} = \left(\frac{d \ln P}{dT} \right)_{\text{equil}} \approx \frac{\Delta H_{\text{vap}}}{nRT^2}$$

because $dP/P = d \ln P$. Thus

$$\left(\frac{d \ln P}{dT} \right)_{\text{equil}} \approx \frac{\Delta \tilde{H}_{\text{vap}}}{RT^2} \qquad (4–18)$$

which is the **Clausius-Clapeyron** relationship. It can be integrated when it is assumed that $\Delta \tilde{H}$ is independent of T, which is approxi-

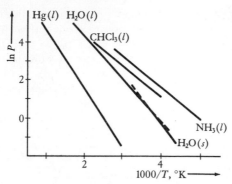

Figure 4–10 Graph of log P versus $1000/T$ for four substances. The slopes of the lines are equal to $-\Delta\tilde{H}_{vap}/2.303R$, except that for $H_2O(s)$ the enthalpy of sublimation enters rather than the enthalpy of vaporization. The intersection of the curves for $H_2O(l)$ and $H_2O(s)$ occur at the triple point of water, where liquid, solid, and vapor are at equilibrium. The slopes are independent of the units in which P is expressed.

mately true for a temperature range that is not too large. It follows that

$$\int d\ln P \approx \left(\frac{\Delta\tilde{H}}{R}\right)\int \frac{dT}{T^2}$$

or

$$\ln P = 2.303\log P \approx \frac{-\Delta\tilde{H}_{vap}}{RT} + \text{const} \qquad (4\text{--}19)$$

It is thus expected that when $\ln P = 2.303\log P$ is plotted against $1/T$, an approximately straight line results. This is indeed usually observed, as illustrated in Fig. 4–10. The slopes of the lines yield $-\Delta\tilde{H}_{vap}/R$. Therefore, if the vapor pressure of a liquid or a solid is measured at a number of temperatures, it is possible to determine $\Delta\tilde{H}_{vap}$ from graphs like Fig. 4–10 *without any calorimetric measurements* entering into the procedure.

One aspect of (4–19) needs special comment, and this is the term $\ln P$ or $\log P$: Taking the logarithm of a physical quantity such as 2 atm looks patently absurd. Backtracking we see that $d \ln P$ in (4–18) should present no real problem, being equal to the ratio dP/P, which is a pure number. This can also be seen by using units: Let P be equal to r atm where r is a pure number. Then $d \ln P = d \ln(r \text{ atm}) = d[\ln r + \ln(\text{atm})]$. But (atm) must be considered a constant, so that whatever $\ln(\text{atm})$ may be, $d \ln(\text{atm})$ is zero. We are thus left with $d \ln P = d \ln r$, where r is a pure number.

Next, we consider the indefinite integral of $d \ln P$,

$$\int d \ln P = \ln P + \text{const}$$

Again assuming P to equal r atm, we see that $\ln P = \ln r + \ln(\text{atm})$, so that the constant of integration must contain a compensating term $-\ln(\text{atm})$. We therefore simply express P in atm and disregard the units atm when taking the logarithm. Another way of avoiding this situation would be to write $\ln(P/\text{atm})$, where (P/atm) is a pure number. This scheme is not used here, however, because it is cumbersome, particularly when the logarithms of quantities such as mass-action constants are to be taken. This and related matters are discussed further in Sections 5–6, 6–1, 6–6, and 6–7.

It should finally be noted that as long as (4–19) serves only to obtain $\Delta\tilde{H}$, the units in which P is expressed are not important: Curves of $\ln P$ versus $1/T$ with P in different units are parallel to each other and thus have the same slope $-\Delta\tilde{H}/R$.

EXAMPLE 3

The enthalpy of vaporization of water at 100°C is $\Delta H_{\text{vap}} = 9.71$ kcal/mole. What is the boiling point of water at 761.00 torr? The pressure change is small, so that the change in the boiling point is expected to be small also. To imply small quantities the symbols δP and δT are used. In the present situation the left side of the Clausius-Clapeyron equation may be approximated by $d \ln P/dT \approx (1/P)(\delta P/\delta T)$, and therefore

$$\delta T \approx \frac{RT^2}{\Delta H} \frac{\delta P}{P} = \frac{(1.99 \times 373^2) \text{ cal-deg/mole}}{9.71 \times 10^3 \text{ cal/mole}} \frac{1}{760} = 0.037 \text{ deg}$$

The boiling point at 761 torr is thus expected to be **100.037°C,** as is actually observed.

PROBLEMS

4–1. *Melting ice.* Find ΔS for the change in state $H_2O(s,$ $0°C) = H_2O(l, 25°C)$. The molar enthalpy of fusion of ice at $0°C$ is 1.44 kcal/mole; $\tilde{C}_P$ for $H_2O(l)$ is 18.0 cal/mole-deg and is to be assumed constant.

4–2. *Mixing snow and water.* A thermos bottle contains 100 ml of H_2O at 25°C with which are mixed 10 g of snow of $-10°C$. What is the final temperature and what is ΔS? The enthalpy of fusion of ice is 79.7 cal/g, and the specific heat capacities (assumed to be constant) are (in cal/g-deg), 0.50 for ice and 1.00 for liquid water.

4–3. *Mixing water.* One kilogram of liquid water at temperature T_1 is mixed with 1 kg of liquid water at temperature T_2. Assume that the specific heat capacity C_P for water is constant at 1 cal/g-deg. Show that $\Delta S = 2000 \ln[(T_1 + T_2)/2\sqrt{T_1 T_2}]$ cal/deg and prove that this quantity is positive for all possible values of T_1 and T_2.

4–4. *Entropy of vaporization.* The normal boiling point of methanol is 64.6°C and the enthalpy of vaporization 8.43 kcal/mole. What is the entropy of vaporization?

4–5. *Entropy.* Is it possible to decrease the entropy of a fluid of any sort by (*a*) an adiabatic expansion? (*b*) an adiabatic compression? Explain.

4–6. *Entropy a state function.* (*a*) One mole of a perfect gas at 300°K at 1 atm is compressed reversibly and isothermally to half its volume. (*b*) Another mole of the gas at the same initial conditions is heated reversibly to 600°K at constant volume and then cooled reversibly to 300°K at constant pressure. Assure yourself that the final state is the same in both cases and calculate ΔS for the two paths, assuming a constant $\tilde{C}_P$ of 5.0 cal/mole-deg.

4–7. *Change of state of helium.* One mole of helium may undergo the change in state from 100°C, 2 atm, and the volume V_1 to 25°C, 1 atm, and the volume V_2 by each of the following *reversible* processes: (1) The gas is cooled at constant pressure to 25°C. It is then expanded isothermally until its pressure is 1 atm. (2) The gas is heated at the constant pressure of 2 atm, until its volume is V_2 and its temperature T_3. It is then cooled at constant volume until its temperature is 25°C. (3) The gas is cooled at the constant volume V_1 until its pressure is 0.5 atm and its temperature T_4. It is next heated at constant pressure until its volume is V_2 and its temperature T_5 and then at constant volume until its temperature is 25°C.

(a) Calculate the temperatures T_3, T_4, and T_5. (b) For each of processes (1) to (3), calculate w, q, ΔU, and ΔS. Employ the calorie as the unit of energy and tabulate the results. Assume helium to be a perfect gas and its molar heat capacity at constant pressure to be 4.97 cal/mole-deg at all temperatures. Illustrate the processes by P-V diagrams.

4–8. *Entropy change.* Develop a general expression for ΔS for an isobaric change of the temperature of a substance, in a range in which C_P is constant.

4–9. *Vaporization of water.* Suppose 1 mole $H_2O(l)$ at 100°C and 1 atm is introduced into an evacuated space of such size that on restoration of the temperature to 100°C, the pressure is found to be 0.368 atm. What is the entropy change of the water? Assume water vapor to be a perfect gas. The enthalpy of vaporization is 9.71 kcal/mole at 100°C.

4–10. *Crystallization of supercooled water.* The molar enthalpy of fusion of ice at 0°C is 1.44 kcal/mole and the molar heat capacity of supercooled water 18.0 cal/mole-deg. (a) One mole of supercooled water at -10°C is induced to crystallize in a heat-insulated vessel. The result is a mixture of ice and water at 0°C. What fraction of this mixture is ice? (b) What is ΔS for the system?

4–11. *Refrigerator.* What is the minimum electrical energy, in kilowatt-hours, to make 20 lb (that is, 500 moles) of ice from the same amount of liquid water at 0°C, on a warm day at a temperature outside the refrigerator of 40°C. The molar enthalpy of fusion of ice at 0°C is 1.44 kcal/mole.

4–12. *Clapeyron equation.* State the conditions under which the following relationships apply and any approximations made in their derivation: (a) $dP/dT = \Delta H/T \Delta V$; (b) $dP/dT = P \Delta \tilde{H}/RT^2$; (c) $\ln(P_2/P_1) = (\Delta \tilde{H}/R)[(1/T_1) - (1/T_2)]$.

4–13. *Change of melting point of ice by pressure.* From the Clapeyron equation, find the melting point of ice that is subject to a pressure of 10 atm rather than the usual 1 atm. The density of water at 0°C is 0.999841 g/cm³ and that of ice 0.917 g/cm³. The enthalpy of fusion is 1.44 kcal/mole.

4-14. *Enthalpy of vaporization.* Find the molar enthalpy of vaporization of water at 120.5°C from the following data. At 120.5°C the volume of 1 g of liquid water is 1.05 cm³ and of vapor, 875.5 cm³. The vapor pressure at 120.0°C is 1489.2 torr and at 121.0°, 1536.9 torr.

4-15. *Enthalpy of vaporization.* The vapor pressure of benzene at 21°C is 76 torr and its normal boiling point is 80°C. Calculate an approximate value of ΔH for the process $C_6H_6(l) = C_6H_6(g)$ assuming that ΔH is independent of the temperature in the interval considered.

4-16. *Vapor pressure and enthalpy of vaporization.* The vapor pressure of acetaldehyde, CH_3CHO, is approximated in the range -25 to 27°C by the formula $\log [P(\text{torr})] = -1447.14/T + 7.8206$. Find an approximate value of the enthalpy of vaporization in the same temperature range. State assumptions made.

4-17. *Vapor pressure of benzene.* Benzene melts at 6°C and boils at 80°C. Estimate $\Delta \tilde{H}_{\text{vap}}$ from Trouton's rule and find an approximate value of the vapor pressure at the melting point.

4-18. *Boiling point increase.* Let the increase of the boiling temperature T_b of a liquid caused by a pressure increase of δP be δT. Derive, by use of Trouton's rule, the approximate relationship $\delta T/T_b \approx \delta P/10$, where δP must be expressed in atmospheres.

4-19. *Hildebrand's rule.* The boiling point of NO is 121°K and the molar enthalpy of vaporization is 3.29 kcal/mole. (*a*) What is the entropy of vaporization? Is the rule of Pictet and Trouton satisfied? (*b*) The vapor pressure of liquid NO is 36 torr at 100°K, 176 torr at 110°K, and 760 torr at the boiling point. By graphical or other methods (for example, plot log P against $1/T$), find the temperature T', where the molar volume of the saturated vapor (of pressure equal to the vapor pressure) is 22.4 liters. Assume that ΔH_{vap} is independent of the temperature and find the entropy of vaporization at T'. Is Hildebrand's rule better obeyed than was the rule of Pictet and Trouton? (*c*) Nitric oxide in the liquid state is believed to exist largely as the dimer $(NO)_2$, whereas in the gas NO is monomeric. What deviations from the rules of Pictet-Trouton and of Hildebrand would be expected?

4–20. *Enthalpy and entropy of vaporization.* The enthalpy of vaporization of ethanol at its boiling point of 78.3°C is 9.25 kcal/mole. Find the enthalpy of vaporization at 100°C assuming the following molar heat capacities $\tilde{C}_P$: 13.4 cal/mole-deg for the vapor and 29.3 cal/mole-deg for the liquid. What is ΔS for the vaporization of 1 mole of ethanol (*a*) at 100°C and its vapor pressure of 2.23 atm; (*b*) at 78.3°C and 1 atm? Discuss the difference between these two values of ΔS.

4–21. *Condensation of acetone.* The normal boiling point of acetone is 56°C and the enthalpy of vaporization is 6.95 kcal/mole. A closed flask that contains 1 mole of acetone vapor at 56°C and 760 torr is cooled to 25°C. How much of the acetone condenses? Assume that ΔH is constant, that the vapor behaves like a perfect gas, and that the volume of the liquid is negligible compared to that of the gas.

4–22. *Dissociation of AgCl · NH₃.* Solid silver chloride and gaseous ammonia form the solid compound $AgCl \cdot NH_3$. At 16°C the dissociation pressure of this compound is 42 torr and the enthalpy for the dissociation reaction

$$AgCl \cdot NH_3(s) = AgCl(s) + NH_3(g)$$

is 11.11 kcal/mole. One-tenth mole of $AgCl \cdot NH_3$ is placed in an evacuated container at 16°C. (*a*) For what size container will exactly half of the $AgCl \cdot NH_3$ decompose into AgCl and NH₃? (*b*) What is the dissociation pressure at 50°C and how much of the $AgCl \cdot NH_3$ would be dissociated in the same container at 50°C? Assume that ΔH is constant, that NH₃ behaves like a perfect gas, and that the volumes of the solids are negligible compared to that of the gas.

5 Equilibrium and Spontaneous Processes

A new function of state, the free energy G, is introduced, and its virtue in the treatment of equilibria and in the formulation of stability conditions is shown. The two driving principles of reaction—lowering of enthalpy and increase of entropy—are discussed and a simple system on the molecular plane considered. Standard free energies are defined and their application explained. The pressure and temperature dependence of the free energy is derived and the differentials dU, dH, dA, and dG are developed. They are used to derive relationships among thermodynamic quantities and to prove that for a perfect gas U is a function of T alone.

5–1 FREE ENERGY

As discussed earlier, all reactions in an adiabatic system must satisfy the condition $dS \geqq 0$, where the *larger than* pertains to reactions that can actually occur, and the *equals* sign to reversible reactions—reactions that are in equilibrium. In an adiabatic system the *equilibrium condition* for a reaction is thus that $dS = 0$ when the reaction is pushed by an infinitesimal amount in either direction.

The requirement for the *absolute thermodynamic stability* of an adiabatic system is that S must have reached its maximum value for *all possible* adiabatic paths. Along any such path there must either exist equilibrium ($dS = 0$), or else the path must be prohibited by thermodynamics ($dS < 0$).

The situation in chemistry is that most systems are not truly at equilibrium, but that reactions for which equilibrium does not exist are so slow that they can be neglected. The emphasis is therefore usually on equilibrium conditions for *specific* reactions, phase transformations, etc., rather than on equilibrium for a *system as a whole*.

For example, nitrogen dioxide, NO_2, and nitrogen tetroxide, N_2O_4, are both unstable relative to decomposition into N_2 and O_2, but under normal conditions the rates of this decomposition are immeasurably small. These reactions can therefore be disregarded when establishing thermodynamic criteria for the equilibrium $2NO_2 = N_2O_4$. (Another possible reaction, the decomposition of NO_2 into oxygen and nitric oxide $2NO_2 = O_2 + 2NO$, proceeds at measurable rates, but the equilibrium is completely on the side of NO_2 below 130°C.)

A second example concerns hydrogen peroxide, for which the equilibrium

$$H_2O_2(l) = H^+ + HO_2^-$$

is established rapidly and can be examined by experiment, even though the possible equilibrium

$$H_2O_2(l) = H_2O(l) + \tfrac{1}{2}O_2(g)$$

lies overwhelmingly on the side of H_2O and O_2. The rate of decomposition of H_2O_2 is, however, very slow in the absence of catalysts.

In a system that is not adiabatic, the more general relationship

$$dS \geqslant \frac{Dq}{T} \tag{5–1}$$

applies (Section 3–1). The *larger than* applies to actually possible, irreversible (and infinitesimal) changes, and the *equals* sign to reversible changes and thus to equilibrium situations. Processes for which $dS < Dq/T$ are unnatural and prohibited.

For many chemical applications it is useful to transform (5–1) by the following development. Insertion of $Dq = dU - Dw$ from the first law and multiplication by T yields

$$T \, dS \geqslant dU - Dw \tag{5–2}$$

By rearrangement,

$$Dw \geqslant dU - T \, dS \tag{5–3}$$

A new function of state, the **free energy** G, used first by Gibbs, is now introduced:

$$G = U + PV - TS = H - TS \qquad (5\text{--}4)$$

To see the usefulness of this function a consideration of the differential dG of G is helpful. Since the differential of a product, $d(xy)$, is $y\,dx + x\,dy$, we obtain from (5–4)

$$dG = dU - T\,dS - S\,dT + P\,dV + V\,dP$$

By rearrangement $dU - T\,dS$ is placed on one side, and (5–3) is applied,

$$dU - T\,dS = dG + S\,dT - P\,dV - V\,dP \leqslant Dw$$

Next, $P\,dV$ is added on both sides of the inequality:

$$dG + S\,dT - V\,dP \leqslant Dw + P\,dV = Dw'$$

On the right side is what we have called the infinitesimal *net work* Dw', the infinitesimal work other than the reversible pressure-volume work (2–8). The final expression is a restatement of the one just given,

$$dG + S\,dT - V\,dP \leqslant Dw' \qquad (5\text{--}5)$$

This relationship is generally valid, but it is particularly useful for systems and paths for which the *temperature* and the *pressure* are kept *constant*. These conditions are attractive to the chemist, because they are realized in containers that are surrounded by a constant-temperature bath and that are open and thus under atmospheric pressure. The changes in the atmospheric pressure during the course of chemical reactions are usually negligible. Because $dT = 0$ and $dP = 0$, only dG remains on the left side of (5–5), and

$$dG \leqslant Dw' \qquad \text{when } P = \text{const}, \ T = \text{const} \qquad (5\text{--}6)$$

The *equals* sign applies to a reversible, constant-temperature, constant-pressure process, the *smaller than* sign to an irreversible, actual process.

To see one of the meanings of (5–6), we write it for the moment in the form

$$-Dw' \leqslant -dG \qquad (5\text{–}7)$$

On the left side, $-Dw'$ is the net work done by the system on the surroundings, and on the right side, $-dG$ is the loss of the free energy of the system. Our relationship (5–6) thus states that $-dG$ is the maximum net work that the system is capable of performing at constant temperature and pressure. This fact is, of course, the origin of the name free energy—that part of the energy of the system that is "freely convertible" into net work. This maximum net work can be obtained under reversible or equilibrium conditions only, that is, in the limit of an infinitesimally slow, idealized process.

Unfortunately, another state function, $A = U - TS$, has also been called "free energy." It is widely used, but in general not by chemists. It is particularly useful in constant-temperature constant-volume processes. The pressure-volume work is not taken into account automatically in the function A, but at constant volume there is no work of this kind. To distinguish between A and G, A is often called the **Helmholtz free energy,** and G the **Gibbs' free energy.** The terms **Gibbs' energy** and **Helmholtz energy** have also been recommended. In the more recent European literature, G is also called the free enthalpy, because of the relationship $G = H - TS$. In the older literature such precautions are, however, often lacking; to add to the confusion even the same letter, F, has been used for both functions in the past. In most older American literature F stands for the Gibbs' free energy, but it is always a good idea to make sure. In this book the function G is used exclusively.

5–2   CONDITIONS FOR EQUILIBRIUM AND
SPONTANEOUS PROCESSES

Many chemical processes occur along paths for which *all* work is of the pressure-volume type. In this case $Dw' = 0$, and therefore $dG \leqslant 0$ along such paths.

Cases where w' is not zero are those involving, for example, electrical, magnetic, or gravitational work. Of these the electrical case is discussed in a later chapter on electrochemical cells. Gravitational work is negligible in most chemical considerations but must be included, for example, in a thermodynamic treatment of the atmosphere. A similar type of work occurs in centrifugation. Mechanical work that is not of the pressure-volume type is in general of no interest in chemical thermodynamics, but is important, for example, in the thermodynamic treatment of gas turbines.

Returning to chemical processes, three cases can be distinguished. At constant temperature and pressure, and for pressure-volume work only:

(1) A chemical or any other process is at equilibrium when

$$dG = 0 \qquad (5-8)$$

as the process is made to proceed in any direction by an infinitesimal amount.

(2) An actual process must occur in the direction in which

$$dG < 0 \qquad (5-9)$$

(3) A process for which

$$dG > 0 \qquad (5-10)$$

is thermodynamically forbidden.

For finite changes that occur at constant temperature and pressure, and involve only pressure-volume work,

$$\Delta G = 0 \qquad (5-11)$$

when equilibrium exists;

$$\Delta G < 0 \qquad (5-12)$$

for any actual process; and

$$\Delta G > 0 \qquad (5-13)$$

for any unnatural process (Section 3-1).

5–3 DRIVING FORCES OF REACTIONS

A ball on a hill is pulled by gravity in a downward direction, and stable equilibrium with no pull on the ball exists only when the potential energy is at a minimum, with the ball at the lowest point. By analogy it might be expected that the direction in which a thermodynamically stable equilibrium lies is that of lowest energy for constant-volume and temperature processes and that of lowest enthalpy for constant-pressure and temperature processes, the conditions of interest here. Indeed, Berthelot and Thomsen recognized just about a hundred years ago that the production of heat of reaction, or lowering of the enthalpy in our terms, is an important driving principle. It was realized only later that this is not the whole story and that what matters is the free energy G, that is, the combination $H - TS$ rather than just H alone. By (5–12), the direction in which constant temperature and pressure processes tend to proceed is toward *lower free energy*.

At constant temperature, $\Delta G = \Delta H - T \Delta S$, and the condition (5–12) for the direction of actual processes becomes

$$\Delta G = \Delta H - T \Delta S < 0 \qquad (5-14)$$

It is seen that while decrease of H (or a negative ΔH) is indeed desirable, increase of S (or a positive ΔS) is also desirable, and that the influence of the entropy change becomes more important as the absolute temperature increases. The temperature is a weighting factor of the importance of the entropy change, relative to that of the enthalpy change. Temperature exerts a randomizing influence. At low temperatures ΔH is important, at high temperatures ΔS.

In more detail, depending on the signs of ΔH and ΔS, four different cases exist:

(1) When $\Delta H < 0$ and $\Delta S > 0$, the reaction may proceed at *any temperature*. The signs of ΔH and ΔS may, of course, change with temperature, in which case ΔG may not be negative at all temperatures.

(2) When $\Delta H < 0$ and $\Delta S < 0$, the reaction may proceed *only* when $|T \Delta S| < |\Delta H|$. The reaction must thus be sufficiently

Table 5–1
Influence of Enthalpy and Entropy Changes
on Chemical Reactions

Case	ΔH	ΔS	Reaction proceeds
1	<0	>0	Always
2	<0	<0	When T sufficiently low
3	>0	>0	When T sufficiently high
4	>0	<0	Not at all

exothermic to overcome the handicap of the entropy decrease. At sufficiently large T, the term $T\,\Delta S$ will overcome the ΔH term, and the reaction can no longer proceed. When ΔH and ΔS are known at a given temperature T', the temperature T above which the reaction becomes prohibited by thermodynamics is, by (5–14), approximately equal to the ratio $\Delta H(T')/\Delta S(T')$; the relationship is approximate only, because both ΔH and ΔS depend to some extent on the temperature.

(3) When $\Delta H > 0$ and $\Delta S > 0$, the reaction tends to proceed *only as long as* $T\,\Delta S > \Delta H$. Here the advantage of the entropy increase must overcome the handicap of the endothermic nature of the reaction, and for this T must be sufficiently large. The heat required by the reaction comes, of course, from the surroundings, that is, from the constant-temperature bath needed to maintain the temperature at a constant level. When T is too small, the reaction is prohibited.

(4) When $\Delta H > 0$ and $\Delta S < 0$, the reaction *is prohibited thermodynamically at any temperature*, unless a sign change of ΔH or ΔS with temperature occurs in such a way that the sign of ΔG changes also.

Table 5–1 is a summary of the four cases just discussed.

There is no assurance that a reaction actually proceeds if it is permitted by thermodynamics, since no prediction of rates can be made. For example, for a mixture of hydrogen and oxygen at room temperature, the tendency to form water is large ($\Delta G \sim -57$ kcal/mole), but the rate is approximately zero. When the rate of a reaction permitted by thermodynamics is small or zero, there is no reason why a diligent search for suitable catalysts should not succeed. However, no catalyst *can* exist for reactions that are in violation of thermodynamics. The presence of catalysts cannot affect ΔG, because G is a function of state and depends on the nature of the reactants and products only, not on the path that relates them.

This does not rule out the possibility of preparing substances that are thermodynamically unstable, as long as the rates of decomposition are slow. For example, the reaction $2N_2 + O_2 = 2N_2O$ corresponds to a free-energy increase of about 50 kcal and is thus forbidden by thermodynamics. No catalyst can exist that furthers a reaction between N_2 and O_2 to produce nitrous oxide. It may, however, be formed by gentle heating of ammonium nitrate,

$$NH_4NO_3(s) = N_2O(g) + 2H_2O(g)$$

because NH_4NO_3 is less stable thermodynamically than N_2O and H_2O; that is, ΔG for the foregoing reaction is negative. Once formed, N_2O does not decompose into its elements, because the rate is too small.

The *condition for equilibrium* is that $\Delta G = \Delta H - T\,\Delta S = 0$ or that

$$\Delta H = T\,\Delta S \qquad (5\text{–}15)$$

for a reaction taking place at constant T and P with pressure-volume work only. The two terms ΔH and $T\,\Delta S$ are thus exactly equal *at equilibrium*. If they are both positive, the tendency toward greater randomness, measured by ΔS and weighted by multiplication with T, is just sufficient to compensate for the endothermic nature of the reaction. If they are both negative, the exothermic character of the reaction just compensates for the decrease in randomness, again weighted by T.

At equilibrium there is no change in free energy G when one phase is transformed into another, or when reactants are transformed into products, *provided equilibrium concentrations and pressures of all reaction participants are maintained.*

EXAMPLE 1

Consider the phase transformation

$$H_2O(l) = H_2O(g)$$

at 25°C and 1 atm. Calculate ΔG from the values of ΔH and ΔS, $\Delta H = 10.5195$ kcal, $\Delta S = 28.391$ cal/deg, and discuss the result. We find $T \, \Delta S = 8.4648$ kcal and, therefore, $\Delta G = \Delta H - T \, \Delta S = \mathbf{2.0547 \ kcal.}$

At 25°C, $T \, \Delta S$ is smaller than ΔH, and ΔG is positive. For the reverse process, condensation, ΔG is therefore negative, so that water vapor of 1 atm, at 25°C, is unstable and condenses.

A more general question is at what temperature would equilibrium between vapor of 1 atm and liquid water be achieved? To this end ΔH and $T \, \Delta S$ must be made equal, and since at 298°K ΔH is larger than $T \, \Delta S$, the temperature must be raised. The equilibrium temperature T_{eq} may be estimated to be

$$T_{eq} \approx \frac{\Delta H(298)}{\Delta S(298)} = 370.5°\text{K} \qquad (5-16)$$

assuming that ΔH and ΔS depend little on the temperature. The actual equilibrium temperature is, of course, 100°C or 373.15°K. Figure 5–1 shows the actual behavior of ΔH and $T \, \Delta S$ as functions of

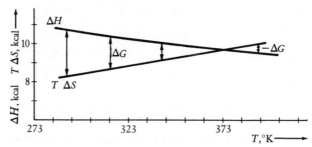

Figure 5–1 ΔH **and** $T \, \Delta S$ **for the phase transformation** $\mathbf{H_2O}(l)$ $= \mathbf{H_2O}(g, \ \mathbf{1 \ atm}).$ At the point where the two curves cross (373.15°K) there is equilibrium, since $\Delta H = T \, \Delta S$ implies that $\Delta G = 0.$ To the left of this intersection the difference between the two curves is $+\Delta G$ because ΔH is larger than $T \, \Delta S;$ on the right the difference is $-\Delta G$ because ΔH is now smaller than $T \, \Delta S.$ Thus, ΔG for the reaction $H_2O(l) = H_2O(g, \ 1 \ atm)$ is positive below 373.15°K and negative above. Below 373.15°K liquid water is more stable than vapor at 1 atm, above 373.15°K vapor at 1 atm is more stable, and at 373.15°K there is equilibrium.

the temperature. It is seen that ΔH slowly decreases with the temperature. For the approximate relationship (5–16), a constant ΔH was assumed, and the reasonable agreement between the estimated and actual equilibrium temperatures (370.5 and 373.15°K) is due in part to a cancellation of errors: ΔS slowly decreases with temperature also, and the curve $T\,\Delta S$ rises less steeply than it would if ΔS were constant.

At equilibrium, where the two curves intersect, $\Delta H = T\,\Delta S$, and $\Delta G = 0$. There is no change in free energy when liquid water is converted into vapor at 1 atm and 100°C. Above 100°C, $T\,\Delta S$ is larger than ΔH, and ΔG is therefore negative, confirming that above 100°C steam at 1 atm is more stable than liquid water. Below 100°C, ΔG is positive, and liquid water is more stable than steam at 1 atm.

The following examples of chemical reactions illustrate the cases of different signs of ΔH and ΔS given in Table 5–1. The numbers on the right of the chemical equations are, in sequence, ΔH, $T\,\Delta S$, and ΔG, all in kcal at 25°C, and at 1 atm.

Case 1

$$2H_2O_2(g) = 2H_2O(g) + O_2(g) \qquad -50.5;\ 9.4;\ -59.9$$

There is a strong tendency of the reaction to proceed to the right. At no temperature is this tendency expected to be reversed.

Case 2

$$3H_2(g) + N_2(g) = 2NH_3(g) \qquad -22.1;\ -14.1;\ -8.0$$

Again, this reaction tends to go to the right. As the temperature is increased, this tendency becomes less, and at elevated temperatures the reaction tends to proceed to the left.

Case 3

$$N_2O_4(g) = 2NO_2(g) \qquad 13.9;\ 12.6;\ 1.3$$

At 25°C, ΔG is positive, and the reaction cannot proceed to the right. However, as the temperature is raised, $T\,\Delta S$ increases and is eventually expected to become larger than ΔH, so that the reaction may proceed to the right.

Case 4

$$N_2(g) + 2O_2(g) = 2NO_2(g) \qquad 16.2; \; -8.6; \; 24.8$$

Since $\Delta H > 0$ and $\Delta S < 0$, there is no temperature at which the reaction is expected to proceed to the right.   There is instead a strong tendency toward the left.

The examples chosen illustrate again the importance of rates. In the absence of catalysts, H_2O_2 does not decompose appreciably at room temperature, and the rate of formation of NH_3 from H_2 and N_2 is zero for all practical purposes.   Although NO_2 is unstable at room temperature (reaction of case 4 going to the left), the rate of decomposition is immeasurably small.

5–4   AN EXAMPLE ON THE MOLECULAR PLANE

It is of interest to consider the results of statistical mechanics for particularly simple systems, in which only a discrete set of energy levels is accessible to the particles of the system, and for which the spacing ϵ of these levels is constant.   The methods of statistical mechanics permit the calculation of the enthalpy, the entropy, and the free energy for such a system, as functions of the temperature.

It is admittedly difficult to grasp all the intricacies of the present example, but an understanding of the *details* is not essential.   What is illuminating are the fundamental ideas involved.

We recall that in Fig. 4–4 a system with constant level spacing was shown at two temperatures.   At the higher temperature the spread over the energy levels and the entropy S of the system were larger than at the lower temperature.

Here we are interested in comparing systems with different, though constant, level spacings ϵ at the *same temperature* T.   Figure 5–2 shows four such systems, one with ϵ infinite and the others with ϵ equal to kT, $kT/2$, and $kT/4$, where kT is an energy per molecule characteristics of T; per mole of molecules this energy is $NkT = RT$. The occupancies of the levels are again determined by the Boltz-

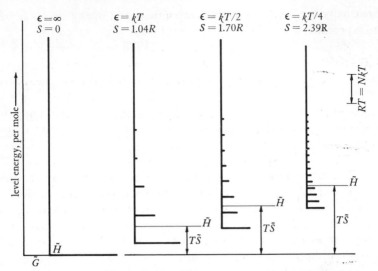

Figure 5–2   Systems with constant level spacing at constant
T **and** $\tilde{G}$.   For these independent systems of energy levels the
energy of the ground level has been adjusted so that the molar free
energy $\tilde{G} = \tilde{H} - T\tilde{S}$ is the same for each system, and they are
therefore in equilibrium with each other at temperature T.   The
level spacing in the system on the far left is infinite, while those of
the other systems are kT, $kT/2$, and $kT/4$ on a molecular basis,
or RT, $RT/2$, and $RT/4$ on a molar basis.   The size of RT is also
shown.   The relative occupancies are indicated by the lengths of
the horizontal lines, which add up to the same total in each diagram.   As the level spacing is decreased, going from left to right,
the spread over the levels increases and so does the entropy.   The
enthalpy increases also, because it has been arranged that $\tilde{G}$ stays
constant, and $\tilde{H} = \tilde{G} + T\tilde{S}$.   The example shows—going from
left to right—how a system can soak up more enthalpy from a
constant-temperature bath as the energy levels are spaced more
closely, or—going from right to left—how the enthalpy of a system
must be expended to lower the entropy.

mann factor, as they were in the example of Fig. 4–4.   Since there
is no PV term, the enthalpy H is identical with the total energy of
each system, the N molecules being distributed over the levels as
indicated.   The entropy $\tilde{S}$ is determined by the spread over the
levels.   The free energy $\tilde{G} = \tilde{H} - T\tilde{S}$ has been arranged to be con-

stant by suitable choice of the ground levels of the systems. Since G is constant, all systems are at equilibrium with each other.

When ϵ is infinite, all molecules are in the ground level and $\tilde{S} = 0$, because there is only one way for the molecules to be distributed. In this case $\tilde{H} = \tilde{G}$. When the level spacing is decreased, the spread and thus S increases, so that at constant $\tilde{G}$ and T, $\tilde{H} = \tilde{G} + T\tilde{S}$ also increases: The closer the spacing of the energy levels, the more enthalpy is soaked up by a system kept at constant temperature and free energy.

The different systems might, for example, be isomers with different bond enthalpies as well as different spacing of the levels, caused by different stiffness of the bonds and different masses of directly linked atoms. The constant spacing of the levels is, of course, an idealization. It could also not be expected that the various systems all have their ground levels and level spacings accidentally adjusted so that the free energy is the same for all. But for any two cases in which the system with the higher ground level has also more closely spaced energy levels, there exists a temperature at which the free energies are equal.

It is seen that when $kT \ll \epsilon$ it is the energy or enthalpy that counts; when $kT \gg \epsilon$ it is the number of levels that are populated as a result of thermal excitation. Quite generally, at $T = 0$ matter is most stable in its lowest state of energy or enthalpy, while at very high temperatures a large number of accessible energy levels, permitting the acquisition of a large entropy, is decisive.

5–5 STANDARD FREE ENERGIES

Because the free energy is a function of state, values of ΔG for different chemical reactions may be combined in the same way that the chemical equations of the reactions considered may be combined into the equations of new reactions. All this is analogous to the behavior of ΔH values (Section 2–4).

EXAMPLE 2

Given below are the over-all equations (1) and (2) of two chemical reactions. On the right are given the values of ΔG at 298°K for transforming as many moles of reactants into products as is indicated by the coefficients in the equations, with ions at concentrations of 1 mole/liter and gases at partial pressures of 1 atm. What is ΔG for reaction (3) that may be obtained by suitably combining reactions (1) and (2)?

(1) $16H^+ + 2MnO_4^- + 10Cl^- = 5Cl_2(g) + 2Mn^{2+} +$

$$8H_2O(l) \qquad \Delta G_1 = -43.62 \text{ kcal}$$

(2) $\qquad Cl_2(g) + 2Fe^{2+} = 2Fe^{3+} + 2Cl^-$

$$\Delta G_2 = -27.14 \text{ kcal}$$

(3) $\quad 8H^+ + MnO_4^- + 5Fe^{2+} = 5Fe^{3+} + Mn^{2+} +$

$$4H_2O(l) \qquad \Delta G_3 = ?$$

The third equation can be obtained by adding one-half of the first and five-halves times the second equation. Therefore, $\Delta G_3 = \frac{1}{2}\Delta G_1 + \frac{5}{2}\Delta G_2 = \frac{1}{2}(-43.62) + \frac{5}{2}(-27.14) \text{ kcal} = $ **−89.66 kcal.**

Since only free energy differences are defined by thermodynamics, it is possible, just as in the case of enthalpies, to agree on certain reference states that are assigned zero free energy of formation *by convention.* These are exactly the same reference states that were assigned zero standard enthalpies of formation—the elements at standard conditions in their most stable forms (see Section 2–5). The **standard molar free energies of formation** G_f^0 of compounds, and of elements in less stable modifications, are then their *free energies of formation at standard conditions from the elements* in their most stable forms. For substances in aqueous solution, standard conditions imply unit concentration (or more precisely, activity), and the standard free energies of formation of ionic species are defined by the convention that the standard free energy of H^+ is zero. Appendix 4 contains a representative list of such standard free energies of formation or, more simply, **standard free energies,** as they will usually be called. In many texts these quantities are given the symbols ΔG_f^0 or ΔGf^0. Unless otherwise indicated, standard free energies refer to 25°C or 298.15°K. Occasionally another temperature T is more useful and molar standard free energies at T are indicated by the symbol $G_f^0(T)$. Thus $\tilde{G}_f^0(500)$ is the free energy of formation of the substance in question from the elements at standard conditions and at 500°K. Again the convention is to take as reference states the elements in their most stable forms at 1 atm and the temperature T, to which are thus assigned zero standard free energies of formation.

The standard free energy change for any reaction can be found from the standard free energies of all substances involved by the relationship

$$\Delta G^0 = \sum G_{f,\text{ prod}}^0 - \sum G_{f,\text{ reac}}^0$$

This quantity is meaningful only if the explicit over-all balanced equation of the reaction it applies to is given. It refers to the complete conversion into products of as many moles of reactants as are indicated by the coefficients in the chemical equation, all at standard conditions. A temperature of 298°K is implied here also unless another temperature is specifically mentioned.

EXAMPLE 3

What is the standard free energy for burning ammonia in oxygen to NO?

$$4NH_3(g) + 5O_2(g) = 4NO(g) + 6H_2O(l)$$
$$-3.98 \qquad 0 \qquad 20.72 \qquad -56.69$$

This is an important industrial reaction, being a step in manufacturing nitric acid from synthetic ammonia. The standard molar free energies of formation of the substances involved are found in Appendix 4 and are shown under the chemical symbols. Combining them, $\Delta G^0 = (4 \times 20.72 - 6 \times 56.69 + 4 \times 3.98)$ kcal = **−241.34 kcal.** This value refers, of course, to 298°K or 25°C.

Standard free energies of formation of substances may be obtained experimentally *from thermal measurements alone*, which determine H, T, and S. Other experimental approaches, the measurement of equilibrium constants and of electric cell potentials, are discussed later.

The standard molar entropies of formation S_f^0 mentioned earlier are related to $\tilde{H}_f^0$ and $\tilde{G}_f^0$ by the equation $\tilde{S}_f^0 = (\tilde{G}_f^0 - \tilde{H}_f^0)/$ 298.15 or more generally, $\tilde{S}_f^0(T) = [\tilde{G}_f^0(T) - \tilde{H}_f^0(T)]/T$. Absolute molar entropies S^0 are generally given preference, because of their connection with the third law.

5–6 DEPENDENCE OF G ON PRESSURE AND TEMPERATURE

The state of a given quantity of a phase of given composition is completely defined by prescribing the values of two independent variables that will be chosen to be T and P. In particular, the free energy is a function of T and P, $G = G(T,P)$.[1]

Consider now the portion of the relationship (5–5) that has an *equals* sign and write it in the form

$$dG = Dw' - S\,dT + V\,dP$$

It applies to an infinitesimal change for any system. If the change is such that there is pressure-volume work only, $Dw' = 0$, and

$$dG = -S\,dT + V\,dP \qquad (5\text{–}17)$$

It is important to realize that this expression for dG remains unchanged when the specifications "reversible" and "pressure-volume work only" are dropped. The reason is that G is a function of state so that dG is the difference between the values G assumes at $T + dT$ and $P + dP$, and at T and P,

$$dG = G(T + dT, P + dP) - G(T,P)$$

---

[1] It is useful to note the following usage peculiar to thermodynamics. When a function $f(x,y)$ is expressed in terms of new variables s and t, it is the general practice in mathematics to use a new letter, say g, to describe the relationship: $f(x,y) = g(s,t)$. This practice is not followed in thermodynamics, where the *same* letter is always used for a given quantity, regardless of the choice of independent variables. Thus $G(T,P)$ is the free energy when T and P are the independent variables, while $G(S,V)$ is the free energy for the independent variables S and V. This does not imply, of course, that the functional dependence of G on S is the same as that of G on T, and similarly for P and V.

The difference cannot depend on the path, and it is permissible to evaluate it in whatever way desirable. This is precisely what has been done to obtain (5–17), which is thus of general validity.

The foregoing development implies that Dw' must be zero for an isothermal, isobaric, and reversible process. This is indeed the case unless external fields of electric, magnetic, gravitational, or other nature are present, which require the introduction of additional independent variables and cause work terms other than $-P\,dV$ to appear. For an isothermal isobaric and *irreversible* process, dG is still zero (external fields being absent), because G is a state function. But all we can say about Dw' now is that $Dw' > 0$, by considering that the left side of (5–5) is zero under the circumstances. An example is the isothermal isobaric vaporization of a liquid that is agitated mechanically, the agitation representing non-volume-pressure work of an irreversible nature.

When the pressure is kept constant and only the temperature is changed, $dP = 0$, and therefore

$$dG_P = -S\,dT \tag{5–18}$$

For changes of G with pressure at constant temperature, $dT = 0$, and thus

$$dG_T = V\,dP \tag{5–19}$$

These are important relationships. They are further developed in Section 5–7 and used in Chapter 6 to rederive the Clapeyron equation and to find the temperature dependence of the mass-action constant.

Equation (5–19) is used now, to find the pressure dependence of the free energy for a perfect gas. From the equation $V = nRT/P$ it follows that $dG_T = V\,dP = (nRT/P)\,dP$. The change in free energy for a change in pressure from P_1 to P_2 at constant temperature is therefore

$$\Delta G = \int_1^2 V\,dP = nRT\int_{P_1}^{P_2}\frac{dP}{P} = nRT\ln(P_2/P_1) \tag{5–20}$$

One important application of (5–20) is that it permits the calculation of the free energy of formation $\tilde{G}_f$ of a mole of ideal gas at *any* pressure from the *standard* free energy of formation $\tilde{G}_f^0$. Let P_1 in (5–20) be equal to the standard pressure $P^0 = 1$ atm, let P_2 be equal to the general pressure P, and let n be 1 mole. To find $\tilde{G}_f$ we add (5–20) to $\tilde{G}_f^0$:

$$\tilde{G}_f = \tilde{G}_f^0 + \Delta\tilde{G} = \tilde{G}_f^0 + RT \ln \frac{P}{P^0} = \tilde{G}_f^0 - RT \ln P^0 + RT \ln P$$
(5–21)

However, $RT \ln P^0$ is zero because P^0 is 1 atm, so that

$$\tilde{G}_f = \tilde{G}_f^0 + RT \ln P$$
(5–22)

This relationship is used in Chapter 6.

Equation (5–21) again contains a term $\ln P$ such as the one discussed on p. 112. Here it arises because in (5–21) the ratio P/P^0 was separated into two terms,

$$\ln \frac{P}{P^0} = \ln P - \ln P^0$$
(5–23)

Being a ratio, P/P^0 is a pure number, although P and P^0 themselves are not. However, assume, for example, that P is 2 atm while P^0 is 1 atm, so that the right side of (5–23) is $\ln(2 \text{ atm}) - \ln(1 \text{ atm}) = \ln 2 + \ln(\text{atm}) - \ln 1 - \ln(\text{atm}) = \ln 2$. Although the meaning of the terms $\ln(\text{atm})$ is not defined, they are seen to cancel. Inspection further shows that going from (5–21) to (5–22) the $\ln(\text{atm})$ arising from the term $\ln P^0$ has been combined with $\tilde{G}_f^0$. The standard enthalpy of formation of a gas thus always contains the term $-\ln(\text{atm})$, without this being explicitly stated. We essentially imply this by the statement that G_f^0 refers to a standard state of 1 atm pressure, and imply further that P has to be expressed in atm and the $\ln(\text{atm})$ disregarded in the quantity $\ln P$. When P is given in torr or other units, it must of course be converted to atmospheres before taking the logarithm.

In a similar way, in the term $\ln T$ that may occur in connection with expressions for the entropy such as (4–12), T is to be expressed in degrees Kelvin and the units disregarded when taking the logarithm. In connection with the mass-action law, terms such as $\ln(\text{mole/liter})$ may arise and are to be treated in the same way, as will be discussed in Sections 6–6 and 6–7.

After this digression we return to a numerical application of the more general equation (5–20).

EXAMPLE 4

Find the standard free energy of formation of water vapor at 25°C from that of liquid water (-56.6902 kcal/mole) and from the vapor pressure of water at 25°C, 23.76 torr. The free energy of the vapor at its equilibrium pressure is equal to that of liquid water, because the two phases are at equilibrium,

$$\widetilde{G}(H_2O, g, 23.76 \text{ torr}) = \widetilde{G}^0(H_2O, l)$$

Therefore, by (5–22),

$$G^0(H_2O, g) \approx G^0(H_2O, l) + RT \ln(760/23.76)$$
$$= (-56.6902 + 1.987 \times 10^{-3} \times 298.15 \times 2.303 \times$$
$$\log 31.99) \text{ kcal/mole}$$
$$= (-56.6902 + 2.0534) \text{ kcal/mole} = \mathbf{-54.637}$$

$$\mathbf{kcal/mole}$$

These calculations are approximate only, because water vapor does not behave exactly as a perfect gas.

5–7 RELATIONSHIPS AMONG THERMODYNAMIC QUANTITIES

It is useful at this point to review the fundamental relationships among the quantities U, H, and G, and to include also the Helmholtz free energy $A = U - TS$ that was mentioned in Section 5–1, even though no application of A will be made in this book.

By the first law, $dU = Dq + Dw$. For a reversible path involving volume-pressure work only, $Dw = -P \, dV$, whereas the second law states that for a reversible path $dS = Dq/T$ or $Dq = T \, dS$. Therefore,

$$dU = -P \, dV + T \, dS \tag{5–24}$$

Although this result was derived under special conditions, it is generally valid, because all quantities involved are state functions.   The only restriction is the absence of external fields of electric, gravitational, or similar nature that would require the introduction of additional variables.

Next, we consider $H = U + PV$ and form $dH = dU + P\,dV + V\,dP$. Inserting dU from (5–24) we note that $P\,dV$ cancels, so that

$$dH = V\,dP + T\,dS \qquad (5\text{–}25)$$

A similar consideration of $A = U - TS$ and $dA = dU - T\,dS - S\,dT$ shows that cancellation of $T\,dS$ occurs so that

$$dA = -P\,dV - S\,dT \qquad (5\text{–}26)$$

Finally, we note that $G = H - TS$ and that therefore $dG = dH - T\,dS - S\,dT$. Insertion of (5–25) shows that $T\,dS$ vanishes, so that

$$dG = V\,dP - S\,dT \qquad (5\text{–}27)$$

which is identical with (5–17).

As implied by the foregoing development, two independent variables are sufficient to specify the state of a given system in the absence of external fields. These may be chosen almost at random, such as P and T, V and S, etc. However, the simplicity of the expression (5–24) for dU suggests that the energy U is particularly suited to being expressed as a function of the independent variables V and S. Equations (5–25) through (5–27) suggest similarly that the most natural independent variables for H are P and S, whereas, V and T are most suitable for A, and P and T most convenient for G. This last fact is an indication of why the function G is of such importance in discussing thermodynamic equilibrium conditions at constant P and T. To explore equilibrium conditions at constant V and T the function A is preferable to G, as might be expected.

A complete appreciation of the developments to follow requires an understanding of *partial differentiation* of a function of several variables. However, many aspects of this mathematical development are so closely analogous to ordinary differentiation of a function of *one* variable that it should not prove difficult to grasp at least the spirit of the material in the remainder of this section.

Suppose we decide to express the energy U as a function of the independent variables V and S, $U = U(V,S)$. Since U is a state function, its differential dU is

$$dU = \left(\frac{\partial U}{\partial V}\right)_S dV + \left(\frac{\partial U}{\partial S}\right)_V dS \qquad (5\text{--}28)$$

To analyze this formula we let dS be zero for a moment, whence $dU = (\partial U/\partial V)_S dV$, as it would be if U were a function of V only. On the other hand, when dV is set equal to zero, $dU = (\partial U/\partial S)_V dS$, which is the change that would be expected if U were a function of S alone. The content of (5–28) is thus that when both V and S are altered, the change in U is the sum of the changes that would result if V and S were to be varied alone. The expressions in parentheses are the partial derivatives referred to in the footnote on p. 36. For example, $(\partial U/\partial V)_S$ is the partial derivative of $U(V,S)$ with respect to V, with S being treated as a constant. The subscript S is to some extent redundant, because the symbol $(\partial/\partial V)$ intimates that only V is to be considered a variable in the differentiation. However, a reminder is needed that S is the other independent variable, because the independent variables are often changed in thermodynamics and must therefore be kept track of.

An important fact is that the expression (5–28) of dU in terms of dV and dS is *unique*. The coefficients of dV in (5–24) and (5–28) must therefore be identical, and so must the coefficients of dS, so that

$$\left(\frac{\partial U}{\partial V}\right)_S = -P \qquad \text{and} \qquad \left(\frac{\partial U}{\partial S}\right)_V = T \qquad (5\text{--}29)$$

The same procedure can be applied to the quantities $H(P,S)$, $A(V,T)$, and $G(P,T)$. For example,

$$dG = \left(\frac{\partial G}{\partial P}\right)_T dP + \left(\frac{\partial G}{\partial T}\right)_P dT \qquad (5\text{--}30)$$

and comparison with (5–27) yields

$$\left(\frac{\partial G}{\partial P}\right)_T = V \qquad \text{and} \qquad \left(\frac{\partial G}{\partial T}\right)_P = -S \qquad (5\text{--}31)$$

The content of these relationships is identical to that of (5–18) and (5–19).

The simple form of the partial derivatives (5–29) and (5–31) illustrates again the appropriateness of using the independent variables V and S when dealing with U, variables P and T when working with G, etc. There is, of course, no rule against expressing the energy, for example, in terms of the variables V and T, leading to the correct equation

$$dU = \left(\frac{\partial U}{\partial T}\right)_V dV + \left(\frac{\partial U}{\partial V}\right)_T dT \qquad (5\text{--}32)$$

The coefficient of dV is by definition equal to C_V (p. 36),

$$\left(\frac{\partial U}{\partial T}\right)_V = C_V \qquad (5\text{--}33)$$

but the coefficient of dT does not lend itself to being expressed simply, as will be seen shortly. Note that $(\partial U/\partial V)_T$ is by no means equal to $(\partial U/\partial V)_S$.

An important property of partial derivatives is that in a so-called "mixed second derivative," $\partial^2 G/\partial T\, \partial P$, the sequence of differentiation, does not matter:

$$\frac{\partial^2 G}{\partial T\, \partial P} = \frac{\partial^2 G}{\partial P\, \partial T}$$

or written in more detail,

$$\frac{\partial}{\partial T}\left(\frac{\partial G}{\partial P}\right) = \frac{\partial}{\partial P}\left(\frac{\partial G}{\partial T}\right) \qquad (5\text{--}34)$$

The subscripts on the parentheses have been deleted, because no reminder that the independent variables are T and P is needed. Equations of the type (5–34) are called **Euler** or **Maxwell relations** and lead to interesting connections between partial derivatives. Thus, inserting the two parts of (5–31) into (5–34), we learn that

$$\left(\frac{\partial V}{\partial T}\right)_P = -\left(\frac{\partial S}{\partial P}\right)_T \qquad (5\text{--}35)$$

where subscripts are again needed. The rate of change of the entropy with pressure at constant temperature is thus negatively equal to the rate of change of the volume with temperature at constant pressure. The importance of such relationships is that they often relate a quantity that is hard to measure to one that is readily accessible to experimentation. Thus, the left side of (5–35) is easily determined, whereas the right side is not.

Still other relationships may be obtained, as follows. For example, solve (5–24) for dS,

$$dS = \left(\frac{1}{T}\right) dU + \left(\frac{P}{T}\right) dV \qquad (5–36)$$

and compare this with

$$dS = \left(\frac{\partial S}{\partial U}\right)_V dU + \left(\frac{\partial S}{\partial V}\right)_U dV$$

treating S as function of U and V. Comparison yields

$$\left(\frac{\partial S}{\partial U}\right)_V = \frac{1}{T} \qquad \text{and} \qquad \left(\frac{\partial S}{\partial V}\right)_U = \frac{P}{T} \qquad (5–37)$$

The first of these two relationships is the reciprocal of the second relationship in (5–29)..

As an application of these ideas, it is possible to demonstrate that for a perfect gas $(\partial U/\partial V)_T = 0$, because of the perfect gas equation, $PV = nRT$, so that U is a function of the temperature only: First, we divide (5–24) by dV, keeping T constant:

$$\left(\frac{\partial U}{\partial V}\right)_T = -P + T\left(\frac{\partial S}{\partial V}\right)_T \qquad (5–38)$$

The procedure just used is questionable, but the same result may be derived by sound methods.

The next step is a transformation of $(\partial S/\partial V)_T$. To this effect we derive from (5–26) that

$$dA = -P\,dV - S\,dT = \left(\frac{\partial A}{\partial V}\right)_T dV + \left(\frac{\partial A}{\partial T}\right)_V dT$$

so that

$$\left(\frac{\partial A}{\partial V}\right)_T = -P \quad \text{and} \quad \left(\frac{\partial A}{\partial T}\right)_V = -S \qquad (5\text{–}39)$$

Forming the mixed second derivative $\partial^2 A / \partial V \, \partial T$ we find the Maxwell relation,

$$\left(\frac{\partial S}{\partial V}\right)_T = \left(\frac{\partial P}{\partial T}\right)_V \qquad (5\text{–}40)$$

which is the desired equation. Insertion in (5–38) yields the general result

$$\left(\frac{\partial U}{\partial V}\right)_T = -P + T\left(\frac{\partial P}{\partial T}\right)_V \qquad (5\text{–}41)$$

Note that this expression is more complicated than that for $(\partial U / \partial V)_S$, (5–29), demonstrating again that S is a natural independent variable for U, whereas T is not.

Specializing, finally, to an ideal gas, we differentiate the equation $P = nRT/V$ with respect to T at constant V:

$$\left(\frac{\partial P}{\partial T}\right)_V = \frac{\partial}{\partial T}\left(\frac{nRT}{V}\right)_V = \frac{nR}{V} = \frac{P}{T}$$

Inserting in (5–41) yields

$$\left(\frac{\partial U}{\partial V}\right)_T = -P + T\left(\frac{P}{T}\right) = 0$$

which is the desired result. It follows that U is a function of T only, $U = U(T)$ for an ideal gas, and $d\,U = C_V \, dT$.

This is only a small taste of partial derivatives, the use of which is one of the more common and powerful methods of thermodynamics. They are particularly useful in the treatment of solutions where so-called "partial molar quantities" play an important role.

PROBLEMS

5–1. *Thermodynamic criteria.* State the conditions for which:
(*a*) $\Delta G = 0$ indicates a reversible process.
(*b*) $\Delta S = 0$ indicates a reversible process.

(c) $\Delta G = w'$ (net work).

(d) $\Delta G = \Delta H - T \Delta S$.

(e) $\Delta H = \Delta U + V \Delta P$.

(f) $\Delta H = q + V \Delta P$.

(g) What is the sign of ΔG for a spontaneous process under the conditions of (a)?

(h) What is the sign of ΔS for a spontaneous process under the conditions of (b)?

5–2. *Triple point of water.* At the triple point of water, 273.16°K, the phases ice, liquid, and vapor of a pressure of 4.58 torr are stable. Under these conditions ΔH_{vap} is 10.767 kcal/mole and $\Delta S_{vap} = 39.416$ cal/mole-deg; the values for ΔH_{melt} and ΔS_{melt} are, respectively, 1.4363 kcal/mole and 5.2585 cal/mole-deg. For the solid-to-vapor transition calculate ΔH_{sub}, ΔS_{sub}, and ΔG_{sub}.

5–3. *Vaporization of ethanol.* The enthalpy of vaporization of ethanol is 9.25 kcal/mole at its boiling point, 78.3°C. Calculate q, w, ΔU, ΔS, and ΔG for vaporizing 1 mole of ethanol reversibly at 78.3°C and 1 atm. Neglect the volume of liquid ethanol and assume the vapor to behave as a perfect gas.

5–4. *Free energy and vapor pressure.* The *standard* molar free energies of benzene at 25°C are 29.76 kcal/mole for the liquid and 30.99 kcal/mole for the vapor. What is the vapor pressure of benzene at 25°C, assuming the vapor to behave as a perfect gas?

5–5. *Iron oxides.* From the values in Appendix 4 calculate ΔH^0, ΔS^0, and ΔG^0 for the reaction $3Fe_2O_3(s) = 2Fe_3O_4(s) + \frac{1}{2}O_2(g)$ at 25°C. Which of the two oxides is more stable at 25°C and $P_{O_2} = 1$ atm?

5–6. *Thermodynamic quantities for unknown equilibrium.* From the tables in Appendix 4 calculate ΔH^0, ΔS^0, $T \Delta S^0$, and ΔG^0 for the following reaction, at 298°K and at standard conditions: $6CH_4(g) + 4\frac{1}{2}O_2(g) = C_6H_6(l,$ benzene$) + 9H_2O(l)$. Check the equality of ΔG^0 and $\Delta H^0 - T \Delta S^0$ but note that no direct experimental information on the existence of this equilibrium exists.

5–7. *Vaporization of water.* Find the quantities ΔU, ΔH, ΔS, and ΔG for the vaporization of 1 mole of water at 100°C and 1 atm. At the conditions stated the enthalpy of vaporization is 9.71 kcal/mole, the molar volume of liquid water is 18.0 ml, and that of water vapor is 30.2 liters.

5–8. *Chemistry of molecules.* The strongest chemical bond known is that in carbon monoxide, CO, with a bond enthalpy of 250 kcal/mole. Furthermore, the entropy increase in a gaseous dissociation of the kind AB = A + B is about 30 cal/mole-deg. These factors establish a temperature beyond which there is essentially no chemistry of molecules. Show why this is so and find the temperature.

5–9. *Vaporization of dimethyl ether.* One mole of dimethyl ether is vaporized at its boiling point of 24.8°C into a previously evacuated space of a size such that the pressure of the resulting vapor is just 760 torr at the end. The temperature is maintained at 24.8°C. The enthalpy of vaporization is 5.141 kcal/mole. Assume that the vapor behaves as a perfect gas and that the volume of the liquid is negligible. Find ΔU, ΔS, and ΔG for the process. Explain the value of ΔG in the light of the fact that the process considered is irreversible.

5–10. *Supercooled water.* (a) Find the quantities ΔH, ΔS, and ΔG for the transformation of 1 g of undercooled water at −10°C to ice at the same temperature. Data: specific heat capacities: liquid water, 1.00 cal/g-deg; ice, 0.50 cal/g-deg. Enthalpy of melting at 0°C, 79.7 cal/g. (b) Find ΔG for the same transformation from the vapor pressures at −10°C, 1.950 torr for ice and 2.149 torr for supercooled water.

5–11. *Change of state.* Two moles of $H_2O(l)$ at 25°C are surrounded by a vacuum jacket that springs a leak so that water begins to evaporate into the jacket until the jacket is filled with water vapor. No leak develops toward the outside, but heat is transferred from the outside to the system that comprises the two forms of H_2O. Although the temperature of the system drops at the beginning, it is finally restored to the outside temperature of 25°C. At the end, exactly 1 mole of water has evaporated. The vapor pressure of water at 25°C is 23.8 torr. The enthalpy of vaporization at 25°C is 10.52 kcal/mole. What are the values of q, w, ΔU, ΔH, ΔS, and ΔG? Assume that the vapor behaves as a perfect gas, and that the volume of liquid water is negligible compared to that of its vapor.

5–12. *Thermodynamic relationships.* Find relationships that involve $(\partial H/\partial P)_S$, $(\partial H/\partial S)_P$, $(\partial V/\partial S)_P$, $(\partial T/\partial P)_S$, and $(\partial S/\partial P)_H$.

6 The Chemical Potential

This chapter deals with the chemical potential and its value as related to phase equilibria and chemical equilibria. With its use the Clapeyron equation is rederived, and Henry's law and the osmotic pressure law discussed. A thermodynamic treatment of the mass-action law follows, including the relationship between the equilibrium constant and the difference between the standard free energies of products and reactants. A derivation of the temperature dependence of the equilibrium constant concludes the chapter.

6–1 CHEMICAL POTENTIAL

It is possible to assign to any chemical species an intensive quantity called the chemical potential that characterizes the thermodynamic behavior of this species when reacting with other chemical species, both as to the direction in which reactions are permitted to occur and the positions of chemical equilibria. This applies not only to **homogeneous reactions**—reactions that occur in a single phase—but also to reactions at the interface between different phases, which are called **heterogeneous reactions.** Chemical potentials also apply to phase transformations and equilibria, regardless of whether they occur in pure substances or in mixtures.

A detailed treatment of chemical potentials requires the full apparatus of partial derivatives and will not be attempted here. Instead, some of the facts about chemical potentials are presented in the remainder of this section, without proof. They will, however, be made plausible to some extent by analogy, and to some extent by the demonstration that their application leads to well-known laws such as Henry's law (Section 6–4), Raoult's law (Problem 6–1), and the osmotic pressure law (Section 6–5).

Consider a mixture of n_1 moles of species 1, n_2 moles of species 2, etc. The **chemical potential** μ_i of each species i has the property that the free energy of the mixture is the sum of the μ_i, multiplied by the respective number of moles n_i,

$$G = \sum_i n_i \mu_i \tag{6-1}$$

As already stated, the chemical potentials μ_i are intensive quantities. They depend on the composition of the mixture, the temperature T, and the pressure P. They are of particularly simple form for a mixture of perfect gases and for dilute solutions. For a pure substance, $\mu = \tilde{G}_f$.

In a *mixture of perfect gases* labeled by the subscripts $i = 1, 2,$ . . . , the chemical potential of the species i is given by the expression

$$\mu_i = \mu_i^0(T) + RT \ln P_i \tag{6-2}$$

where P_i is the partial pressure in atmospheres of the species i, and $\mu_i^0(T)$ is the chemical potential of the species i at a standard pressure of 1 atm and at a temperature T, chosen to be 298°K unless another temperature is mentioned specifically; $\mu_i^0(T)$ may be set equal to $\tilde{G}_f^0(T)$, the standard molar free energy of formation for the pure gas i. Equation (6–2) is very similar to (5–22) for the molar free energy of the pure component i at pressure P_i and temperature T. Indeed, for pure gases the content of these two equations is identical.

As for the term $\ln P_i$, the earlier discussion applies here as well. The logarithm of the numerical part only of P_i is to be taken; the term $RT \ln(\text{atm})$ is automatically compensated by a term $-RT \ln(\text{atm})$ in μ_i^0 that is usually not mentioned explicitly. Finally, it is always useful to check formulas for special cases. Thus, when $P_i = 1$ atm, $\mu_i = \mu_i^0$ by (6–2), as it should.

For *dilute solutions* the chemical potential of the solute species i is

$$\mu_{is} = \mu_{is}^0 + RT \ln c_i \tag{6-3}$$

where c_i is the concentration in moles per liter of the species i—also denoted by $[i]$ in mass-action expressions—and μ_{is}^0 is the chemical potential of the species i in a solution at standard concentration (1 M), at temperature T (usually 298°K), and at 1 atm; μ_{is}^0 may be set equal to $\tilde{G}_f^0(T)$, the standard molar free energy of formation for the species i in question. The subscript s is used to differentiate the chemical potential of the species i in a solution from that in a gas mixture as shown in (6–2); μ_{is} depends on T and the total pressure P.

Although the units of c_i are moles per liter, the logarithm in $\ln c_i$ pertains only to the numerical part of c_i. The term $RT \ln(\text{moles/liter})$, whatever it may be, is automatically compensated by a term $-RT \ln(\text{moles/liter})$ in μ_{is}^0 that is usually not mentioned. Note that when $c_i = 1$ mole/liter, $\mu_{is} = \mu_{is}^0$, as it should.

Expressions (6–2) and (6–3) are very similar. In both cases there is a logarithmic term, and both μ_i and μ_{is} are independent of the nature and the concentrations of the other components of the mixture. For other than dilute (about 0.01 M) solutions, expression (6–3) remains valid if the concentrations are replaced by the quantities a_i, called **activities,** that represent effective concentrations and are obtained by multiplying the concentrations by **activity coefficients** γ_i: $a_i = \gamma_i c_i$ and thus

$$\mu_{is} = \mu_{is}^0 + RT \ln a_i = \mu_{is}^0 + RT \ln \gamma_i c_i \qquad (6\text{–}4)$$

Similarly, for a mixture of *real* gases, (6–2) remains valid if the partial pressures P_i are replaced by *corrected* partial pressures, also called **fugacities.**

The chemical potential of a *pure* solid, liquid, or gas may be set equal to the *molar* free energy of formation of the substance.

EXAMPLE 1

What are the chemical potentials at 298°K for the species in a three-phase system comprised of $AgCl(s)$; $H_2O(l)$ containing Ag^+, H^+, and Cl^-; and $HCl(g)$? Using the values for G_f^0 in Appendix 4 we find

Solid phase:
$$\mu_{AgCl} = \mu_{AgCl}^0 = -26.22 \text{ kcal/mole}$$
Liquid phase:
$$\mu_{H_2O} \approx \mu_{H_2O}^0 = -56.69 \text{ kcal/mole}$$
$$\mu_{Ag^+} = 18.43 \text{ kcal/mole} + RT \ln[Ag^+]$$
$$\mu_{H^+} = RT \ln[H^+]$$
$$\mu_{Cl^-} = -31.35 \text{ kcal/mole} + RT \ln[Cl^-]$$

Vapor phase:

$$\mu_{HCl} = -22.77 \text{ kcal/mole} + RT \ln P_{HCl}$$

No superscripts have been used to identify the μ's as belonging to different phases, as might be necessary in some situations. The chemical potential of AgCl(s) is constant unless the pressure is changed to several hundred atmospheres. Similarly, μ for $H_2O(l)$ in dilute solutions is approximately equal to that of *pure* water (however, see Section 6–5). For really accurate results, the concentrations of the dissolved species should be replaced in the foregoing expressions by effective concentrations or activities, unless these concentrations are less than about 0.01 M.

6–2   APPLICATION TO PHASE TRANSFORMATIONS

First, consider two phases of a pure substance—phase I, containing n_I moles, and phase II, with n_{II} moles. If the substance is not composed of molecules, quantities such as number of moles and molecular weight have to be interpreted suitably. The free energy of the system is

$$G = n_I\mu_I + n_{II}\mu_{II}$$

where the chemical potentials μ of the two phases are identical here with the molar free energies $\tilde{G}_I$ and $\tilde{G}_{II}$. Suppose now that dn moles of phase I are changed into phase II, at constant P and T. The change in the number of moles of phase I is thus $dn_I = -dn$, that of phase II, $dn_{II} = dn$, and

$$dG = \mu_I dn_I + \mu_{II} dn_{II} = (\mu_{II} - \mu_I)dn \qquad (6\text{--}5)$$

When the two phases are at equilibrium, $dG = 0$ for this process, from which the equilibrium condition follows:

$$\mu_I = \mu_{II} \qquad \text{or} \qquad \tilde{G}_I = \tilde{G}_{II} \qquad (6\text{--}6)$$

When equilibrium has not been reached, $dG < 0$ for any spontaneous process, so that when $\mu_I > \mu_{II}$, dn must be positive, and when

$\mu_{II} > \mu_I$, negative. That is, the phase with the lower chemical potential or molar free energy is the more stable, and a given phase can transform spontaneously only into one of lower chemical potential. Note the analogy between chemical potential and the potential in a mechanical system, where the force is also in the direction of lower potential.

For more than two phases, the situation is analogous. The phase with the lowest chemical potential is the most stable, that with the highest potential the least stable. Equilibrium exists between phases that have the same chemical potential.

The equilibrium condition (6–6), together with (5–18) and (5–19), permits a rederivation of the Clapeyron equation (4–17), as follows.

Suppose two phases are at equilibrium at T and P, so that

$$\tilde{G}_I(T, P) = \tilde{G}_{II}(T, P) \qquad (6\text{–}7)$$

The temperature is changed by dT; if equilibrium is to be maintained, the pressure must be changed by an amount dP such that an equilibrium condition like (6–7) applies also at $T + dT$ and $P + dP$,

$$\tilde{G}_I(T + dT, P + dP) = \tilde{G}_{II}(T + dT, P + dP) \qquad (6\text{–}8)$$

The difference between the left sides of (6–8) and (6–7) is, by (5–18) and (5–19),

$$d\tilde{G}_I = -\tilde{S}_I\, dT + \tilde{V}_I\, dP \qquad (6\text{–}9)$$

It must be equal to the difference between the right sides of (6–8) and (6–7),

$$d\tilde{G}_I = d\tilde{G}_{II} = -\tilde{S}_{II}\, dT + \tilde{V}_{II}\, dP \qquad (6\text{–}10)$$

Combining (6–9) and (6–10) and rearranging leads to

$$(\tilde{S}_I - \tilde{S}_{II})\, dT = (\tilde{V}_I - \tilde{V}_{II})\, dP$$

Thus, when equilibrium is maintained, dP and dT must be related by

$$\left(\frac{dP}{dT}\right)_{\text{equil}} = \frac{S_{\text{II}} - S_{\text{I}}}{V_{\text{II}} - V_{\text{I}}} = \frac{\Delta S}{\Delta V}$$

Finally, for a phase transformation at equilibrium, $\Delta S = \Delta H/T$, whence

$$\left(\frac{dP}{dT}\right)_{\text{equil}} = \frac{\Delta H}{T \, \Delta V} \qquad (6\text{--}11)$$

which is the Clapeyron equation. It should be noted that no assumption need be made about the nature of the two phases, so that (6–11) is of general validity. It applies, for example, to the change in melting point of ice with pressure,

$$\left(\frac{\delta T}{\delta P}\right)_{\text{equil}} \approx \left(\frac{dT}{dP}\right)_{\text{equil}} = \left(\frac{T \, \Delta V}{\Delta H}\right)$$

The melting point of ice is lowered by an increase in pressure, because ΔV is negative.

EXAMPLE 2

Orthorhombic sulfur, stable at room temperature, transforms into monoclinic sulfur at 96°C. The densities at this temperature are, respectively, 1.98 g/cm³ and 1.93 g/cm³. The enthalpy of transformation is 96 cal/mole. By how much is the transformation temperature changed when the pressure is increased by 1 atm?

The reciprocal of the Clapeyron equation is $dT/dP = T \, \Delta V/\Delta H$, so that $\delta T \approx (T \, \Delta V/\Delta H)\delta P$. This approximation is valid as long as δT is small compared to T, and ΔH and ΔV are not affected by the pressure change. One mole (32.1 g) of sulfur atoms takes up $32.1/1.98 = 16.21$ cm³ in the orthorhombic and $32.1/1.93 = 16.63$ cm³ in the monoclinic state, so that $\Delta \tilde{V} = \tilde{V}_{\text{mon}} - \tilde{V}_{\text{orth}} = 0.42 \times 10^{-3}$ liter/mole, and $\Delta H = (96 \text{ cal/mole}) \times (0.0413)$ liter-atm/cal $= 3.96$ liter-atm/mole. Hence, $\delta T = [369 \text{ deg} \times 0.42 \times 10^{-3}$ (liter/mole) $\times 1$ atm]/3.96 (liter-atm/mole) $= \mathbf{0.04 \text{ deg}}$.

6–3 PHASE EQUILIBRIA BETWEEN MIXTURES

Suppose two phases are both mixtures of the pure substances $i = 1, 2, \ldots$, and that there are no chemical equilibria between the different substances. Let n_i^I be the number of moles of substance i, of chemical potential μ_i^I in the mixture, and similarly for phase II, so that the free energy of the system is

$$G = n_1^I \mu_1^I + n_2^I \mu_2^I + \cdots + n_1^{II} \mu_1^{II} + n_2^{II} \mu_2^{II} + \cdots$$

Suppose that dn_i moles of substance i are removed from phase I and added to phase II. The change in G is, by the argument used preceding (6–5),

$$dG = (\mu_i^{II} - \mu_i^I)\, dn_i \qquad (6\text{--}12)$$

Thus at equilibrium

$$\mu_i^I = \mu_i^{II} \qquad (6\text{--}13)$$

for all components i. If equilibrium for a component has not been reached, this component can only move to the phase in which its chemical potential is lower, because (6–12) applies and $dG < 0$ for any natural process.

Nothing is changed when there are more than two phases. It can also be shown that the conclusions are unchanged when chemical equilibria exist between the different substances involved. In all cases there is equilibrium only when the chemical potentials for a given substance are the same in all phases, and when this is true for all substances concerned. Furthermore, if equilibrium has not been reached, a given substance can move only to a phase in which its chemical potential is lower.

Figure 6–1 shows the chemical potential of ice, liquid water, and water vapor at different pressures. For the condensed phases μ (and G) are only slightly sensitive to changes of pressure, and for the range of pressures shown, the change in μ would not be discernible in the figure. This is different for the vapor phase, as is evident.

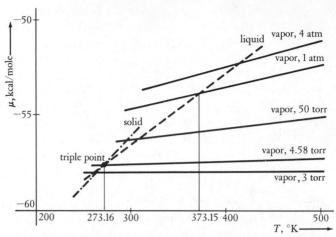

Figure 6–1 The chemical potential of water in different states of aggregation. The solid curves indicate μ for the vapor at different pressures ranging from 3 torr to 4 atm. The dashed curve shows μ for liquid water and the dot-dashed curve represents ice. For these condensed phases the change of μ with pressure is about 0.4 cal/atm-mole which is less than the widths of the curves shown. In the pressure range of 3 torr to 4 atm, there is thus only one curve for liquid water and one curve for ice. The phase of the lowest chemical potential is always the most stable. Thus vapor at 1 atm is more stable than liquid water when the solid curve "vapor, 1 atm" is below the dashed curve; in the converse situation liquid water is more stable, and at the intersection point there is equilibrium—this is the normal boiling point of water. At other vapor pressures the situation is analogous. Similarly, vapor of a given pressure is more stable than ice when the corresponding solid curve is below the dot-dashed curve and less stable in the opposite case; the point of intersection is the sublimation point of ice at the pressure concerned. The intersection of the curves for ice and liquid water is also crossed by the curve for vapor at 4.58 torr. This is thus a triple point at which three phases are stable: ice, liquid water, and vapor at 4.58 torr. The slopes of the different curves give $-\Delta \tilde{S}_f$, the negative of the entropy of formation of H_2O at the conditions given from $H_2(g)$ and $O_2(g)$ at 1 atm [see Eq. (5–18)].

At a given pressure and temperature the phase with lowest μ is the most stable. At intersections of the chemical potential lines of two phases there is equilibrium. Thus the curve for vapor of 4 atm intersects the curve for the liquid at 417°K, which is the boiling point of water at 4 atm. The curve for vapor of 3 torr intersects the curve for ice at 268°K, which is the sublimation temperature of ice at a pressure 3 torr. Liquid water has a higher μ than ice under these conditions and is therefore less stable. By careful cooling it can nevertheless be cooled to 268°K, and even lower, without freezing. The curve showing μ for vapor of 3 torr intersects that for water at 267°K, indicating that the vapor pressure of supercooled water of 267°K is 3 torr. At 273.1600°K and 4.58 torr the curves for ice, liquid water, and water vapor intersect, and these phases are thus at equilibrium with each other. This is the **triple point** of water. The portion of the curve for ice above the triple point is experimentally not accessible, because "superheated" ice does not exist.

The following analogies among the temperature T, the pressure P, the electric potential $\mathcal{V}$, and the chemical potential μ are illuminating. All these quantities are intensive, and all are of consequence (1) in determining the direction of irreversible processes, and (2) in establishing criteria for equilibrium. In detail, between two constant-temperature baths of different temperature there is heat flow to the bath at the lower temperature, and thermal equilibrium exists at temperature equality. When the pressures on the two sides of a movable wall are different, the wall moves in the direction of the lower pressure, and the wall is in equilibrium when the pressures are equal. Electric current moves in the direction of lower electric potential, and there is electric equilibrium when the electric potentials are equal. At a phase boundary, a substance tends to pass into the phase in which its chemical potential is lower, and the condition for equilibrium across a phase boundary is the equality of the chemical potentials.

6–4 HENRY'S LAW

To show an application we consider the equilibrium between a dilute solution of gases and a gas phase. The chemical potential of gas i is given by (6-2) in the gas phase, and by (6-3) in solution. Equating the two,

$$\mu_i^0(T) + RT \ln P_i = \mu_{is}^0 + RT \ln c_i \qquad (6\text{-}14)$$

Rearrangement leads to

$$-\ln P_i + \ln c_i = \ln \frac{c_i}{P_i} = \frac{\mu_i^0 - \mu_{is}^0}{RT}$$

The right side is constant at a constant temperature, and it is convenient to call this constant $\ln k_i$, that is, $(\mu_i^0 - \mu_{is}^0)/RT = \ln k_i$. Taking the antilogarithms of $\ln(c_i/P_i)$ and $\ln k_i$ results in

$$\frac{c_i}{P_i} = k_i \qquad \text{or} \qquad c_i = k_i P_i \qquad (6\text{-}15)$$

This is **Henry's law,** by which the concentration of a volatile species in a solution is proportional to the partial pressures of the species above the solution. The value of the proportionality constant depends on the nature of the species i, the solvent, and the temperature, because the quantities μ_i^0 and μ_{is}^0 depend on these factors. It must be realized that this is not a thermodynamic derivation of Henry's law from first principles, and that such a derivation does not exist. What has been shown is that expressions (6-2) and (6-3) for the chemical potential contain, or are consistent with, Henry's law.

6-5   OSMOTIC PRESSURE LAW

Suppose two phases are separated by a semipermeable diaphragm through which some of the substances concerned can pass but others cannot (Fig. 6-2). The argument used to derive (6-5) and (6-12) can then be used only for the substances that may pass the membrane. Thus the conditions of equal chemical potential at equilibrium and of substances passing into phases of lower chemical potential apply only to those substances, and for the other substances there are no conditions on the chemical potentials.

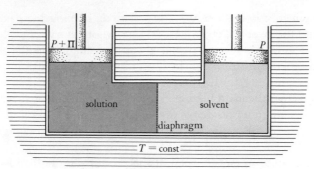

Figure 6–2 Osmotic pressure. The solvent and the solution are separated by a diaphragm that is permeable to the solvent, and impermeable to the solute. Solvent molecules constantly pass through the diaphragm in both directions. If the same pressure P were to be applied to both pistons, more solvent would pass into the solution than out of it, tending to dilute the solution. The piston on the left would rise, that on the right would lower. To prevent this, an additional pressure Π must be applied to the piston on the left. This pressure Π is called the osmotic pressure.

Derivation of the osmotic pressure law illustrates the treatment of an equilibrium that involves a semipermeable membrane. *First*, it is useful to express concentrations in terms of mole fractions. If n_1 is the number of moles of solvent and n_2 the *total* moles of solute, including the contribution of each separate molecular or ionic species, **the mole fraction** x_1 of solvent is $x_1 = n_1/(n_1 + n_2)$ and the mole fraction of total solute is $x_2 = n_2/(n_1 + n_2)$. Note that $x_1 + x_2 = 1$. The chemical potential of the solvent in terms of its mole fraction x_1 is

$$\mu_1 = \mu_1^0 + RT \ln x_1 \qquad (6\text{--}16)$$

This expression will not be justified, but it can be shown that it is consistent with Raoult's law (Problem 6–1). The quantity μ_1^0 is the standard potential of the pure solvent, which may be set equal to the standard molar free energy $\tilde{G}_f^0(T)$ of the pure solvent at T and at 1 atm. Indeed if $x_1 = 1$ (indicating pure solvent) is inserted in (6–16), the logarithmic term vanishes, yielding $\mu_1 = \mu_1^0$, as it should.

For a solution x_1 is always less than 1, making $\ln x_1$ negative. If (6–16) were complete and told the whole story, the chemical potential μ_1 of the solvent would always be smaller on the solution side than on the side of the pure solvent. Solvent would continuously pass the membrane in the direction of the lower value of μ_1, diluting the solution further and further. Equality of the chemical potentials for the solvent on both sides of the membrane (and thus equilibrium) could be achieved only by letting the solution become infinitely dilute.

This would in fact happen, if the pressures on both sides of the membrane were to be kept equal. However, if the pressures on both sides are not equal the situation is changed, because μ_1 depends also on the pressure and this is not shown by (6–16). As will be seen shortly, increase of the pressure increases μ_1. By increasing the pressure on the solution side, μ_1 can thus be increased until it matches $\mu_1 = \mu_1^0$ on the pure solvent side. The excess pressure needed to achieve equality of μ_1 and thus equilibrium is, by definition, the **osmotic pressure** II (Fig. 6–2).

The pressure dependence of μ_1 at constant composition and temperature is given by an equation just like (5–19):

$$(d\mu_1)_{T,\,x} = \tilde{V}\,dP \qquad (6\text{–}17)$$

where $\tilde{V}$ is the molar volume of the solvent. Thus if the pressure on the solution is changed from P to $P + \Delta P$,

$$\Delta\mu_1 = \int_P^{P+\Delta P} \tilde{V}\,dP \approx \tilde{V}\,\Delta P \qquad (6\text{–}18)$$

provided $\tilde{V}$ is assumed to be constant, which means that the compressibility of the solvent is neglected. The complete expression for the chemical potential of the *solvent in the solution* is therefore

$$\mu_1(T, P + \Delta P, x_1) \approx \tilde{G}_f^0(T) + RT \ln x_1 + \tilde{V}\,\Delta P \qquad (6\text{–}19)$$

where $\tilde{G}_f^0(T)$ is the standard molar free energy of the pure solvent. Thus a higher pressure on the solution side (ΔP positive) causes a positive contribution to μ_1, which thus counteracts the negative term

$RT \ln x_1$ in (6–19). By variation of ΔP, this μ_1 can thus be made smaller or larger than μ_1 on the pure solvent side, where $\mu_1 = \tilde{G}_f^0(T)$, and since solvent always passes the membrane in the direction of the lower μ_1, it can be made to pass in either direction by adjustment of the pressure. There is equilibrium when the chemical potential of the solvent is equal on both sides, and for this situation ΔP is by definition equal to Π. The condition for equilibrium is

$$\tilde{G}_f^0(T) = \tilde{G}_f^0(T) + RT \ln x_1 + \Pi \tilde{V} \qquad (6\text{–}20)$$

Rearrangement leads to

$$RT \ln x_1 = - \Pi \tilde{V} \qquad (6\text{–}21)$$

The next step is to develop an approximation to $\ln x_1$, using the fact that $\ln(1 - \delta) \approx -\delta$ when $\delta \ll 1$. We note that $x_1 = 1 - x_2$ and that $x_2 \ll 1$ for a dilute solution. Therefore, $\ln x_1 = \ln(1 - x_2) \approx -x_2 = -n_2/n$, where n_2 is the total number of moles of solutes, and $n = n_1 + n_2$ is the total number of moles, including solvent and all solutes. This leads to

$$RTn_2 \approx n\Pi\tilde{V} = \Pi V$$

and finally to the **osmotic pressure law,**

$$\Pi \approx \frac{n_2 RT}{V} \qquad (6\text{–}22)$$

where $V = n\tilde{V} \approx n_1\tilde{V}$ is the total solution volume. The osmotic pressure Π needed to maintain equilibrium across a semipermeable membrane (Fig. 6–2) is thus proportional to the total molar concentration n_2/V of solute species, V being the volume that contains the n_2 total moles of solute. Although the similarity between (6–22) and the perfect gas equation should be noted, no deeper meaning must be attached to the similarity.

The development of (6–22) is again not a derivation from first principles, but depends on the physical content of (6–16), which cannot be derived from thermodynamics. However, (6–16) and thus (6–22) are compatible with Raoult's law, so that Raoult's law and the osmotic pressure law are related by thermodynamics.

EXAMPLE 3

What is the osmotic pressure at 298°K of salt water that is 0.5 M in Na^+ and 0.5 M in Cl^- (approximately the salt concentration in ocean water)? One liter contains a total of $n_2 = 1.0$ mole of solute, so that $\Pi = 1.0$ mole $\times$ 0.082 (liter-atm/mole-deg) $\times$ 298 deg/liter = **24 atm.**

There exist membranes permeable to water but not to salt, and a process is under development for the desalination of ocean water by forcing it through such membranes, fresh water emerging on the other side. For the salt solution considered earlier, the pressure on the salt-water side must be 24 atm above the pressure on the other side, just to maintain equilibrium. To produce 1 liter of pure water reversibly from a large supply of salt water thus takes the work of 1 liter $\times$ 24 atm = 24 liter-atm $\approx$ 600 cal. A large supply is presupposed, so that removal of the liter of fresh water does not increase the salt concentration, which would increase the osmotic pressure and the work needed to obtain fresh water.

In actual practice a pressure that is larger than 24 atm would be needed to force the water through the membrane. Furthermore, because the 600 cal calculated earlier represent reversible work, this is the *minimum work* required for 1 liter of fresh water no matter whether it is obtained by distillation, by freezing out of the salt, by an ion-exchange column, or by any other method.

6–6 CHEMICAL EQUILIBRIUM—GAS REACTIONS

Consider the gas reaction

$$3H_2(g) + N_2(g) = 2NH_3(g) \qquad (6-23)$$

It is useful to treat this equation as algebraic and to move the reactants to the right side, with a change of sign of the coefficients

$$0 = 2NH_3(g) - 3H_2(g) - N_2(g) \qquad (6-24)$$

The general balanced equation of a chemical reaction, written in this form, is

$$0 = \sum_i \nu_i A_i \qquad (6\text{–}25)$$

where the ν_i are the coefficients of the species A_i and are by definition always negative for the reactants, positive for the products. In the example given,

$$\nu_1 \equiv \nu_{NH_3} = 2 \qquad \nu_2 \equiv \nu_{H_2} = -3 \qquad \nu_3 \equiv \nu_{N_2} = -1 \qquad (6\text{–}26)$$

Suppose that at the beginning of a reaction the number of moles of the different species A_i are n_i^0, where i ranges over all reactants and products. Often the n_i^0 for all products are zero, but this need not be the case. The extent to which a reaction has occurred is conveniently described by the **reaction variable** ξ. It is defined by the statement that at the point considered the change in the moles of species A_i has been $\xi\nu_i$, that is, of the species with positive ν_i (products), $\xi\nu_i$ moles have been formed, whereas of those with negative ν_i (reactants), $\xi|\nu_i|$ moles have disappeared. Since the ν_i are numbers, the units of ξ are moles. At any point the number of moles A_i is thus

$$n_i = n_i^0 + \nu_i\xi \qquad (6\text{–}27)$$

and the signs of the ν_i take the loss of reactants and the gain of products automatically into account. At the start of a reaction ξ is zero. When ξ is 1, as many moles of reactants as is indicated by the coefficients $|\nu_i|$ have reacted to form products. However, ξ is limited by the magnitudes of the n_i^0 of the reactants, because none of the n_i in (6–27) may become negative. The upper limit that ξ can assume may thus be smaller or larger than 1, depending on the case. Increase of ξ means progress of the reaction to the right, while a decrease indicates that the reaction proceeds in the direction opposite from that written, the moles of reactants increasing at the expense of the products. To an infinitesimal change in ξ correspond the changes of moles

$$dn_i = \nu_i \, d\xi \qquad (6\text{–}28)$$

In terms of the ammonia example, and for $n^0_{H_2} = 3$ moles, $n^0_{N_2} = 1$ mole, $n^0_{NH_3} = 0$ mole,

$$n_{H_2} = 3(1 - \xi) \qquad n_{N_2} = (1 - \xi) \qquad n_{NH_3} = 2\xi \qquad (6\text{--}29)$$

and

$$dn_{H_2} = -3d\xi \qquad dn_{N_2} = -d\xi \qquad dn_{NH_3} = 2d\xi \qquad (6\text{--}30)$$

The free energy of the system of reactants and products is

$$G = \sum_i n_i \mu_i = \sum_i (n^0_i + \nu_i \xi) \mu_i \qquad (6\text{--}31)$$

where μ_i is the chemical potential of the species A_i. When ξ is changed by $d\xi$, the change in G is

$$dG = \sum_i \nu_i \mu_i \, d\xi \qquad (6\text{--}32)$$

In particular, for *equilibrium* at constant P and T, dG must be zero, which requires

$$\sum_i \nu_i \mu_i = 0 \qquad (6\text{--}33)$$

since $d\xi$ is by definition not zero. This is the important **general equilibrium condition** for chemical reactions, at constant P and T.

For the ammonia case,

$$\sum \nu_i \mu_i = 2\mu_{NH_3} - 3\mu_{H_2} - \mu_{N_2} \qquad (6\text{--}34)$$

and this is just the increase ΔG in the free energy when 3 moles of H_2 and 1 mole of N_2 are reacted to form 2 moles of NH_3 all at the prevailing, *constant* partial pressures. This is seen to be a general result, the coefficients ν_i being by definition positive for the products and negative for the reactants:

$$\sum \nu_i \mu_i = \Delta G = \sum G_{prod} - \sum G_{reac} \qquad (6\text{--}35)$$

The content of (6–33) is thus that $\Delta G = 0$ *for the reaction at equilibrium conditions.*

When all species A_i are gases, as in the ammonia example, the μ_i are given by expressions (6–2) and

$$\Delta G = \sum_i \nu_i \mu_i = \sum_i \nu_i \mu^0 + RT \sum_i \nu_i \ln P_i \qquad (6\text{–}36)$$

The first term on the right is ΔG^0, the increase in the free energy that would be incurred if the reactants at *standard conditions* were to be changed into products at *standard conditions*, to an extent indicated by the coefficients of the reaction equation, so that the change in the number of moles of the species A_i would be ν_i. This ΔG^0 is also called the **standard free energy of the reaction.**

Next we consider the sum in the last expression on the right and use the properties of the logarithm that $a \ln b = \ln(b^a)$ and that $\ln c + \ln d = \ln cd$:

$$\nu_1 \ln P_1 + \nu_2 \ln P_2 + \cdots = \ln P_1^{\nu_1} + \ln P_2^{\nu_2} + \cdots$$
$$= \ln (P_1^{\nu_1} \cdot P_2^{\nu_2} \cdots) \qquad (6\text{–}37)$$

The meaning of the product of which the logarithm is to be taken is seen most easily by returning to the ammonia reaction, where the ν_i are given by (6–26), so that

$$P_1^{\nu_1} \cdot P_2^{\nu_2} \cdots = \frac{P_{\mathrm{NH_3}}^2}{P_{\mathrm{H_2}}^3 P_{\mathrm{N_2}}} \qquad (6\text{–}38)$$

which is the mass-action quotient Q for the ammonia reaction. This is a general result, and therefore

$$\Delta G = \sum_i \nu_i \mu_i = \Delta G^0 + RT \ln Q \qquad (6\text{–}39)$$

By (6–33) this must be zero at equilibrium, so that

$$RT \ln Q = -\Delta G^0(T) \qquad (6\text{–}40)$$

At constant T the right side is constant and so is RT, and therefore

$$Q = K(T) \qquad (6\text{–}41)$$

This is the mass-action law, and $K(T)$ is the mass-action constant, for which thus by (6–40)

$$\Delta G^0(T) = -RT \ln K(T) \qquad (6\text{–}42)$$

or also

$$K(T) = \exp\left[-\Delta G^0(T)/RT\right] \qquad (6\text{–}43)$$

These are two important relationships between the equilibrium constant K and the standard free energy of the reaction.

For the example considered $\Delta G^0(T)$ is the increase in the free energy that corresponds to the transformation of 3 moles of $H_2(g)$ at 1 atm and 1 mole of $N_2(g)$ at 1 atm, to 2 moles of $NH_3(g)$ at 1 atm, all at T. The participants in this change of state are in general not at equilibrium with each other, because the partial pressures of the gases involved satisfy the mass-action law only when the equilibrium constant is accidentally equal to 1. However, to find $\Delta G^0(T)$ a reaction does not actually have to be carried out. All that has to be known are the free energies of all reaction participants at standard conditions, from which $\Delta G^0(T)$ is found by algebraic combination as in Example 4 below. If the values of G_f^0 in Appendix 4 are used to evaluate ΔG^0 the result applies to 298°K. For other temperatures more elaborate tabulations are available.

Note that the units of Q are those appropriate to the mass-action quotient of the chemical equation being considered, such as atm^{-2} for the ammonia example. The mass-action constant $K(T)$ has the same units and when $\ln K(T)$ is formed in (6–42), only the logarithm of the numerical part is to be taken. The term containing the logarithm of the units of $K(T)$ is compensated by a similar logarithmic term in $\Delta G^0(T)$, which follows from the discussion on p. 142. Similarly in (6–43) the appropriate units, such as atm^{-2} for the ammonia example, have to be supplied. Indeed, ΔG^0 turns out to contain a term $-RT \ln(atm^{-2})$, which in fact generates the proper units for $K(T)$ when inserted in (6–43), because $\exp[\ln(atm^{-2})] = atm^{-2}$. After convincing oneself that this always works out, it is simplest just to forget about the logarithms of units and provide the units for K that are appropriate to the case considered.

The reason why partial pressures must be expressed in atmospheres in Q and $K(T)$ is that standard states refer to 1 atm. It would be possible to use any other pressure unit such as the torr, but then standard states would have to be redefined as pertaining to 1 torr, with corresponding changes in the tabulated values of $\tilde{G}_f^0$, $\tilde{H}_f^0$, etc.

EXAMPLE 4

What are the values for ΔG^0 and K at 298°K for the formation of ammonia by the reaction discussed earlier, (6-23)? From the values in Appendix 4, $\Delta G^0 = 2\mu_{NH_3}^0 - 3\mu_{H_2}^0 - \mu_{N_2}^0 = 2\tilde{G}_{fNH_3}^0 - 3\tilde{G}_{fH_2}^0 - \tilde{G}_{fN_2}^0 = [2(-3.98) - 3 \times 0 - 0]$ kcal $= -7.96$ kcal. Thus, $\log K = 7960/(1.99 \times 298 \times 2.30) = 5.84$; $K = \mathbf{6.9 \times 10^5}$ **atm**$^{-2}$. This reaction is discussed further in Chapter 8.

Figure 6-3 shows the typical behavior of the free energy of a reaction mixture in dependence of ξ. For the equilibrium value ξ_{equil}, the free energy of the system assumes a minimum.

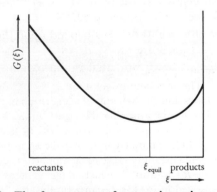

Figure 6-3   The free energy of a reaction mixture. As the reaction proceeds from left to right the concentrations of the reagents change in such a way that the free energy of the system is lowered. Equilibrium is established when the free energy has reached its minimum value. Starting with the products, the reaction would proceed toward the left, until the same minimum free energy had been reached.

6–7   CHEMICAL EQUILIBRIUM—GENERAL SOLUTION REACTIONS

It should be realized that most of the results and discussion of the preceding section apply to any kind of chemical equilibrium. This is particularly true for the general equilibrium condition

$$\Delta G = \sum_i \nu_i \mu_i = 0 \qquad (6\text{--}44)$$

and the relationships (6–42) and (6–43) between $K(T)$ and $\Delta G^0(T)$.

Consider, for example, the following reaction in a dilute solution:

$$4H^+ + MnO_2(s) + 2Cl^- = Mn^{2+} + Cl_2(g) + 2H_2O \qquad (6\text{--}45)$$

Aside from the ions this reaction involves H_2O, as well as a gas and a solid that are both at equilibrium with the solution. Written in the general form (6–25) the reaction equation reads

$$Mn^{2+} + Cl_2(g) + 2H_2O - 4H^+ - MnO_2(s) - 2Cl^- = 0 \qquad (6\text{--}46)$$

For the ions the chemical potentials depend upon the concentrations (or activities) as shown by (6–3) or (6–4). For H_2O it can be assumed that the chemical potential is approximately constant and equal to that of pure water

$$\mu_{H_2O} \approx \text{const} \approx \mu^0_{H_2O} = \tilde{G}^0_{f,H_2O}$$

The chemical potential of the dissolved Cl_2 is equal, at equilibrium, to that of the Cl_2 in the gas phase, so that

$$\mu_{Cl_2} = \mu^0_{Cl_2} + RT \ln P_{Cl_2}$$

Finally, the chemical potential in the solution of the MnO_2 is equal at equilibrium to that of pure, solid MnO_2, G^0_{f,MnO_2},

$$\mu_{MnO_2} = \mu^0_{MnO_2} = \tilde{G}^0_{f,MnO_2}$$

Combining the chemical potentials for the different species,

$$\Delta G = \sum_i \nu_i \mu_i = \mu_{Mn^{2+}} + \mu_{Cl_2} + 2\mu_{H_2O} - 4\mu_{H^+} - \mu_{MnO2} - 2\mu_{Cl^-}$$

$$= \mu^0_{Mn^{2+}} + \mu^0_{Cl_2} + 2\mu^0_{H_2O} - 4\mu^0_{H^+} - \mu^0_{MnO_2} - 2\mu^0_{Cl^-}$$

$$+ RT(\ln[Mn^{++}] + \ln P_{Cl_2} - 4\ln[H^+] - 2\ln[Cl^-])$$

$$(6\text{--}47)$$

This is equal to $\Delta G^0 + RT \ln Q$ [see (6–39)], with

$$Q = \frac{P_{Cl_2}[Mn^{++}]}{[H^+]^4[Cl^-]^2} \qquad (6\text{--}48)$$

Again, the equilibrium condition $\Delta G = 0$ leads to the mass-action law, $Q = K(T)$, and to $\Delta G^0(T) = -RT \ln K(T)$.

It is seen that Q has the form demanded by the conventions generally adopted for the mass-action expression. These are the following: (1) The reactants appear in the denominator, the products in the numerator. (2) For a gas—often specifically designated by a (g) in the chemical equation—the partial pressure must be used in Q because the standard state refers to the gas, at a pressure of 1 atm; (3) for a dissolved species the concentration must be used, because the standard state refers to the dissolved species at a concentration of 1 mole/liter; (4) solids, often specified by an (s) in the chemical equation, do not appear in Q, because their chemical potentials are constant and have thus no term contributing to Q; (5) H_2O does not appear in Q when the solution is dilute, because the concentration of the water and thus its chemical potential remain approximately constant in spite of the reaction considered.

Note should again be taken of the unit situation: Q and thus $K(T)$ have the units appropriate to mass-action expressions, which is atm (mole/liter)$^{-5}$ in the present case. When forming $\ln K(T)$ the logarithm is to be taken of the numerical value of $K(T)$ only. The term containing the logarithm of the units of $K(T)$ is compensated by an analogous term in ΔG^0 that can be traced to the corresponding terms μ^0 (see p. 146 and p. 147). The units used in $K(T)$ must always be combinations of atm and mole/liter, because standard states refer to 1 atm and 1 mole/liter. However, the units of $K(T)$ are often not stated, being rather cumbersome.

EXAMPLE 5

What are ΔG^0 and K at 298°K for the oxidation of Cl$^-$ by MnO$_2(s)$ in the example considered earlier, with the over-all equation

$$4H^+ + MnO_2(s) + 2Cl^- = Mn^{2+} + Cl_2(g) + 2H_2O?$$
$$ 0 \qquad -111.1 \qquad -31.35 \quad -53.4 \qquad 0 \qquad -56.69$$

The free energies $\tilde{G}_f^0$ of the species involved as found in Appendix 4 are listed underneath the chemical symbols. Therefore, $\Delta G^0 = -53.4 - 2 \times 56.69 + 111.1 + 2 \times 31.35 = \mathbf{7.02\ 1\ kcal}$, and $\log K = -7.0_2 \times 10^3/1.99 \times 298 \times 2.30 = -5.1_5$, $K = \mathbf{7 \times 10^{-6}\ atm\ (mole/liter)^{-5}}$.

EXAMPLE 6

What is the partial pressure of HCl(g) above a solution that is 2 M in H$^+$ and 2 M in Cl$^-$? The reaction involved is

$$H^+ + \quad Cl^- = HCl(g)$$
$$ 0 \qquad -31.35 \qquad -22.77$$

with values $\tilde{G}_f^0$ indicated underneath the chemical equation. Therefore, $\Delta G^0 = -22.77 + 31.35 = 8.58$ kcal, and $\log K = -8.58 \times 10^3/1.99 \times 298 \times 2.30 = -6.29$.

$$K = \frac{P_{HCl}}{[H^+][Cl^-]} = 5.1 \times 10^{-7}\ atm\ (mole/liter)^{-2}$$

Finally, $P_{HCl} = 2 \times 2 \times 5.1 \times 10^{-7} = \mathbf{2.0 \times 10^{-6}\ atm}$
This is an example of an equilibrium for a substance that exists as different species in a solvent phase and in a gas phase.

It should be clear that similar reasoning applies to any other chemical equilibrium; in other words, the mass-action law, with the usual conventions, is expected to apply. It must be noted, however, that the developments in Sections 6–6 and 6–7 are not derivations of the mass-action law from first principles, but depend on the specific form of the chemical potential given by (6–2) and (6–3). Furthermore, although the equilibrium condition $\Sigma \nu_i \mu_i = 0$ is exact and general, the expressions used for the chemical potentials are valid only for perfect gases and for dilute solutions. The same is thus true for the mass-action expressions that follow. However, all these expressions can be made exact by replacing concentrations by activities (6–4) and pressures by fugacities.

It is instructive to consider that a negative ΔG^0 corresponds by (6–42) to a mass-action constant K larger than one. The thermodynamic rule that a negative ΔG^0 indicates the tendency of the reactants to form products, all in their standard states, is thus paralleled by the observation that when K is larger than 1, the numerator of the mass-action expression Q and thus the right side of the reaction equation is favored. Indeed, the more negative ΔG^0, the larger K. Conversely, a positive ΔG^0 implies a K smaller than 1, both favoring the left side of the reaction equation. When ΔG^0 is zero, K equals 1, indicating that equilibrium exists between reactants and products, all in their standard states.

Another point is that a change of the balanced chemical equation by multiplying all the coefficients by the same (positive, negative, integral, or fractional) factor does not change the fundamental relationship $\Delta G^0 = -RT \ln K$. For example, if all coefficients are multiplied by the factor $-\frac{1}{2}$, ΔG^0 is replaced by $\Delta G^{0\prime} = -\frac{1}{2}\Delta G^0$, the mass-action expression Q by $Q' = Q^{-1/2}$, and K by $K' = K^{-1/2}$. However,

$$\Delta G^{0\prime} = -\tfrac{1}{2}\Delta G^0 = +\tfrac{1}{2}RT \ln K = -RT \ln(K)^{-1/2} = -RT \ln K'$$

so that the new $\Delta G^{0\prime}$ and K' are related in the correct way. As a special case, when the reaction equation is written in the reverse direction, ΔG^0 changes its sign, so that K is replaced by $1/K$.

Thirdly, if a reaction mixture is at equilibrium with respect to a number of possible reactions, it is at equilibrium also with respect to all reactions that are combinations of the reactions considered first. When the balanced equations of any two reactions are multiplied by coefficients and added, the related ΔG^0 values combine in the same way. As a consequence of (6–42), the logarithms of the equilibrium constants also combine in the same way, so that the equilibrium constant of the combination reaction is the product of the constants of the original reactions, raised to appropriate powers.

For example, in the over-all reactions considered earlier (Section 5–5),

(1) $16H^+ + 2MnO_4^- + 10Cl^- = 5Cl_2(g) + 2Mn^{2+} + 8H_2O$

(2) $\qquad\qquad Cl_2(g) + 2Fe^{2+} = 2Fe^{3+} + 2Cl^-$

(3) $\quad 8H^+ + MnO_4^- + 5Fe^{2+} = 5Fe^{3+} + Mn^{2+} + 4H_2O$

the third equation can be obtained by adding $\frac{1}{2}$ times the first and $\frac{5}{2}$ times the second equation. Therefore, the equilibrium constant K_3 of reaction (3) is equal to the following combination of the constants K_1 and K_2 for reactions (1) and (2):

$$K_3 = K_1^{1/2} K_2^{5/2}$$

As a by-product of the thermodynamic development of the mass-action law from expressions for the chemical potentials, the important relationships (6–42) and (6–43) between K and ΔG^0 have emerged. They are important for two reasons: (1) They permit the derivation of the temperature dependence of the mass-action constant K, as shown in Section 6–8; (2) they show that values of ΔG^0 may be determined experimentally by measuring equilibrium constants. This is a very valuable method. Experimental determination of K usually offers no problems for equilibria that are readily established and that are not strongly one-sided. Many standard free energy values have been determined in this way. On the other hand, many equilibria are either not readily established, or are so one-sided that it is not a simple matter to measure the mass-action constant. In such cases K may be calculated, provided the standard free energies of all participating species are known. It is particularly intriguing that it is therefore possible to determine equilibrium constants by thermal measurement (of ΔH and C_P values) alone, so that it is possible to make quantitative statements about chemical reactions without ever performing them.

For example, it is possible to determine ΔH for the reaction of ethylene with water to form ethanol,

$$C_2H_4(g) + H_2O(g) = C_2H_5OH(g)$$

by determining the heats of combustion of C_2H_4 and C_2H_5OH, all at any desirable temperature T. The entropies at T of all three substances can be determined by measuring the molar heat capacities $\bar{C}_P$ and the enthalpies of all pertinent phase transformations of the three substances, as explained in Section 4–8. This yields ΔS for the reaction. Adjustments to standard conditions yield $\Delta H^0(T)$, $\Delta S^0(T)$, and thus $\Delta G^0(T) = \Delta H^0(T) - T \Delta S^0(T)$, from which $K(T)$ can be calculated. The reaction considered forms the basis for the large-scale industrial production of ethanol from ethylene.

Furthermore, a listing of equilibrium constants of reactions can be replaced by a listing of standard free energies $\tilde{G}_f^0$ or μ^0 of the substances involved with far fewer entries. From such a free-energy table, equilibrium constants can be calculated for all the innumerable possible combinations as reactants and products, of the substances listed.

It is also of interest to establish *experimental criteria* to decide whether a mixture of substances that do not react represents equilibrium or whether there is "no" reaction because the rates of possible reactions are very slow. Two such criteria exist: (1) One or more variables that may affect a possibly existing equilibrium are changed. If this affects the concentrations and partial pressures of the substances involved, and if the original concentrations and partial pressures are again assumed when the original values of the variables are restored, an equilibrium situation exists. The variables being changed may be the temperature or the total pressure; concentrations and partial pressures may also be varied directly by addition or removal of substances. (2) A possible equilibrium may be approached from the side of the reactants or the side of the products. If the final concentrations and partial pressures are the same in either case, a real equilibrium exists.

6–8 TEMPERATURE DEPENDENCE
OF THE EQUILIBRIUM CONSTANT

In this section the temperature dependence of the free energy for constant-pressure processes is discussed. The basic equation is (5–18), which may be restated in the form

$$\left(\frac{\partial G}{\partial T}\right)_P = -S \qquad (6\text{–}49)$$

Consider the initial and the final states of a reaction, both at the same temperature and pressure. Let the free energy of the initial state 1 be G_1, its entropy S_1, and its enthalpy H_1. The values of the same quantities for the final state 2 are denoted by G_2, S_2, and H_2, and the differences by ΔG, ΔS, and ΔH. The temperature derivatives at constant pressure are

$$\left(\frac{\partial G_1}{\partial T}\right)_P = -S_1$$

$$\left(\frac{\partial G_2}{\partial T}\right)_P = -S_2$$

By substraction,

$$\left[\frac{\partial(G_2 - G_1)}{\partial T}\right]_P = -S_2 + S_1$$

or in brief

$$\left[\left(\frac{\partial}{\partial T}\right)\Delta G\right]_P = -\Delta S \qquad (6\text{--}50)$$

The derivative of the ratio $(\Delta G/T)$ proves particularly useful:

$$\frac{\partial}{\partial T}\left(\frac{\Delta G}{T}\right)_P = -\frac{\Delta G}{T^2} + \frac{1}{T}\left(\frac{\partial}{\partial T}\Delta G\right)_P$$

from which, by the use of (6--50),

$$\frac{\partial}{\partial T}\left(\frac{\Delta G}{T}\right)_P = -\frac{\Delta G}{T^2} - \frac{\Delta S}{T} = -\frac{\Delta G + T\,\Delta S}{T^2}$$

But $\Delta G = \Delta H - T\,\Delta S$, because T is constant, and therefore

$$\frac{\partial}{\partial T}\left(\frac{\Delta G}{T}\right)_P = -\frac{\Delta H}{T^2} \qquad (6\text{--}51)$$

This important equation is known as the **Gibbs-Helmholtz equation.** It applies in particular to the standard free energy of a reaction, which by (6–42) is related to the mass-action constant: $(\Delta G^0 / T) = -R \ln K$. Insertion in (6–51) yields

$$\frac{\partial}{\partial T}\left(\frac{\Delta G^0}{T}\right)_P = -\left(\frac{\partial R \ln K}{\partial T}\right)_P = -\frac{\Delta H^0}{T^2} \qquad (6\text{–}52)$$

and therefore,

$$\left(\frac{\partial \ln K}{\partial T}\right)_P = \frac{\Delta H^0}{RT^2} \qquad (6\text{–}53)$$

This is known as the **van't Hoff equation.** It is seen that ΔH^0 of a reaction is important for two reasons: (1) Together with an entropy term it determines the equilibrium constant; (2) It governs the temperature dependence of this equilibrium constant.

The van't Hoff equation (6–53) is the quantitative statement of the qualitative consequence of the **Le Châtelier-Braun** principle that upon temperature increase the equilibrium of an endothermic reaction is shifted to the right, while it is shifted to the left for an exothermic reaction.

Equation (6–53) can be integrated, to relate equilibrium constants at two different temperatures:

$$\ln \frac{K_2}{K_1} = \int_{T_1}^{T_2} \frac{\Delta H^0}{RT^2} \, dT \qquad (6\text{–}54)$$

The integral can be evaluated when ΔH^0 is known as the function of the temperature in the interval considered. In particular, when ΔH^0 is approximately constant,

$$\ln \frac{K_2}{K_1} = 2.303 \log \frac{K_2}{K_1} \approx -\left. \frac{\Delta H^0}{RT} \right|_{T_1}^{T_2}$$

$$= \frac{\Delta H^0}{R}\left(\frac{1}{T_1} - \frac{1}{T_2}\right) \qquad (6\text{–}55)$$

Consideration of the indefinite integral of (6–53) for the case that ΔH^0 can be regarded as constant is also very useful:

$$\ln K = \int \frac{\Delta H^0}{RT^2} dT \approx - \frac{\Delta H^0}{RT} + \text{const} \qquad (6\text{–}56)$$

Accordingly, enthalpies of reaction may be determined by measuring the equilibrium constant at several temperatures and plotting $\ln K$ as a function of $1/T$. If ΔH^0 is constant in the temperature range of the measurements, the experimental points should lie on a straight line. The negative slope of this is $\Delta H^0/R$ (Fig. 6–4). It is therefore possible to measure enthalpies of reaction without performing any calorimetric experiments.

It should be noted that (6–56) implies exponential dependence of K on $\Delta H^0/RT$,

$$K \approx \text{const} \times \exp \frac{-\Delta H^0}{RT}$$

a temperature-dependence characteristic of many phenomena. An-

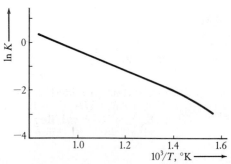

Figure 6–4   Graph of ln T **versus 1000/T for the reaction** $CO_2(g) + H_2(g) = CO(g) + H_2O(g)$. The slope of the curve is equal to $-\Delta H^0(T)/R$. It is thus possible to determine $\Delta H^0(T)$ indirectly from the temperature dependence of the equilibrium constant. The value of ΔH^0 is seen to change slightly with temperature.

other example of the same temperature dependence is the approximate relationship for the vapor pressure of a substance,

$$P \approx \text{const} \times \exp \frac{-\Delta H}{RT}$$

a consequence of the Clausius-Clapeyron equation (4–18).

EXAMPLE 7

It has been reported that the equilibrium constant for the reaction

$$\tfrac{1}{2}I_2(g) + \tfrac{1}{2}Br_2(g) = IBr(g)$$

can be represented by the equation

$$\log K(T) = 277.4/T + 0.3811 \text{ cal}$$

Find ΔG^0, ΔH^0, and ΔS^0 for this reaction. First, ΔG^0 pertains to $T = 298.15°K$, so that $\Delta G^0 = -RT \ln K = -2.303 \, RT \log K = -2.303 \times 1.987 \, (277.4 + 0.3811 \times 298.15) \text{ cal} = -1790 \text{ cal.}$ Second,

$$\Delta H^0(T) = RT^2 d \ln K/dT$$
$$= RT^2(d/dT)[2.303(277.4/T + 0.3811)]$$
$$= -1.987 T^2(2.303 \times 277.4/T^2) \text{ cal} = -1270 \text{ cal.}$$

Within the accuracy of the data provided, $\Delta H^0(T)$ is seen to be constant, so that at $298.15°K$, $\Delta H^0 = -1270 \text{ cal.}$ Finally, $\Delta S^0 = (\Delta H^0 - \Delta G^0)/298.15 = 1.74 \text{ cal/deg.}$

PROBLEMS

6–1. *Raoult's law.* This law relates the vapor pressures P_1 of the solvent above a solution to the vapor pressure P_1^{pure} of the pure solvent, all at a given, constant temperature. If x_1 is the mole fraction of solvent in the solution, Raoult's law states that $P_1 = x_1 P_1^{\text{pure}}$. Derive this relationship from considerations of the chemical potential.

6-2. *The distribution law.* Consider the equilibrium distribution of a molecular species between two immiscible liquid phases I and II such as ether and water. Let c^I and c^{II} be the concentrations of the species in phases I and II, respectively. From considerations of the chemical potential derive the distribution law, $c^I/c^{II} = k$, where k depends on the nature of the two liquid phases, the molecular species involved, and the temperature.

6-3. *Two solid phases.* A certain substance consists of two modifications A_1 and A_2, and ΔG^0 for the transition from A_1 to A_2 is positive. Both modifications produce the same vapor. Which has the higher vapor pressure? Which is the more soluble in a solvent common to both?

6-4. *Equilibrium constants.* Find ΔG^0 and the equilibrium constant K for the following reactions by referring to the values of the standard free energies of formation listed in Appendix 4:

(a) $4I^-(aq) + O_2(g) + 4H^+ = 2H_2O(l) + 2I_2(g)$

(b) $CO(g) + 2H_2(g) = CH_3OH(l)$

(c) $3H_2(g) + SO_2(g) = H_2S(g) + 2H_2O(l)$

(d) $Ca(s) + CO_2(g) = CaO(s) + CO(g)$

6-5. *Stability of hydrogen halides.* (a) Consider the free energies of formation of HCl, HBr, and HI listed in Appendix 4, and discuss qualitatively the theoretical degree of purity expected for forming these compounds by direct combination of the elements at 25°C. (Note, however, that in the absence of catalysts and in the dark the reaction between hydrogen and halogens is slow, whereas the reaction between hydrogen and chlorine is explosive in the presence of light of suitable wavelength.) (b) Repeat your considerations quantitatively for HCl and HI.

6-6. *Solubility products.* Find K_{SP} for the following salts by using the values of the standard free energies of formation given below and those listed in Appendix 4: (a) AgCl(s), $\tilde{G}_f^0 = -26.22$; (b) AgBr(s), $\tilde{G}_f^0 = -22.93$; (c) AgI(s), $G_f^0 = -15.85$.

6-7. *Free energy of atoms.* The standard molar free energy of Cl atoms at 25°C is 25.19 kcal/mole. What is the partial pressure of atomic chlorine that would be at equilibrium with $Cl_2(g)$ at 25°C and 1 atm?

6–8. *Equilibrium pressure of CO_2.* From $\tilde{G}_f^0$ for $CO_2(g)$ and $H_2CO_3(aq)$ find the partial pressure of CO_2 at equilibrium with a 1-M solution of H_2CO_3.

6–9. *Gas equilibria.* At 1000°K the free energies of formation of CO and CO_2, are, respectively, -47.97 and -94.65 kcal/mole. What are the equilibrium constants, at 1000°K, of the reactions $C(\text{graphite}) + \frac{1}{2}O_2(g) = CO(g)$; $C(\text{graphite}) + O_2(g) = CO_2(g)$; and $CO_2(g) + C(\text{graphite}) = 2CO(g)$?

6–10. *Gas equilibrium.* At 3500°K the equilibrium constant for the reaction $CO_2(g) + H_2(g) = CO(g) + H_2O(g)$ is 8.28. What is $\Delta G^0(3500)$ for this reaction? What is ΔG for transforming at 3500°K 1 mole each of CO_2 and H_2, both held at 0.1 atm to 1 mole each of CO and H_2O, both held at 2 atm? In which direction would this last reaction run spontaneously?

6–11. *Free energy from equilibrium measurements.* At 35°C and a *total* pressure of 1 atm, $N_2O_4(g)$ is dissociated 27.2 per cent into $NO_2(g)$. What is ΔG^0 at 35°C for the reaction $N_2O_4(g) = 2NO_2(g)$?

6–12. *Free energy changes.* At 800°C the reaction $CaCO_3(s) = CaO(s) + CO_2(g)$ is at equilibrium when the pressure of the carbon dioxide is 180 torr. (*a*) What is ΔG for changing 1 mole of $CaCO_3(s)$ into 1 mole $CaO(s)$ and 1 mole of $CO_2(g)$ at 180 torr, all at 800°C? (*b*) What is ΔG for the same change but with the carbon dioxide at 1 atm?

6–13. *Standard molar free energy.* The equilibrium constant for the reaction $2HI(g) = H_2(g) + I_2(g)$ is 0.01984 at 717°K. What is the free energy of formation of $HI(g)$ at 717°K?

6–14. *ΔG^0 from equilibrium data.* At 1200°K and in the presence of solid carbon an equilibrium mixture of CO and CO_2 ("producer gas") contains 98.3 mole per cent CO and 1.69 mole per cent CO_2 with the total pressure at 1 atm. What are P_{CO} and P_{CO_2}, what is K, and what is ΔG^0 associated with the reaction

$$CO_2(g) + C(\text{graphite}) = 2CO(g)$$

at 1200°K?

6–15. *Temperature dependence of G_f^0.* The free energy of formation $\tilde{G}_f^0$ of phosgene gas, $COCl_2$, is -44.77 kcal/mole and the entropy of formation $\tilde{S}_f^0$ is -9.152 cal/mole-deg, both at $800°K$. (*a*) What is $\tilde{G}_f^0$ at $1000°K$ assuming S_f^0 to be constant? (*b*) What is $\tilde{H}_f^0$ at $800°K$?

6–16. *Temperature dependence of solubility.* State a quantitative relationship between the solubility of a substance and the enthalpy of solution.

6–17. *Enthalpy of neutralization and K_w.* At $24°C$, K_w is equal to 1.0×10^{-14}. Find the enthalpy of the reaction $H_2O(l) = H^+(aq) + OH^-(aq)$ from the values in Appendix 4. Assume that this enthalpy of neutralization is temperature-independent and use it to estimate K_w at $100°C$.

6–18. *Free energy, enthalpy, and entropy for the dissociation of an acid.* Calculate ΔG^0, ΔH^0, and ΔS^0 for the reaction $HCOOH(aq) = H^+(aq) + HCOO^-(aq)$ from the following data: $K_a(25°C) = 1.8 \times 10^{-4}$; $dK_a/dT = 0$.

6–19. *Acid constants.* (*a*) Calculate the acid constants K_1 and K_2 of H_2CO_3 from the values of the free energies of formation given in Appendix 4. (*b*) Find $d \log K_1/dT$ and $d \log K_2/dT$ from the enthalpies of formation.

6–20. *Entropy and enthalpy of formation.* The free energy of formation $\tilde{G}_f^0$ for CO is -43.57 kcal/mole at $800°K$ and -47.93 kcal/mole at $1000°K$. (*a*) What is the entropy of formation S_f^0 in this temperature range, assuming it to be constant? (*b*) What is $\tilde{H}_f^0$ in the same range, assuming it to be constant also?

6–21. *Synthesis of ethanol.* Examine the thermodynamic feasibility of synthesizing ethanol from (*a*) acetylene and (*b*) ethylene. Use the standard enthalpies and free energies of formation given in Appendix 4 and discuss whether increase in temperature would be advantageous in either case. Would increase in pressure be of advantage?

7 Electrochemical Phenomena

Electrochemical concepts such as anode, cathode, and galvanic and electrolytic cells are reviewed, and a notation for describing electrochemical cells is introduced. Cell potential and electromotive force are explained and related to the free energy of the cell reactions. The equilibrium of a cell under an applied external potential is discussed, the Nernst equation is derived, and rules are developed by which half-cell emf's can be used to obtain equilibrium constants and the emf's of new half-cells. Finally, the temperature dependence of cell emf's is derived and its thermodynamic implications are discussed.

7–1   REVIEW OF ELECTROCHEMICAL CONCEPTS

An **electrochemical cell** is a device with two electric terminals or poles that links the course of a chemical reaction to the flow of an electric current.   When the reaction occurs in the spontaneous direction we speak of a **galvanic cell.**   The reaction generates a potential capable of sustaining the flow of current between the electrodes.   In the reverse situation the reaction is driven by an external potential that is applied to the electrodes.   The reaction is termed **electrolysis** and the cell an **electrolytic cell.**   The same electrochemical cell may be galvanic or electrolytic, depending on whether the cell reaction proceeds spontaneously or is driven in the opposite direction by a potential applied externally.

Chemists find it useful to label electrical terminals by the type of electrode reaction associated with them.   If the reaction is a reduction, the terminal is called the **cathode;** if an oxidation, the **anode.** The electrons therefore always enter an electrochemical cell at the cathode and leave at the anode.   (This direction of electron flow corresponds to a current of positive electricity in the opposite direction.)

178

Electrical terminals are also labeled *plus* and *minus*, but whether the electrons enter at the plus or minus terminal depends on the nature of the device of which the terminal is a part. If the device produces a voltage, the minus terminal is the one in which the electrons accumulate to give it a negative charge. If the device is driven by an external voltage, the minus terminal is the one into which the electrons are forced by the external voltage, charging it negatively. Thus in a galvanic cell the minus pole is the electrode by which the electrons leave the cell while the minus pole of an electrolysis cell is the electrode by which the electrons enter (Fig. 7–1).

The plus and minus labels are convenient when connecting terminals of a dc-generating to a dc-utilizing device: minus goes to minus, plus to plus. Furthermore, it is possible to label the terminals of a storage battery plus and minus permanently, because the signs of the terminals remain the same whether the battery is being charged or discharged. However, the terms "anode" and "cathode" do not go hand in hand with "plus" and "minus." In an electrolytic cell the negative pole is the cathode; in a galvanic cell, the anode.

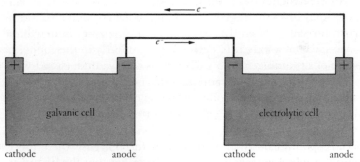

Figure 7–1 Plus and minus terminals, anode and cathode. In a galvanic cell the minus terminal is the one by which the electrons leave; in an electrolytic cell it is the terminal by which they enter. The two minus terminals are thus connected by a wire, as are the two plus terminals. The cathode is always the electrode where reduction takes place, regardless of whether the cell is galvanic or electrolytic. At the anode oxidation occurs, and electrons thus always enter at the cathode and leave at the anode.

The plus terminal in a storage battery is the cathode when the battery is discharged and the anode when the battery is charged.

In any electrochemical process the number of electrons leaving through the anode equals the number of electrons entering through the cathode, since the net charge on the electrolyte remains zero. This number of electrons also governs the stoichiometric aspects of the electrode reactions. If n is the number of electrons participating in the reaction of *one* molecule or ion, then the reaction of 1 mole of substance involves n faradays of electricity, where 1 faraday, $\mathfrak{F}$, is the same as 1 mole or Avogadro's number of electrons. This essentially is **Faraday's law of electrolysis.** In terms of coulombs,

$$\mathfrak{F} = 96,487.0 \text{ coulombs/mole}$$

The value of $\mathfrak{F}$ given is based on the C^{12} scale of atomic weights and is usually rounded to 96,500 coulombs/mole, correct to 0.01 per cent.

Electrochemical cells are often described by a shorthand notation that is explained by the following example. Consider a cell with a zinc electrode dipping into a 1-M Zn^{2+} solution and a copper electrode surrounded by a 0.1-M Cu^{2+} solution, the two solutions being connected by a **salt bridge,** which is an inverted U-tube containing KCl solution (Fig. 7–2). There must be, of course, an adequate supply of negative ions such as Cl^- in the zinc compartment to balance the charges of the Zn^{2+} ions, and similarly in the copper compartment. The presence of such ions is always understood without explicit mention. The shorthand notation for this cell is

$$Zn|Zn^{2+} (1 \ M)| \ |Cu^{2+} (0.1 \ M)|Cu \qquad (7–1)$$

Single vertical lines indicate phase boundaries across which there are potential differences. The double line signifies that the **liquid junctions** between the solutions containing Zn^{2+}, KCl, and Cu^{2+} make only a negligible contribution to the cell potential. This happens to be the case when a KCl (or NH_4NO_3) salt bridge is present, for reasons not examined here, which depend on the fact that the ions K^+ and Cl^- move with approximately equal speed but in opposite directions in an electric field, as do the ions NH_4^+ and NO_3^-. Instead of the KCl salt bridge the Zn^{2+} and the Cu^{2+} solutions may be per-

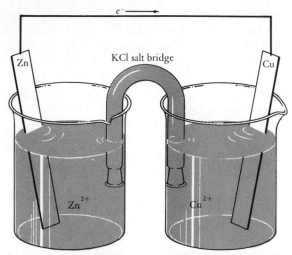

Figure 7–2   An electrochemical cell.   This cell is composed of an anode of zinc in a solution containing Zn^{2+} ions and a cathode of copper in a solution containing Cu^{2+} ions.   The KCl salt bridge contains a concentrated KCl solution, usually in a gel of agar that impedes mixing with the solutions in the two beakers, but permits the migration of ions.   It minimizes potential differences at the interfaces between the different solutions.

mitted to be in direct contact, separated only by a porous membrane that impedes their becoming mixed.   Under these circumstances a potential difference arises at the interface of the two liquids.   This complicates matters, and our discussions are restricted to situations where there are no liquid-junction potentials.

The sequence in which cell descriptions such as (7–1) are written is tied to the *convention* that *electrons are to enter by the electrode on the right and to leave by the electrode on the left* regardless of whether this is the direction in which the electrons would flow spontaneously upon short-circuiting the cell or whether an external potential would be needed to drive the electrons in this direction.   This implies that the electrode reaction on the right is always a reduction, making that electrode always the cathode; the electrode on the left is always the anode.

In the example given, the electrons that enter on the right re-duce Cu^{2+} to Cu by the half-reaction

$$Cu^{2+} + 2e^- = Cu(s) \qquad (7\text{--}2)$$

The electrons leaving on the left are the result of the oxidation of Zn to Zn^{2+} by the half-reaction

$$Zn(s) = Zn^{2+} + 2e^- \qquad (7\text{--}3)$$

The over-all cell reaction is the combination of (7–2) and (7–3):

$$Cu^{2+} + Zn(s) = Cu(s) + Zn^{2+} \qquad (7\text{--}4)$$

The Cu electrode is the cathode and the Zn electrode the anode.

If it is to be implied that the cell reaction is run in the opposite direction (spontaneously or by an external potential),

$$Cu(s) + Zn^{2+} = Cu^{2+} + Zn(s) \qquad (7\text{--}5)$$

the cell description must by convention be inverted also,

$$Cu|Cu^{2+} \ (0.1 \ M)| \ |Zn^{2+} \ (1 \ M)|Zn \qquad (7\text{--}6)$$

because electrons are always to enter on the right. In other words, the Zn electrode is now the cathode and the Cu electrode the anode.

In the example given the electrodes are simply pieces of metal. More complex electrodes also exist, such as gas electrodes. An ex-ample is the hydrogen electrode in which hydrogen gas is bubbled over a platinum electrode coated by a special process with finely divided platinum (called platinum black) and surrounded by a solu-tion containing H^+ ions (Fig. 7–3). The half-reaction at this elec-trode is

$$2H^+ + 2e^- = H_2(g) \qquad (7\text{--}7)$$

The platinum acts as catalyst for the reaction between H^+ ions and H_2 molecules and acquires a potential characteristic of this reaction.

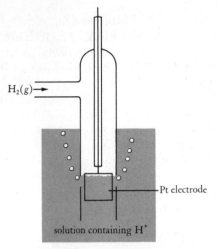

Figure 7–3 A hydrogen electrode. A piece of platinized platinum is saturated with H_2 gas that is bubbled over it and is immersed into a solution containing H^+ ions. The potential of the electrode depends on the partial pressure of the H_2 gas and the H^+ ion concentration. Accurate measurements require a more elaborate design than that shown.

Other gas electrodes may be constructed along similar lines. Examples are the oxygen electrode with the half-reaction

$$4H^+ + O_2(g) + 4e^- = 2H_2O \qquad (7\text{--}8)$$

and the chlorine electrode with the half-reaction

$$Cl_2(g) + 2e^- = 2Cl^- \qquad (7\text{--}9)$$

Electrodes may be characterized by the redox couple they represent, such as Cu^{2+}/Cu, Zn^{2+}/Zn, H^+/H_2, O_2/H_2O, and Cl_2/Cl^- for the electrodes mentioned so far. We shall always list the oxidized form first, followed by the reduced form.

For both, simple metal electrodes and gas electrodes, the concentrations of the solution species that participate in the electrode reaction may be varied at will within a wide range. Such electrodes are called **electrodes of the first kind.** In **electrodes of the second kind** the concentration of the cations associated with the electrode metal is kept fixed through the solubility-product principle by the presence of a salt of low solubility. An example is the AgCl/Ag electrode, which consists of a silver wire coated with AgCl(s) and surrounded by a solution of a soluble chloride. Since AgCl(s) is present, the solution is saturated with silver chloride to the extent that at all times $[Ag^+][Cl^-] = K_{sp}$, where K_{sp} is the solubility-product constant. If any Ag^+ ions are reduced to Ag by the gain of electrons, they are replenished by the dissolving of AgCl(s). The dissolving of AgCl(s) also produces Cl^- ions, and the concurrent reactions may be described by the equations

$$Ag^+ + e^- = Ag(s)$$

$$AgCl(s) = Ag^+ + Cl^-$$

Conversely, if any Ag(s) is oxidized to Ag^+ by loss of electrons, AgCl(s) is precipitated to keep the product $[Ag^+][Cl^-]$ equal to K_{sp}. The half-reaction of this electrode is most simply described as the sum of the foregoing reactions:

$$AgCl(s) + e^- = Ag(s) + Cl^- \tag{7-10}$$

It is a reduction of Ag(I) to Ag(0) in which the predominant form of Ag(I) is AgCl(s).

Another example of an electrode of the second kind is the calomel electrode, in which liquid mercury (connected with the outside by a Pt wire) is in contact with solid calomel (Hg_2Cl_2) and a solution containing chloride ions. Its half-reaction is

$$Hg_2Cl_2(s) + 2e^- = 2Hg(l) + 2Cl^- \tag{7-11}$$

The potentials of these two electrodes depend on the electrode material and the concentration of the chloride ions. Electrodes of this type behave well experimentally and furnish particularly reproducible potentials. They are often chosen as reference electrodes. For example, the two electrodes mentioned are commonly used in pH meters.

Still other electrodes represent redox couples in which both oxidized and reduced forms are ionic species in the solution, and the electron transfer occurs at an inert electrode. An example is provided by a solution containing Fe^{2+} and Fe^{3+} ions and a gold or platinum electrode. The potential corresponds to the Fe^{3+}/Fe^{2+} couple with the half-reaction

$$Fe^{3+} + e^- = Fe^{2+} \qquad (7\text{--}12)$$

A platinum electrode immersed in a solution containing MnO_4^-, Mn^{2+}, and H^+ ions may assume under favorable conditions the potential characteristic of the MnO_4^-/Mn^{2+} couple with the half-reaction

$$MnO_4^- + 8H^+ + 5e^- = Mn^{2+} + 4H_2O \qquad (7\text{--}13)$$

EXAMPLE 1

What are the cathode, anode, and over-all reactions of the cell

$$Ag(s), AgCl(s)|Cl^- \ (0.5 \ M| \ |H^+ \ (0.1 \ M)|H_2 \ (0.5 \ atm), Pt$$
$$(7\text{--}14)$$

Since electrons always enter on the right, the electrode at the right is reducing and functions as a cathode. It consists in this case of a hydrogen gas electrode with H_2 at 0.5 atm and an H^+ concentration of 0.1 M. The cathode reaction is

$$2H^+ + 2e^- = H_2(g) \qquad (7\text{--}15)$$

The anode consists of silver coated with $AgCl(s)$ and surrounded by a 0.5-M Cl^- solution. The anode reaction is

$$Ag(s) + Cl^- = AgCl(s) + e^- \qquad (7\text{--}16)$$

The over-all cell reaction is that combination of (7–15) and (7–16) in which the electrons just cancel, i.e., $1 \times$ (7–15) + $2 \times$ (7–16), or

$$2Ag(s) + 2Cl^- + 2H^+ = 2AgCl(s) + H_2(g) \qquad (7\text{--}17)$$

7–2   CELL POTENTIAL AND CELL EMF

When a quantity Q of (positive) electricity is passed reversibly through an electrochemical cell, work is performed on the system or on the surroundings, depending on the direction in which the electricity is passed. As was pointed out in Section 1–9, the quantity of work involved equals $\mathcal{V}Q$, ignoring the sign for the moment, where $\mathcal{V}$ is the potential of the cell.

This **cell potential** $\mathcal{V}$ is defined as the potential difference that physically exists between the electrodes of the cell, a potential difference that can be measured by a high-resistance voltmeter. It is the potential of the positive pole minus that of the negative pole (relative to the same arbitrary reference point), irrespective of which pole is used as the anode. The cell potential is by definition a *positive* quantity.

Suppose the cell is used as an electrolytic cell, reversibly and at constant T and P, and a quantity of electricity Q is forced by an external potential $\mathcal{V} + d\mathcal{V}$ to pass through the cell. The cell reaction is forced to proceed against the spontaneous direction. The work $\mathcal{V}Q$ is performed on the system, and this work is just the net work w' that automatically includes pressure-volume work:

$$w' = +\mathcal{V}Q \qquad \text{(electrolysis cell; forced reaction)} \qquad (7\text{–}18)$$

When the cell is used as a galvanic cell, the outside voltage is adjusted to be $\mathcal{V} - d\mathcal{V}$, and the cell reaction goes in the spontaneous direction. In this case the cell performs the net work $\mathcal{V}Q$ on the surroundings and

$$w' = -\mathcal{V}Q \qquad \text{(galvanic cell; spontaneous reaction)} \qquad (7\text{–}19)$$

The dependence of the sign of w' on whether a cell is operated in the galvanic or electrolytic direction is inconvenient. This can be avoided by using another quantity, the **cell electromotive force** or **cell emf** $\mathcal{E}$, defined to be the potential of the cathode minus the potential of the anode. In terms of our shorthand description of a cell $\mathcal{E}$ is also the potential of the right side minus the potential of the left side. We shall show that by the use of $\mathcal{E}$, (7–18) and (7–19) can be written as one formula,

$$w' = -\mathcal{E}Q \tag{7–20}$$

Indeed, when the cell is used as a galvanic cell, the cathode is positive relative to the anode; $\mathcal{E}$ is positive, $\mathcal{E} = +\mathcal{V}$, and (7–20) and (7–19) have equivalent content. When the cell is used as an electrolysis cell, the cathode is negative relative to the anode; $\mathcal{E}$ is negative, $\mathcal{E} = -\mathcal{V}$, and (7–20) and (7–18) are seen to be identical and (7–20) is thus generally valid. However, the convenience of having just one expression for w' is bought at a price: The labeling of the poles as anode and cathode depends on the direction in which the current passes the cell, and the sign of $\mathcal{E}$ depends therefore on this direction also. The cell emf, unlike the cell potential, is a *sign-bivariant* quantity.

Let the reaction of an electrochemical cell be symbolized by the equation

$$\sum_i \nu_i A_i = 0 \tag{7–21}$$

and let the number of moles of electrons involved be n. For a change $d\xi$ in the reaction variable, the quantity of electricity passing the cell is thus

$$dQ = n\mathcal{F} \, d\xi \tag{7–22}$$

where $\mathcal{F}$ is the faraday. If this change is reversible, the net work associated with it is

$$Dw' = -\mathcal{E} \, dQ = -n\mathcal{E}\mathcal{F} \, d\xi \tag{7–23}$$

By (5–6) this is the change dG in the free energy, at constant P and T, so that

$$dG = -\mathcal{E} \, dQ = -n\mathcal{E}\mathcal{F} \, d\xi \tag{7–24}$$

But dG is also related to the chemical potentials of the reagents involved, $dG = \sum_i \nu_i \mu_i\, d\xi$ (6–32). It follows that

$$-n\mathcal{E}\mathfrak{F} = \sum_i \nu_i \mu_i \qquad (7\text{–}25)$$

Furthermore,

$$\sum_i \nu_i \mu_i = \sum_{\text{prod}} |\nu_i| \mu_i - \sum_{\text{reac}} |\nu_i| \mu_i = \Delta G$$

so that

$$-n\mathcal{E}\mathfrak{F} = \Delta G \qquad (7\text{–}26)$$

where ΔG is the difference between the free energy of the products and reactants, at the prevailing concentrations.

The basic reason that dG can be related to the cell emf in this way is that G is a function of state, so that dG is independent of the path and can be evaluated if a reversible path is found that connects the two neighboring states involved. This is just what has been done. The path chosen happens to be the one for which the maximum electrical work available at constant temperature and pressure is realized. But this does not imply that the actual change of state has to take place along this particular path. Along nonreversible paths that connect the same two states part of the change in free energy may appear as heat; or irreversible work may be performed on the system. Furthermore, performance of electrical work is just one way in which the *maximum* net work possible can be realized for the change of state considered. There might also be work against a gravity field, work against a magnetic field, or work to drive another chemical reaction.

Equation (7–26) may be solved for $\mathcal{E}$:

$$\mathcal{E} = \frac{-\Delta G}{n\mathfrak{F}} \qquad (7\text{–}27)$$

A special case of this relationship is that of a cell with all reactants and products at standard conditions, in which case the emf is called the **standard emf** $\mathcal{E}^0$ and is related to ΔG^0 of the cell reaction by

$$\mathcal{E}^0 = \frac{-\Delta G^0}{n\mathcal{F}} \qquad (7\text{-}28)$$

Note that the right sides of both equations contain the ratio of two extensive quantities, ΔG and n. This is in agreement with the fact that $\mathcal{E}$ and $\mathcal{E}^0$ are *intensive* quantities. Voltages of cells do not depend on their sizes.

It will be recalled that the criterion for a reaction proceeding spontaneously in the direction written is that ΔG is negative. By (7-27) this corresponds to a positive cell emf $\mathcal{E}$. Thus, *when $\mathcal{E}$ for an electrochemical cell as written is positive, the cell is galvanic and the cell reaction proceeds spontaneously* as written. The cell voltage in the limit of no current flow is $\mathcal{E}$. (If there is current flow, part of the cell potential is used to overcome the internal resistance of the cell and the potential available at the electrodes is diminished. It may be diminished further by other phenomena that will not be discussed.)

Suppose an external voltage that is opposite and equal in magnitude to $\mathcal{E}$ is applied to the cell. The cell reaction is thus kept exactly in balance, and the cell is just on the point of being run as an *electrolytic cell*, reversing the electrode reactions and interchanging the roles of anode and cathode. The voltage required to bring the cell to this point is called the **equilibrium decomposition potential.**

To make electrolysis proceed at a finite rate, additional voltage is needed to overcome the ohmic resistance represented by the cell. This voltage is equal to $I\mathcal{R}$ where I is the current and $\mathcal{R}$ the resistance. Sometimes further voltage, called **overvoltage,** is required because of irreversible phenomena that occur when a gas is evolved or a solid substance is deposited at an electrode.

When $\mathcal{E}$ for an electrochemical cell as written is negative, the cell is electrolytic, because the spontaneous direction of the cell reaction is opposite to the way the cell is written. The equilibrium decomposition voltage is $|\mathcal{E}|$, and to actually run the cell in the direction written requires additional voltage for overcoming resistance and possible overvoltage.

7–3   EQUILIBRIUM WITH APPLIED POTENTIAL

The following reconsideration of this situation is illuminating. Suppose that we apply an external potential $\mathcal{U}_{ext}$ that keeps the cell reaction just in balance at constant P and T. What is the value of $\mathcal{U}_{ext}$ at equilibrium? In other words, we are interested in the equilibrium situation that includes the presence of an external potential. The thermodynamic relationship to be considered is no longer $dG \leqslant 0$, but the more general one, $dG \leqslant Dw'$, because electrical work is now involved. In particular, under reversible conditions or at equilibrium the equal sign applies. If we therefore let $\mathcal{U}_{ext}$ force the charge $d\mathcal{Q}$ reversibly through the cell, by (7–18)

$$dG = Dw'_{rev} = +\mathcal{U}_{ext}\, d\mathcal{Q} \qquad (7\text{–}29)$$

However, by (7–24) dG is given for any electrochemical cell by

$$dG = -\mathcal{E}\, d\mathcal{Q} \qquad (7\text{–}30)$$

so that the equilibrium condition is

$$\mathcal{U}_{ext} = -\mathcal{E} \qquad (7\text{–}31)$$

The external potential must at equilibrium be equal to minus the cell emf. This is, of course, an expected result, the potential required being the equilibrium decomposition potential. However, the derivation provides a simple example of an equilibrium consideration in which Dw' is not equal to zero. Applications in which Dw' involves gravitational, magnetic, or still other types of work can be treated in a similar way.

When the external potential is not equal to the cell emf, there is a flow of electrons and the cell works as a galvanic or an electrolytic cell. As the cell reaction proceeds, the concentrations of the participating species change until equality of potentials has been achieved and equilibrium exists.

A question that may be asked in this context is: What keeps the cell reaction of an unused battery in check? The answer is that the cell reaction proceeds to a small extent, and builds up electric charges on the electrodes. These charges generate an external potential that opposes the cell emf, and the cell reaction stops when the external potential becomes equal to the cell emf. The number of electrons involved in this charge build-up is exceedingly small compared to 1 mole of electrons, so that the extent to which the cell reaction proceeds is very small.

7–4 THE NERNST EQUATION

To derive an expression for the emf $\mathcal{E}$ of an electrochemical cell we recall the expression for ΔG in terms of ΔG^0 and the mass-action quotient Q developed in Chapter 6,

$$\Delta G = \Delta G^0 + RT \ln Q \tag{7–32}$$

Inserted into (7–27),

$$\mathcal{E} = -\frac{\Delta G^0 + RT \ln Q}{n\mathcal{F}}$$

or, by use of (7–28),

$$\mathcal{E} = \mathcal{E}^0 - \frac{RT}{n\mathcal{F}} \ln Q \tag{7–33}$$

This is the **Nernst equation.** It expresses the emf of an electro-chemical cell in terms of the standard emf, the temperature T, the number n of electrons involved in the over-all cell reaction, and the concentrations and partial pressures of the chemical species in-volved. The conventions that apply to Q in connection with the mass-action law apply here also; products appear in the numerator and reactants in the denominator. Concentrations of dissolved species that participate in the cell reaction must be expressed in moles per liter. Gases must be represented by their partial pres-sures in atmospheres in Q rather than their concentrations, whereas $[H_2O]$ for reactions in dilute aqueous solutions does not appear and

neither do the concentrations of solid reagents.   As mentioned
earlier, the Q in ln Q refers to the numerical values only of Q.   Note
also that ε, as computed from the Nernst equation, is not changed—
as indeed it should not be—if the cell reaction is multiplied by a
factor f.   In detail, this factor changes the number n of electrons
appearing in (7–33) to nf, and Q is changed to Q^f; the two changes
just cancel in (7–33).

EXAMPLE 2

What is the Nernst equation for a cell (7–1) with the over-all
reaction (7–4)?   Since $n = 2$,

$$\varepsilon = \varepsilon^0 - \frac{RT}{2\mathfrak{F}} \ln \frac{[\text{Zn}^{2+}]}{[\text{Cu}^{2+}]} \qquad (7–34)$$

where ε^0 is the cell emf at standard conditions.   Note that when
$[\text{Zn}^{2+}]$ and $[\text{Cu}^{2+}]$ are both 1 M, the logarithmic term in (7–34)
vanishes so that $\varepsilon = \varepsilon^0$ as it should.   Furthermore, when the
cell is written in the opposite direction, ε^0 changes sign and the
logarithmic term contains now $\ln([\text{Cu}^{2+}]/[\text{Zn}^{2+}])$, so that this
term changes sign also; ε thus retains its magnitude but changes
sign, as expected.

EXAMPLE 3

What is the Nernst equation for a cell (7–14) with a reaction
described by (7–17)?   Again $n = 2$, so that

$$\varepsilon = \varepsilon^0 - \frac{RT}{2\mathfrak{F}} \ln \frac{P_{\text{H}_2}}{[\text{H}^+]^2[\text{Cl}^-]^2} \qquad (7–35)$$

The ε^0 in (7–35) is of course different from the ε^0 in (7–34).
Again the logarithmic term in (7–35) vanishes at standard
conditions ($P_{\text{H}_2} = 1$ atm and $[\text{H}^+] = [\text{Cl}^-] = 1$ M), so that
$\varepsilon = \varepsilon^0$.   Numerical examples will be given later.

It is convenient to replace the natural logarithm in the Nernst
equation by the decadic logarithm and to combine the conversion
factor between the logarithms with the value of $RT/\mathfrak{F}$ at 25°C.

First, we change the faraday to new units. By (1–20), 4.1840 coulomb-volts = 1 cal, so that

$$\mathfrak{F} = (96{,}487 \text{ coulombs/mole})/(4.1840 \text{ coulomb-volts/cal})$$

$$= 23{,}061 \text{ cal/volt-mole} = 23.061 \text{ kcal/volt-mole} \qquad (7\text{–}36)$$

These units of $\mathfrak{F}$ are useful also when applying (7–27) and (7–28), because ΔG and ΔG^0 are usually expressed in calories or kilocalories. Next, $RT = 1.9872 \times 298.15 = 592.48$ cal/mole and $\ln x = 2.303 \log x$, so that at 298°K,

$$\frac{RT}{n\mathfrak{F}} \ln Q = \left(\frac{592.5 \times 2.303}{n \times 23{,}061} \log Q \right) \text{volt} = \left(\frac{0.0592}{n} \log Q \right) \text{volt}$$

Thus, at 25°C,

$$\mathcal{E} = \mathcal{E}^0 - [(0.0592/n) \log Q] \text{ volt} \qquad (7\text{–}37)$$

In applications the temperature will always be presumed to be 25°C or 298°K, unless another temperature is explicitly indicated.

7–5 HALF-CELL EMF'S

It is possible to assign to each electrode of an electrochemical cell a **half-cell emf,** defined below by an example, so that the cell emf is the difference between the half-cell emfs. The reference point for this scheme is the standard hydrogen electrode, a hydrogen electrode in which the hydrogen gas is at 1 atm pressure and the H^+ ion concentration is 1 mole/liter.

Consider, for example, a Zn electrode immersed in a Zn^{2+} solution. The half-reaction is

$$Zn^{2+} + 2e^- = Zn(s) \qquad (7\text{–}38)$$

The half-cell emf is *defined* as the emf of the cell

$$\text{Pt, } H_2(1 \text{ atm})|H^+ (1 \text{ } M)| \text{ } |Zn^{2+}|Zn(s) \qquad (7\text{–}39)$$

for which the cell reaction is

$$H_2(g) + Zn^{2+} = 2H^+ + Zn(s) \tag{7-40}$$

By the Nernst equation this emf is

$$\mathcal{E} = \mathcal{E}^0 - \left(\frac{RT}{n\mathcal{F}}\right) \ln Q = \mathcal{E}^0 - \left(\frac{RT}{n\mathcal{F}}\right) \ln \frac{[H^+]^2}{P_{H_2}[Zn^{2+}]} \tag{7-41}$$

where $\mathcal{E}^0$ is the emf of this cell when $[Zn^{2+}] = [H^+] = 1\ M$ and $P_{H_2} = 1$ atm. This emf is characteristic of the Zn^{2+}/Zn half-cell at standard conditions ($[Zn^{2+}] = 1\ M$), granting that the reference point is the standard hydrogen electrode. It is thus often given an identifying subscript: $\mathcal{E}^0_{Zn^{2+}/Zn}$, and is called the *standard* half-cell emf of the Zn^{2+}/Zn half-cell. Furthermore, $Q = 1/[Zn^{2+}]$ in (7-41) because $[H^+]$ is by definition $1\ M$ and P_{H_2} equal to 1 atm so that only $[Zn^{2+}]$ contributes to Q. Equation (7-41) thus has the form

$$\mathcal{E} = \mathcal{E}^0_{Zn^{2+}/Zn} - \left(\frac{RT}{2F}\right) \ln\ (1/[Zn^{2+}]) \tag{7-42}$$

Comparison with the half-reaction (7-38) shows that (7-42) is formally identical to the Nernst equation for this half-reaction, provided the electrons appearing in the half-reaction are ignored when forming Q. This result is general. Values of standard half-cell emfs can be obtained by measurement of voltages of appropriate cells and also from thermodynamic data, as will be seen. By definition, $\mathcal{E}^0_{H^+/H_2}$ is equal to zero. A representative set of values of $\mathcal{E}^0$ is given in Table A4-2 of Appendix 4.

Standard conditions for half-cells pertain to the species that appear in the half-reaction. They are unit molarity for dissolved species, and partial pressures of 1 atm for gases. When the solubility of a substance is small, standard conditions require an excess of the solid form (or liquid—for example, Hg) of the substance to be present to assure saturation.

For example, the standard conditions for the Ag^+/Ag couple are: $[Ag^+] = 1$, presence of $Ag(s)$; for the $AgCl/Ag$ couple, $[Cl^-] = 1$, presence of $AgCl(s)$ and $Ag(s)$; for the MnO_4^-/Mn^{2+} couple, $[MnO_4^-] = [Mn^{2+}] = [H^+] = 1$ [see Eq. (7-13)].

EXAMPLE 4

What is the half-cell emf at 25°C for an AgCl/Ag electrode? The half-reaction is

$$AgCl(s) + e^- = Ag(s) + Cl^-$$

and $\mathcal{E}^0_{Ag/AgCl}$ is found in Appendix 4 to have the value of 0.2224 volt. Therefore,

$$\mathcal{E} = (0.2224 - 0.0592 \log[Cl^-]) \text{ volt} \qquad (7–43)$$

where (7–37) has been used.

It is instructive to set up the cell *defining* the half-cell emf desired in the example. It is

$$Pt, H_2(1 \text{ atm})|H^+(1M)| \; |Cl^-|AgCl, Ag$$

with the cell reaction

$$H_2 + 2AgCl(s) = 2Ag(s) + 2H^+ + 2Cl^-$$

Inserting $P_{H_2} = 1$ atm and $[H^+] = 1 \; M$ into the Nernst equation for *this* cell reaction we obtain

$$\mathcal{E} = \mathcal{E}^0 - \left(\frac{RT}{2\mathfrak{F}}\right) \ln [Cl^-]^2$$

This reduces to (7–43) because $2.303 RT/\mathfrak{F} = 0.0592$ volt at 25°C, and the $\frac{1}{2}$ in front of the logarithm cancels the exponent in $[Cl^-]^2$.

EXAMPLE 5

What is the pH dependence of the emf of the hydrogen half-cell? Since $\mathcal{E}^0 = 0.000$ by definition and the half-cell reaction is $2H^+ + 2e^- = H_2(g)$,

$$\mathcal{E} = -\left(\frac{0.0592}{2}\right) \log\left(\frac{P_{H_2}}{[H^+]^2}\right) \text{ volt}$$

When $P_{H_2} = 1$ atm,

$$\varepsilon = -0.0592 \text{ pH}$$

because $\text{pH} = -\log[H^+]$. The half-cell emf is seen to be directly proportional to the pH, and a hydrogen electrode may thus be used to measure the pH of the solution that surrounds it. Indeed, any other half-cell representing a half-reaction that includes H^+ as a reactant or product may be used to measure the pH of a solution. The concentrations of all other species involved in the half-reaction must, of course, be kept constant. Electrodes of this kind have been used in the past, but all (including the hydrogen electrode) suffer from the disadvantage that, besides responding to the pH, their potential is changed by the presence of redox couples. They may thus be used to measure the pH only when there is no interference from oxidizing or reducing agents. This disadvantage is overcome by the glass electrode that is part of the modern pH meter, which responds only to the pH.

It is customary to assign free-energy changes to half-reactions by assigning the arbitrary value of zero to the standard free-energy change of the hydrogen half-reaction. This is consistent with the convention that the half-cell emf of the standard hydrogen electrode is zero. The fundamental relationship

$$\varepsilon = \frac{-\Delta G}{n\mathfrak{F}} \tag{7-44}$$

is thus applicable to half-reactions also, and similarly under standard conditions

$$\varepsilon^0 = \frac{-\Delta G^0}{n\mathfrak{F}} \tag{7-45}$$

EXAMPLE 6

Find the standard half-cell emf at 298°K for the reaction

$$14H^+ + Cr_2O_7^{2-} + 6e^- = 2Cr^{3+} + 7H_2O$$
$$0 \qquad -315.4 \qquad \qquad -51.5 \quad -56.69$$

from the free energies of formation of the species involved, which are listed in kilocalories per mole underneath the chemical symbols. We calculate $\Delta G^0 = (-2 \times 51.5 - 7 \times 56.69 + 315.4)$ kcal $= -184.4$ kcal and therefore, using $\mathfrak{F} = 23.06$ kcal/volt-mole, $\mathcal{E}^0 = [+184.4/(6 \times 23.06)]$ volt $= $ **1.33 volts.**

When the direction in which the half-reaction is written is reversed, the sign of the half-cell emf is reversed just as was the case for the emf of a complete electrochemical cell. It is a *sign-bivariant* quantity.

Side by side with the half-cell emf there also exists the **electrode potential** $\mathcal{U}$, the potential the electrode assumes relative to the hydrogen electrode when the half-cell considered is combined with the standard hydrogen half-cell. This electrode potential is a physical quantity and therefore does not depend on which way the half-reaction is written. It may be positive or negative, but it is a *sign-invariant* quantity.

The use of half-cell emfs has many adherents, particularly in America, but electrode potentials are preferred in Europe. The names *half-cell emf* for the sign bivariant quantity and *electrode potential* for the sign-invariant quantity, that is, the terms used here, were recommended in 1953 at the Seventeenth Conference of the International Union of Pure and Applied Chemistry.

When a half-reaction is written as a reduction, with the electrons on the left, the half-cell emf is equal to the electrode potential in sign and value. This is the reason why in Table A4–2 the half-reactions are all written as reductions, *with electrons on the left*, so that the $\mathcal{E}^0$ values given represent electrode potentials and half-cell emfs *at the same time*. When a half-reaction is written as an oxidation, with the electrons on the right, the signs of half-cell emfs must be reversed and are thus opposite to those of electrode potentials. Such half-cell emf's must not be called electrode potentials.

To consider an example, the redox couple $Cu^{2+}/Cu(s)$ can be said to have the half-reactions and standard half-cell emf's

$$Cu^{2+} + 2e^- = Cu(s) \qquad \mathcal{E}^0_{Cu^{2+}/Cu} = 0.337 \text{ volt} \qquad (7\text{--}46)$$

and

$$Cu(s) = Cu^{2+} + 2e^- \qquad \mathcal{E}^0_{Cu/Cu^{2+}} = -0.337 \text{ volt} \qquad (7\text{--}47)$$

Equation (7–46) is that used in Table A4–2 and $\mathcal{E}^0_{Cu/Cu^{2+}}$ is the *reduction* half-cell emf, as is indicated by the subscript. Equation (7–47) corresponds to oxidation and leads to the opposite sign of the emf: $\mathcal{E}^0_{Cu/Cu^{2+}}$ is an *oxidation* half-cell emf.

The standard half-cell emf corresponding to the *reduction* is also equal to the standard electrode potential: $\mathcal{V}^0_{Cu^{2+}/Cu} = \mathcal{V}^0_{Cu/Cu^{2+}} = 0.337$ volt. This quantity is independent of whether the half-reaction is written as oxidation or reduction; the Cu electrode of a standard $Cu^{2+}/Cu(s)$ half-cell assumes a physical potential of $+0.337$ volt when this half-cell is combined with the standard hydrogen half-cell.

Thus, quite generally,

$$\mathcal{E}^0_{red} = \mathcal{V}^0 = -\mathcal{E}^0_{ox}$$

We shall usually not use subscripts for reduction half-cell emf's $\mathcal{E}^0$, and, *unless subscripts indicate otherwise, half-cell emf's $\mathcal{E}^0$ and electrode potentials $\mathcal{V}^0$ are thus identical.* This is, for example, the case for the $\mathcal{E}^0$ values in Table A4–2. Note, however, that many other tables of half-cell emf's give *oxidation* values that have signs opposite from the values given here and from electrode potentials. Although this is a disadvantage, a listing of $\mathcal{E}^0_{ox}$ values has the merit of paralleling the electropositive nature of the metals involved. For example, Cu is less electropositive, or more noble, than hydrogen; this is reflected by the oxidation half-cell emf of -0.337 volt that goes with (7–47).

When looking up tabulated $\mathcal{E}^0$ values, it is important to find out whether they correspond to a reduction or an oxidation. If this is not stated explicitly and no half-reactions are shown, it can be found out by looking at $\mathcal{E}^0$ values that involve familiar chemistry, and by remembering that $\mathcal{E}^0$ measures the tendency of a half-reaction to go toward the right, whether oxidation or reduction, relative to that of the standard hydrogen half-cell. For example, you may look at the value for an alkali metal like Na for which there is a strong drive to go to $Na^+ + e^-$. A negative $\mathcal{E}^0$ indicates that Na^+ and thus e^- must appear on the left of the half-reaction. This implies that $\mathcal{E}^0$ is the reduction emf and also the electrode potential. A positive $\mathcal{E}^0$ implies that Na^+ and e^- appear on the right and thus that $\mathcal{E}^0$ is the oxidation emf.

7–6 ELECTROCHEMICAL CELLS

When combining half-cells into an electrochemical cell, it is usually convenient to begin with an *arbitrary* choice of the half-reaction to be reversed and written as an oxidation, without considering whether this choice makes the cell galvanic or electrolytic. The two half-reactions must also be multiplied by suitable factors so that the electrons cancel. The half-reaction that has been reversed represents the anode reaction (oxidation) and its *reduction* emf must be subtracted from the *reduction* emf of the other half-reaction that represents the cathode reaction (reduction):

$$\mathcal{E}_{cell} = \mathcal{E}_{cathode} - \mathcal{E}_{anode} = \mathcal{E}_{right} - \mathcal{E}_{left} \qquad (7\text{--}48)$$

where the last expression refers to the symbolic representation of the cell. Instead of using reduction emf's we could have expressed the same relationship by means of electrode potentials:

$$\mathcal{E}_{cell} = \mathcal{V}_{cathode} - \mathcal{V}_{anode} = \mathcal{V}_{right} - \mathcal{V}_{left}$$

but in this text we shall prefer to stay with reduction emf's.[1]

It follows from the earlier discussion that if $\mathcal{E}_{cell}$ turns out to be positive, the cell reaction has the tendency to go from left to right spontaneously, so that the cell acts as a galvanic cell with the cell reaction as written. If the same cell is run as an electrolytic cell by forcing the reaction from right to left, the equilibrium decomposition potential is $\mathcal{E}_{cell}$.

If $\mathcal{E}_{cell}$ turns out to be negative, the statements in the preceding paragraph must be reversed. The cell reaction has the inherent tendency to occur from right to left with the galvanic cell potential

---

[1] Still another way of expressing (7–48) would be

$$\mathcal{E}_{cell} = \mathcal{E}_{cathode}^{red} + \mathcal{E}_{anode}^{ox} = \mathcal{E}_{right}^{red} + \mathcal{E}_{left}^{ox}$$

taking into account that $\mathcal{E}_{ox} = -\mathcal{E}_{red}$. It is, however, best to choose one mode of representation and to adhere to it, and we chose (7–48).

$|\mathcal{E}_{cell}|$. To run the cell in the electrolytic direction, from left to right, requires an opposed external voltage of $|\mathcal{E}_{cell}|$ and additional voltage for overcoming the ohmic resistance of the cell and possible over-voltage.

The value and sign of $\mathcal{E}_{cell}$ depend not only on the $\mathcal{E}^0$ values of the half-cells but also on the concentrations of the species participating in the cell reaction in the way indicated by the Nernst equation. To appreciate the details we consider the two half-reactions and $\mathcal{E}^0$ values

$$Ag^+ + e^- = Ag(s) \qquad \mathcal{E}^0 = \quad 0.7994 \text{ volt} \qquad (7\text{–}49)$$

$$Zn^{2+} + 2e^- = Zn(s) \qquad \mathcal{E}^0 = -0.7628 \qquad\qquad (7\text{–}50)$$

At 25°C the reduction half-cell emf's are

$$\mathcal{E}_{Ag} = \{0.7994 - 0.0592 \log (1/[Ag^+])\} \qquad (7\text{–}51)$$

$$\mathcal{E}_{Zn} = \{-0.7628 - (0.0592/2) \log (1/[Zn^{2+}]\} \qquad (7\text{–}52)$$

The subscripts of the $\mathcal{E}$ should be Ag^+/Ag and Zn^{++}/Zn but have been shortened for simplicity's sake.

To obtain the cell reaction the half-reactions have to be multi-plied by suitable coefficients to make the electrons cancel. Let the anode reaction arbitrarily be the second of the half reactions, so the Zn is oxidized to Zn^{2+}. The proper combination is $2 \times (7\text{–}49) - 1 \times (7\text{–}50)$:

$$2Ag^+ + Zn(s) = 2Ag(s) + Zn^{2+} \qquad (7\text{–}53)$$

the cell reaction corresponding to an interchange of two electrons. The cell emf is $\mathcal{E} = \mathcal{E}_{Ag} - \mathcal{E}_{Zn}$, but before combining (7–51) and (7–52), it is convenient to make the coefficients of the logarithms equal, changing the exponents of the concentrations to correspond. A convenient common factor is $0.0592/2$, and including signs the logarithmic terms are $-(0.0592/2) \{\log (1/[Ag^+]^2) - \log (1/[Zn^{2+}])\} = -(0.0592/2) \log ([Zn^{2+}]/[Ag^+]^2)$. Combining every-thing we obtain

$$\mathcal{E}_{cell} = [0.7994 + 0.7628 - (0.0592/2) \log ([Zn^{2+}]/[Ag^+]^2)] \text{ volt} \qquad (7\text{–}54)$$

The same result could have been obtained by applying the Nernst equation directly to the whole cell, noting that the standard cell emf is the difference of the standard half-cell reduction emf's, $\mathcal{E}^0_{cell} = \mathcal{E}^0_{cathode} - \mathcal{E}^0_{anode}$. Indeed, (7–54) is identical with

$$\mathcal{E}_{cell} = \mathcal{E}^0_{Ag} - \mathcal{E}^0_{Zn} - [(0.0592/2) \ln Q] \text{ volt}$$

where Q is the mass-action quotient of the cell reaction (7–53), and the number of electrons interchanged is $n = 2$.

Whether $\mathcal{E}$ is positive or negative depends on the concentrations of Ag^+ and Zn^{++}. To fix our ideas, suppose that $\mathcal{E}$ as calculated from (7–54) is positive. The cell is galvanic and, if current is permitted to flow, the reaction as written proceeds from left to right. Inspection shows that as a consequence of reactants being used up and products being formed, Q increases, so that the value of $\mathcal{E}$ decreases. Similarly, if an external voltage is used to drive the cell in the electrolytic direction, the resulting concentration changes make Q larger and $\mathcal{E}$ becomes more positive. The external voltage required for electrolysis thus increases as the electrolysis proceeds. All this makes good physical sense.

Analogous results are obtained when $\mathcal{E}$ turns out to be negative for the direction in which the cell reaction has been written.

EXAMPLE 7

What is the potential at 25°C of the cell

$$Zn|Zn^{2+} (1 \; M)| \; |Cu^{2+} (0.1 \; M)| \; Cu$$

encountered in Section 7–1? By Table A4–2 of Appendix 4 we note that $\mathcal{E}^0_{Zn} = -0.763$ volt and $\mathcal{E}^0_{Cu} = 0.337$ volt. Furthermore, the Zn electrode is the anode for the cell as written, and the cell reaction is

$$Zn(s) + Cu^{2+} = Zn^{2+} + Cu(s)$$

Inserting $[Zn^{2+}]/[Cu^{2+}] = 10$ into the Nernst equation yields

$$\mathcal{E} = [0.337 + 0.763 - (0.0592/2) \log 10] \text{ volt}$$

$$= \mathbf{1.070 \; volt}$$

Since $\mathcal{E}$ is positive the cell is galvanic.

EXAMPLE 8

Calculate the cell potential for the reaction

$$5Cl^- + MnO_4^- + 8H^+ = \tfrac{5}{2}Cl_2(g) + Mn^{2+} + 4H_2O$$

at 25°C, at $P_{Cl} = 1$ atm, at $[H^+] = 1.0$ M, and at concentrations of 0.1 M for all other ionic species. The standard half-cell emf's are $\mathcal{E}^0_{Cl} = 1.36$ volt and $\mathcal{E}^0_{Mn} = 1.51$ volts. For the cell reaction, $n = 5$, so that

$$\mathcal{E} = \left[1.51 - 1.36 - (0.0592/5) \log \frac{P_{Cl_2}^{5/2}[Mn^{2+}]}{[Cl^-]^5[MnO_4^-][H^+]^8} \right] \text{volt}$$

The logarithmic term is equal to $-(0.0592)/5 \log (0.1)^{-5} = -0.059$ and the final result is $\mathcal{E} = \textbf{0.09 volt}$. Since $\mathcal{E}$ is positive, the reaction is spontaneous, and MnO_4^- is capable of oxidizing Cl^- under the conditions stated. However, the small value of $\mathcal{E}$ indicates that the concentrations are not far from equilibrium concentrations.

7–7 EQUILIBRIUM CONSTANTS

When the cell emf is zero, there exists equilibrium at the prevailing concentrations between the two redox couples that constitute cathode and anode of the cell. Under these conditions Q is equal to the mass-action constant K. Setting $\mathcal{E}_{cell}$ equal to zero and substituting K for Q, we obtain an equation for K:

$$\mathcal{E}_{cell} = 0 = \mathcal{E}^0_{cathode} - \mathcal{E}^0_{anode} - \left(\frac{RT}{n\mathfrak{F}} \right) \ln K$$

or

$$RT \ln K = n\mathfrak{F}(\mathcal{E}^0_{cathode} - \mathcal{E}^0_{anode}) = n\mathfrak{F}\mathcal{E}^0_{cell} \qquad (7\text{–}55)$$

and at 25°C,

$$\log K = \frac{n\mathcal{E}^0_{cell}}{0.0592} \qquad (7\text{–}56)$$

It is thus possible to calculate equilibrium constants of a cell reaction from the standard half-cell emf's of the redox couples involved, and conversely. It should be realized that even though (7–55) was derived by an argument using a cell emf, it also ties in with earlier relationships. For by (7–28), $\mathcal{E}^0 = -\Delta G^0/n\mathfrak{F}$, which inserted in (7–55) yields $RT \ln K = -\Delta G^0$, that is, (6–42).

Table 7–1 shows the relationships between the characteristic features of ΔG^0, $\mathcal{E}^0_{cell}$, K, and the direction in which a cell reaction *under standard conditions* is thermodynamically spontaneous. No special significance attaches to the second case ($\Delta G^0 = 0$), because to have the reactants and products at standard conditions and at equilibrium at the same time is an accidental situation.

The relationship between cell emf and ΔG shows the feasibility of obtaining free energy changes by electrical measurements. Other methods for deducing ΔG values mentioned earlier are the determination of thermal properties and the establishment of equilibrium constants.

For redox reactions, any of the three quantities—standard emf, standard free energy change, and equilibrium constant—may be obtained by determining just one of the three. Two of these or all three have been measured for many reactions, with results that have always been consistent with each other within the accuracy of the experiments.

For many other reactions it is, however, impractical or impossible to measure the three quantities separately. The equilibrium may, for example, be very one-sided, and the concentrations of the products may completely dominate those of the reactants, or the

Table 7–1

Correlation among ΔG^0, $\mathcal{E}^0_{cell}$, K, and the Behavior of the Cell Reaction

ΔG^0	$\mathcal{E}^0_{cell}$	K	Cell reaction under standard conditions is:
<0	>0	>1	Spontaneous toward right
0	0	1	At equilibrium
>0	<0	<1	Spontaneous toward left

other way around, so that it is hard to obtain accurate measurements of the equilibrium constant.   To illustrate, in the reaction

$$2Ag^+ + Zn(s) = Zn^{2+} + 2Ag(s)$$

the equilibrium is overwhelmingly in favor of the right side, with a concentration of Ag^+ of the order of 10^{-26} when that of Zn^{2+} is about 1.   It would therefore be impossible to determine the equilibrium constant from concentration measurements.   However, the potential established between a Zn and an Ag electrode dipping into connected half-cells that contain, respectively, Zn^{2+} and Ag^+ ions at standard concentrations can easily be measured, and the equilibrium constant can be computed from that value.

An equilibrium of interest may be reached at a very slow rate, or side reactions may prevent its establishment entirely, so that neither the equilibrium constant nor the cell potential may be measured.   For example, the potential of the couple MnO_4^-/Mn^{2+} cannot be measured in an alkaline or neutral solution, because in such a solution MnO_4^- is reduced to $MnO_2(s)$ rather than to Mn^{2+}. Nevertheless, this potential and the corresponding equilibrium constant may be calculated from free energy considerations—in this particular case by using the standard potential of the MnO_4^-/Mn^{2+} couple measured at zero pH, and calculating the desired quantities from the Nernst equation.

Whenever an equilibrium constant or a cell emf is not accessible to direct measurement, it may be determined from the free energies of all substances involved, provided these are known from thermal measurements or from measurements of equilibrium constants or cell potentials of other reactions that relate the substances considered to still others with known free energy values.   However, as in all thermodynamic considerations, only the position of an equilibrium or the value of a cell emf can be determined, and not whether the rates are such that the equilibrium or the cell emf is actually established.

EXAMPLE 9

What is the equilibrium constant at 25°C for the reaction

$$6H^+ + IO_3^- + 5I^- = 3I_2(s) + H_2O$$

In the reaction considered, iodide is oxidized to iodine by iodate. We note in passing that the $I_2(s)$ in the reaction equation implies that solid iodine must be present, and that there is to be no term $[I_2]$ in the mass-action quotient.

The standard half-cell emfs are 1.19 volts for the IO_3^-/I_2 and 0.534 volt for the I_2/I^- couples. Since the I_2/I^- couple is run as an oxidation, its emf is to be subtracted from that of the IO_3^-/I_2 couple and $\mathcal{E}^0 = (1.19 - 0.534)$ volt $= 0.656$ volt. The number of electrons interchanged is 5, because five I^- are oxidized and one IO_3^- reduced. Thus, by (7–56), log $K = 2 \times 0.656/0.0592 = 22.16$ and $K = \mathbf{1.5 \times 10^{22}}$

EXAMPLE 10

Given are two half-reactions and standard half-cell emfs at 25°C:

$$Ag^+ + e^- = Ag(s) \qquad 0.7994 \text{ volt}$$

$$AgCl(s) + e^- = Ag(s) + Cl^- \qquad 0.2224 \text{ volt}$$

What is the solubility product constant for AgCl?

Reversing the first half-reaction and adding it to the second results in $AgCl(s) = Ag^+ + Cl^-$, the reaction corresponding to $[Ag^+][Cl^-] = K_{sp}$. The cell emf for this reaction is $\mathcal{E}^0 = (0.2224 - 0.7994)$ volt $= -0.5770$ volt. Thus log $K_{sp} = -0.5770/0.0592 = -9.747$ and $K_{sp} = \mathbf{1.8 \times 10^{-10}}$.

Another way to derive this result is to realize that the two half-equations represent two aspects of the same reaction, the reduction of Ag(I) to Ag(0). While the two $\mathcal{E}^0$ values refer to different standard states—one to $[Ag^+] = 1$, the other to $[Cl^-] = 1$ and the presence of $AgCl(s)$, and both to the presence of $Ag(s)$—in a given situation the Nernst equation for either half-reaction must yield the same $\mathcal{E}$. Thus $\mathcal{E} = 0.7994 - 0.0592$ log $[Ag^+]^{-1} = 0.2224 - 0.0592$ log $[Cl^-]$, which is readily transformed into 0.0592 log $[Ag^+][Cl^-] = 0.2224 - 0.7994$. The result is equivalent to that of the preceding paragraph.

7–8   COMBINING STANDARD HALF-CELL EMF'S

There are two ways of combining the emf's of two half-cells: (1) The half-reactions may be combined so that the electrons cancel, yielding the reaction of a completed cell. The cell emf is, as was discussed earlier, $\mathcal{E}^0_{cell} = \mathcal{E}^0_{cathode} - \mathcal{E}^0_{anode}$. (2) If the half-reactions have a species in common that is reduced or oxidized, they may be combined so as to eliminate this species rather than the electrons, the result being a new half-reaction. Consider, for example, the half-reactions (1) and (2) below, which involve the couples MnO_4^-/Mn^{2+} and MnO_2/Mn^{2+}. They have the species Mn^{2+} in common. This species may be eliminated by subtracting (2) from (1) to form the half-reaction (3) for the couple MnO_4^-/MnO_2, written in the proper way with electrons on the left.

(1) $8H^+ + MnO_4^- + 5e^- = 4H_2O + Mn^{2+}$ $\mathcal{E}^0_1 = 1.51$ volts

(2) $4H^+ + MnO_2(s) + 2e^- = 2H_2O + Mn^{2+}$ $\mathcal{E}^0_2 = 1.23$ volts

(3) $4H^+ + MnO_4^- + 3e^- = MnO_2(s) + 2H_2O$ $\mathcal{E}^0_3 = ?$

The question is, how are the $\mathcal{E}^0$ values of (1) and (2) to be combined to furnish $\mathcal{E}^0$ for reaction (3)? The answer is given readily when it is remembered that standard free energies of reactions combine in the same way as do the reaction equations. The values for the ΔG^0 are: $\Delta G^0_1 = -5\mathcal{F}\mathcal{E}^0_1$; $\Delta G^0_2 = -2\mathcal{F}\mathcal{E}^0_2$; $\Delta G^0_3 = \Delta G^0_1 - \Delta G^0_2 = -5\mathcal{F}\mathcal{E}^0_1 + 2\mathcal{F}\mathcal{E}^0_2 = -3\mathcal{F}\mathcal{E}^0_3$. Therefore,

$$\mathcal{E}^0_3 = \frac{5\mathcal{E}^0_1 - 2\mathcal{E}_2}{3} = 1.70 \text{ volts}$$

In other words, the intensive standard emf values $\mathcal{E}^0_i$ are not additive. The quantities that may be added or subtracted are the products $n_i\mathcal{E}^0_i$ that contain as factors the numbers n_i of electrons involved in the half-reaction. The quantities $n_i\mathcal{E}^0_i$ are extensive and proportional to the standard free energy changes ΔG^0_i.

The procedure just described is in contrast to that referred to under (1), since in the equation $\mathcal{E}^0_{cell} = \mathcal{E}^0_{cathode} - \mathcal{E}^0_{anode}$ no attention is paid to the fact that different numbers of electrons may be involved in the half-reactions. It is useful to consider this matter once more: For the two half-reactions we write symbolically

$$A + n_1 e^- = B \qquad \mathcal{E}^0_1$$
$$C + n_2 e^- = D \qquad \mathcal{E}^0_2$$

The corresponding free energy changes are $\Delta G^0_1 = -n_1 \mathfrak{F} \mathcal{E}^0_1$ and $\Delta G^0_2 = -n_2 \mathfrak{F} \mathcal{E}^0_2$. To combine the half-reactions into a cell reaction we multiply the first one by n_2, the second by $-n_1$ (which means that we also reverse its direction), and add:

$$n_2 A + n_1 D = n_2 B + n_1 C$$

The standard free energy change is obtained by combining ΔG^0_1 and ΔG^0_2 in the same way: $\Delta G^0 = n_2 \, \Delta G^0_1 - n_1 \, \Delta G_2 = -n_2 n_1 \mathfrak{F} \mathcal{E}^0_1 + n_2 n_1 \mathfrak{F} \mathcal{E}^0_2$. Finally, we note that the cell reaction involves $n_1 n_2$ electrons, so that the standard cell emf is $\mathcal{E}^0 = -\Delta G^0/n_1 n_2 \mathfrak{F} = \mathcal{E}^0_1 - \mathcal{E}^0_2$, which is the previous result.

EXAMPLE 11

For the half-reaction

(1) $\qquad 4H^+ + MnO_4^- + 3e^- = MnO_2(s) + 2H_2O$

the value $\mathcal{E}^0 = 1.70$ was calculated earlier. What is $\mathcal{E}^0$ for the half-reaction

(2) $\qquad 2H_2O + MnO_4^- + 3e^- = MnO_2(s) + 4OH^-$

which is basically the same reduction as (1) but at different standard conditions. The second half-reaction may be obtained from the first by adding four times the equation

(3) $\qquad H_2O = H^+ + OH^- \qquad K_w = 1.0 \times 10^{-14}$

The standard free energy changes for reactions (1) and (3) are $\Delta G_1^0 = -3\mathfrak{F}\mathcal{E}_1^0$ and $\Delta G_3^0 = -RT \ln K_w$. Combining into ΔG_2^0 and dividing by $-3\mathfrak{F}$ we obtain $\mathcal{E}_2^0 = -(\Delta G_1^0 + 4\ \Delta G_3^0)/3\mathfrak{F} = \mathcal{E}_1^0 + 4(RT/3\mathfrak{F})\ \ln K_w$. Thus at 25°C, $\mathcal{E}_2^0 = [1.70 + (4 \times 0.0592/3)\ \log\ 1.0 \times 10^{-14}]$ volt $= (1.70 - 1.11)$ volt $= \mathbf{0.59}$ **volt.**

7–9   TEMPERATURE DEPENDENCE OF $\mathcal{E}$

By (7–27) the emf of an electrochemical cell is

$$\mathcal{E} = \frac{-\Delta G}{n\mathfrak{F}} \tag{7-57}$$

where ΔG is the increase in free energy that would attend the passage of n faradays through the cell at constant temperature and pressure and *at the prevailing, constant concentrations*. By (6–50),

$$\frac{\partial}{\partial T}(\Delta G)_P = -\Delta S \tag{7-58}$$

and combination with (7–57) yields

$$\left(\frac{\partial \mathcal{E}}{\partial T}\right)_P = \frac{\Delta S}{n\mathfrak{F}} \tag{7-59}$$

By establishing the temperature dependence of the cell emf it is therefore possible to calculate ΔS for the cell reaction. Furthermore, since $\Delta H = \Delta G + T\ \Delta S$, it follows from (7–57) and (7–58) that

$$\Delta H = n\mathfrak{F}\ [T\ \left(\frac{\partial \mathcal{E}}{\partial T}\right)_P - \mathcal{E}] = n\mathfrak{F}\ T^2 \left[\frac{\partial(\mathcal{E}/T)}{\partial T}\right]_P \tag{7-60}$$

and ΔH can thus be calculated also. Conversely, if ΔS or ΔH is known, (7–59) or (7–60) may be used to calculate $(d\mathcal{E}/dT)$ at constant pressure. Equation (7–60) is another version of the Gibbs-Helmholtz equation (6–51).

EXAMPLE 12

The cell

$$Pb(s), PbCl_2(s)|KCl|Hg_2Cl_2(s), Hg(l)$$

has an emf of 0.5359 volt at 25°C, and when the temperature is raised the voltage increases by 1.45×10^{-4} volt/deg. What are ΔG^0, ΔS^0, and ΔH^0 for the cell reaction?

The cell reaction is

$$Hg_2Cl_2(s) + Pb(s) = 2Hg(l) + PbCl_2(s)$$

It should be noted that the cell reaction does not involve any dissolved species and the cell emf is therefore independent of the KCl concentration. For ΔG^0 we find

$$\Delta G^0 = -2 \times 23.06 \times 0.5359 \text{ kcal} = \mathbf{-24.72 \text{ kcal}}$$

Next,

$$\Delta S^0 = n\mathfrak{F}\left(\frac{\partial \mathcal{E}}{\partial T}\right)_P = 2 \times 23.06 \times 145 \times 10^{-3} \text{ cal/deg}$$
$$= \mathbf{6.69 \text{ cal/deg}}$$

Finally,

$$\Delta H^0 = \Delta G^0 + T\,\Delta S^0 = (-24.72 + 298 \times 6.69 \times 10^{-3}) \text{ kcal}$$
$$= \mathbf{-22.73 \text{ kcal}}$$

This example is a good illustration of how thermodynamic quantities may be determined with high accuracy by electrical measurements alone, without thermal measurements.

Incidentally, to ask for a mass-action constant K for the cell reaction would make little sense here, because no species is involved that could change its concentration or partial pressure. In other words, the system as described is inherently *not* at equilibrium. Since ΔG^0 is negative, the reaction continues to run toward the right, furnishing the voltage measured, until all $Pb(s)$ or all $Hg_2Cl_2(s)$ is used up.

PROBLEMS

7–1. *Thermodynamic functions.* State which of the quantities q, w, ΔU, ΔH, ΔS, and ΔG are constant for the following situations:

(*a*) A perfect gas undergoes an isothermal reversible expansion.

(*b*) Liquid water evaporates at 100°C into an evacuated space of such volume that only vapor of 100°C and 1 atm results.

(*c*) A mixture of gaseous hydrogen and gaseous iodine reacts at constant temperature and pressure to give hydrogen iodide. The individual gases are regarded as perfect.

(*d*) The cell H_2 (1 atm) | HCl sol'n | H_2(0.1 atm) operates reversibly at constant temperature and pressures. Hydrogen is to be regarded as a perfect gas.

(*e*) Liquid water and liquid sulfuric acid are mixed adiabatically and at such a constant pressure that only a solution results.

7–2. *Electrochemical cells.* Consider the following cells and state for each (1) the cell reaction; (2) the number of electrons involved; (3) whether $\mathcal{E}$ is negative or positive and the same for ΔG; (4) whether the cell reaction is spontaneous as written:

(*a*) Pt, $Cl_2(g)$ |Cl^-| |Fe^{2+}, Fe^{3+}| Pt; left terminal positive.

(*b*) $Hg(l)$, $Hg_2Cl_2(s)$ |HCl(aq)| $H_2(g)$, Pt; right terminal negative.

(*c*) Pb, $PbSO_4(s)$ |H_2SO_4(aq)| $PbSO_4(s)$, $PbO_2(s)$, Pb; left terminal negative.

7–3. *Cell emf.* What is the emf of the following cell: Ni |Ni^{2+} (0.05 M)| |Zn^{2+}(0.10 M)|Zn? Give the cell reaction, find ΔG and state which terminal is positive. Use the half-cell emfs of Appendix 4.

7–4. *Equilibrium constant.* Use the half-cell emfs in Appendix 4 to calculate the equilibrium constant at 25°C for the reaction $2S_2O_3^{2-} + I_3^- = S_4O_6^{2-} + 3I^-$.

7–5. *Half-cell emf.* The cell Pt |H_5IO_6 (0.01 M), IO_3^- ($10^{-4}\,M$)| |H^+ (1 M)| $H_2(g$, 1 atm), Pt is found to have an emf of -1.48 volts. What is the half-reaction and the standard emf for the H_5IO_6/IO_3^- half-cell?

7–6. *Complex formation constant.* Given are the half-cell emf's of the reactions

$$Al^{3+} + 3e^- = Al(s) \qquad -1.66 \text{ volts}$$
$$Al(OH)_4^- + 3e^- = Al(s) + 4OH^- \qquad -2.35 \text{ volts}$$

Calculate the equilibrium constant for the reaction $Al^{3+} + 4OH^- = Al(OH)_4^-$.

7–7. *Free energy from cell voltage.* The cell $Ag(s)$, $AgCl(s)$ $|HCl\ (0.1\ M)|\ Cl_2(g,\ 1\ atm)$, Pt (s) is galvanic and has the voltage 1.1366 volts. (a) What is the cell reaction? (b) What are the values of ΔG and ΔG^0 for this reaction?

7–8. *Free energy of formation of ions.* From the standard half-cell emf values given below, calculate the standard free energy of formation of the ions Cu^{2+}, Fe^{2+}, and Fe^{3+}, all at 25°C: Cu^{2+}/Cu, 0.337 volt; Fe^{2+}/Fe, -0.440 volt; Fe^{3+}/Fe^{2+}, 0.771 volt.

7–9. *Half-cell emf.* Calculate (a) $\mathcal{E}^0_{Na^+/Na}$ from the standard free energy of $Na^+(aq)$; (b) $\mathcal{E}^0_{MnO_4^-/Mn^{2+}}$ from the standard free energies of the species involved in the half-reaction. (c) $\mathcal{E}^0_{O_2/H_2O}$ from the standard free energy of $H_2O(l)$.

7–10. *Half-cell emf.* The half-cell emf of the reaction

$$H_3AsO_4 + 2H^+ + 2e^- = H_3AsO_3 + 2H_2O$$

is 0.559 volt. What is $\mathcal{E}^0$ for the reaction

$$H_2AsO_4^- + 3H^+ + 2e^- = H_3AsO_3 + 2H_2O$$

The first acid constant of H_3AsO_4 is $K_1 = [H^+][H_2AsO_4^-]/[H_3AsO_4] = 5.6 \times 10^{-3}$.

7–11. *Combination of half-cell emf's.* Given are the standard emf values for two half-reactions:

$$Co^{2+} + 2e^- = Co(s) \qquad \mathcal{E}^0 = -0.28 \text{ volt}$$
$$Co^{3+} + e^- = Co^{2+} \qquad \mathcal{E}^0 = 1.82 \text{ volts}$$

What is $\mathcal{E}^0$ for the half-reaction

$$Co^{3+} + 3e^- = Co(s)$$

7–12. *Cell potential and temperature coefficient.* Consider the cell $Cu(s) |Cu^{2+} (0.1 M)| |Zn^{2+} (0.05 M)| Zn(s)$. Use the values of $\tilde{G}_f^0$ and $\tilde{H}_f^0$ in Appendix 4 to calculate the cell potential at 25°C and its temperature coefficient. Determine which terminal is positive.

7–13. *Weston standard cell.* The negative electrode of this cell is a cadmium-mercury amalgam of definite composition, the positive electrode consists of mercury covered by $Hg_2SO_4(s)$, and the electrolyte is a saturated solution of $CdSO_4$. What is the cell reaction in the spontaneous direction? The cell voltage near 20°C is given by the expression $\mathcal{U} = [1.01827 - 0.0000406 (t - 20)]$ volt, where t is the temperature in centigrade. Calculate ΔG^0, ΔH^0, and ΔS^0 for the cell reaction at 25°C.

7–14. *Free energy and enthalpy of cell reaction.* The cell $Ag(s)$, $AgCl(s) |KCl(aq)| Hg_2Cl_2(s)$, $Hg(l)$ is negative at the silver electrode and has a voltage of 0.0455 volt at 25°C, with a temperature coefficient of 3.38×10^{-4} volt/deg. Give the cell reaction and find ΔG^0, ΔH^0, and ΔS^0 for this reaction.

7–15. *Half-cell emf from nonelectrical measurements.* (a) Find the standard free energy of formation of $Mg(OH)_2$ at 25°C from that of $H_2O(l)$ and the following free energies of reaction, at 25°C and under standard conditions: $Mg(s) + \frac{1}{2}O_2(g) = MgO(s)$, -136.13 kcal and $MgO(s) + H_2O(l) = Mg(OH)_2(s)$, -6.45 kcal. (b) Calculate the standard free energy of $Mg^{2+}(aq)$ from that of $OH^-(aq)$ and from K_{sp} for $Mg(OH)_2(s)$, 9.0×10^{-12}. (c) Calculate $\mathcal{E}^0$ for the half-cell reaction $Mg^{2+} + 2e^- = Mg(s)$.

7–16. *Reaction constant.* Derive the value of the solubility product of cuprous iodide, $CuI(s)$ from the half-cell emfs given in Appendix 4 for the couples Cu^{2+}/Cu^+ and $Cu^{2+}/CuI(s)$.

7–17. *Combination of half-cell emf's.* Given are the standard emf values for two half-cells:

$$Mn^{2+} + 2e^- = Mn(s) \qquad \mathcal{E}^0 = -1.19 \text{ volts}$$
$$MnO_4^- + 8H^+ + 5e^- = Mn^{2+} + 4H_2O \qquad \mathcal{E}^0 = 1.51 \text{ volts}$$

What is $\mathcal{E}^0$ for the half-cell $MnO_4^- + 8H^+ + 7e^- = Mn(s) + 4H_2O$? (Note that half-cell emf values are not necessarily accessible to direct measurement.)

7–18. *Lead storage battery.* The cell reaction of a lead storage battery being charged is $2PbSO_4(s) + 2H_2O = PbO_2(s) + Pb(s) + 4H^+ + 2SO_4^{2-}$. In 1 M H_2SO_4 and between 0 and 60°C, the cell potential has been found to follow the equation $\mathcal{V} = (1.91737 + 56.1 \times 10^{-6}t + 108 \times 10^{-8}t^2)$ volt, where t is the temperature in centigrade. Find ΔG, ΔH, and ΔS at 25°C for the cell reaction as written.

8 Applications

Two industrial applications are discussed in this chapter: the Haber process and fuel cells. Further subjects treated are the Joule-Thomson effect and adiabatic demagnetization. Final sections deal with the van der Waals gas and the entropy of mixing.

8–1   HABER PROCESS

The reaction between hydrogen and nitrogen to produce ammonia provides a good example of the power of the thermodynamic analysis of a chemical reaction. The equilibrium constant for the reaction

$$\tfrac{3}{2}H_2(g) + \tfrac{1}{2}N_2(g) = NH_3(g) \tag{8-1}$$

is 8.3×10^2 at 25°C. This is the square root of the value 6.9×10^5 that was calculated from standard free energy values in Example 4, Section 6–6, for twice the chemical equation (8–1). It is seen that the right side of the reaction equation is heavily favored.

The rate of the reaction is so slow that there is no noticeable production of NH_3 at room temperature, no matter how long N_2 and H_2 are left in contact with each other. It is therefore of interest to examine the equilibrium constant at elevated temperatures. This was done through a thermodynamic investigation by Haber, whose tenacious research eventually made possible the large-scale industrial production of ammonia by the process named after him and based on reaction (8–1). For a thermodynamic analysis, ΔH must be known as a function of the temperature. In a lecture given in June, 1914, Haber presented the following results of careful measurements of the molar heat capacities of H_2, N_2, and NH_3. He expressed his data for the difference of the heat capacities,

$$\Delta C_P = \tilde{C}_P(NH_3) - \tfrac{3}{2}\tilde{C}_P(H_2) - \tfrac{1}{2}C_P(N_2)$$

by the empirical formula

$$\Delta C_P \approx -4.98 - 92 \times 10^{-5}T + 51 \times 10^{-7}T^2 \qquad (8-2)$$

in calories per mole-degree. This information permits finding the temperature dependence of ΔH, by the development explained in Section 2–6, with the difference that in the present case ΔC_P is not even approximately constant. This means that the integral over (8–2) must be taken,

$$\Delta H^0(T) = \int \Delta C_P \, dT$$
$$= -4.98T - 46 \times 10^{-5}T^2 + 17 \times 10^{-7}T^3 + \text{const} \qquad (8-3)$$

The superscript 0 is used because the values for ΔC_P and ΔH refer to partial pressures of 1 atm.

The constant of integration has to be determined experimentally by measuring ΔH^0 at any one temperature. Haber's value for the constant of integration is -9591 and corresponds, at 298.15°K, to $\Delta \tilde{H}^0 = -11.07$ kcal/mole, very close to the value listed in Appendix 4 for $\tilde{H}_f^0$ (11.04 kcal/mole). Insertion in (8–3) and use of (6–53) yields

$$\frac{d \ln K}{dT} = \frac{\Delta H^0(T)}{RT^2}$$

$$R \frac{d \ln K}{dT} = -\frac{4.98}{T} - 46 \times 10^{-5} + 17 \times 10^{-7}T - \frac{9591}{T^2}$$

By integration and insertion of the value for R,

$$1.987 \ln K = -4.98 \ln T - 46 \times 10^{-5}T$$
$$+ 8.5 \times 10^{-7}T^2 + \frac{9591}{T} + \text{const}$$

and thus

$$\log K = \frac{1}{1.987 \times 2.303}$$
$$\left(\frac{9591}{T} - 4.98 \times 2.303 \log T - 46 \times 10^{-5}T + 8.5 \times 10^{-7}T^2 \right)$$
$$+ \text{const}$$

The value of the constant was found to be 2.10 by measuring K at one single temperature. Haber's final formula for K is

$$\log K = 2.10 + \frac{2096}{T} - 2.51 \log T$$
$$- 1.01 \times 10^{-4}T + 1.86 \times 10^{-7}T^2 \quad (8\text{–}4)$$

The value of Haber's constant corresponds to $\Delta G^0 = -3.97$ kcal (at 298.15°K), the value in Appendix 4 being -3.98 kcal/mole.

Equation (8–4) permitted Haber to calculate values of K in a large temperature range: from 0 to 1000°C. His values are close to those currently accepted as best. The second column of Table 8–1 contains a partial set of Haber's K values.

Although the equilibrium constant K is independent of the total pressure P, the degree to which a mixture of N_2 and H_2 is converted to NH_3 at equilibrium does depend on P, as can be seen by the following development. It is convenient to discuss the progress of the reaction (8–1) in terms of the reaction variable ξ introduced in Section 6–6. As there, we consider the initial mixture (at $\xi = 0$) to contain 3 moles of H_2, 1 mole of N_2, and no NH_3, so that ξ measures the **yield** of the reaction or the fraction of the initial mixture converted to NH_3. The moles of component gases are given by (6–29). The total number of moles as a function of ξ is thus $n = 4 - 2\xi$, whence for the partial pressures

Table 8–1
Ammonia Equilibrium

t, °C	K	ξ_{equil} $P = 1$ atm	$P = 200$ atm	$P = 500$ atm
200	0.660	0.266	0.924	0.952
500	4.00×10^{-3}	0.0026	0.300	0.472
1000	1.356×10^{-4}	0.0001	0.0087	0.0413

$$P_{N_2} = \frac{(1 - \xi)P}{4 - 2\xi}$$

$$P_{H_2} = 3P_{N_2} \tag{8-5}$$

$$P_{NH_3} = \frac{2\xi P}{4 - 2\xi}$$

Insertion into the equilibrium expression yields

$$\frac{P_{NH_3}}{P_{H_2}^{3/2}P_{N_2}^{1/2}} = \frac{4\xi(2 - \xi)}{3\sqrt{3}\,(1 - \xi)^2 P} = K \tag{8-6}$$

This is a quadratic equation in ξ, but rather than solving for ξ in the usual way the following manipulations are convenient: By multiplication with $3\sqrt{3}\,P/4$,

$$\frac{\xi(2 - \xi)}{(1 - \xi)^2} = \frac{3\sqrt{3}\,KP}{4}$$

The numerator on the left may be written as $1 - (1 - \xi)^2$, so that

$$1 - (1 - \xi)^2 = \frac{(1 - \xi)^2\,3\sqrt{3}\,KP}{4}$$

Solving for $(1 - \xi)^2$,

$$(1 - \xi)^2 = \frac{1}{(3\sqrt{3}/4)KP + 1} \tag{8-7}$$

Because ξ measures the fraction of the original mixture of N_2 and H_2 converted to NH_3, the quantity $(1 - \xi)$ starts from the other end and indicates the degree of dissociation that would have occurred had we had pure NH_3 at the beginning. It is seen that with rising P, $(1 - \xi)$ decreases. Thus ξ, the degree of completion of reaction (8-1), increases with rising pressure, as expected qualitatively from the principle of LeChâtelier-Braun.

Table 8-1 contains the equilibrium values of ξ for several sets of temperatures and pressures. It is seen that a successful ammonia synthesis at ordinary pressures requires a catalyst that works well at temperatures below 200 to 300°C. The chances of finding such a catalyst were considered to be very small by Haber. Rather, he pioneered high-pressure work with streaming gases that were pumped through a reaction chamber continuously and on an industrial scale, limiting himself first to 200 atm at 500°C, and going later to 500 atm at the same temperature. He discovered that finely divided iron made an effective catalyst. The ammonia present in the gases emerging from the reaction chamber was removed by liquefaction, and the remaining mixture of nitrogen and hydrogen recycled together with fresh gases, thus ensuring eventual 100 per cent conversion to ammonia. The present-day process is fundamentally the same except that pressures as high as 1000 atm are employed.

The ammonia formed in this way is (1) used directly, in part as fertilizer; (2) combined with acids into the fertilizers ammonium sulfate and ammonium phosphate; or (3) oxidized by air to nitric oxide:

$$4NH_3 + 5O_2 = 4NO + 6H_2O$$

This reaction is catalyzed by hot platinum gauze. The resulting NO is oxidized further to NO_2 at room temperatures, and the NO_2 is absorbed in water to form nitric acid. By far the largest part of the world's supply of nitric acid is prepared by this method.

Haber's invention, summed up in his lecture of June 1914, made Germany independent of outside sources of ammonia and nitrate, needed in the production of fertilizers and explosives. It enabled her to wage a war that could not have been sustained without an assured supply of these materials.

8–2 FUEL CELLS

One of the most important methods for the production of energy is the generation of electricity in a steam plant. Coal or heating oil is used as fuel to produce steam, which drives a turbine coupled to an electric generator. Consider the case of coal, based on the reaction

$$C(s) + O_2(g) = CO_2(g) \tag{8–8}$$

for which $\Delta H^0 = -94.05$ kcal and $\Delta G^0 = -94.26$ kcal. Unfortunately, much of the total ΔH^0 available is lost as heat, because by (4–15) the maximum theoretical efficiency of a heat engine is $(T_h - T_l)/T_h$, which at best equals about 0.60 in a modern steam plant, whereas the over-all practical efficiency is 0.35 to 0.40. The situation would be improved vastly if it were possible to invent an electrochemical cell having (8–8) for its over-all reaction. The **fuel cell** is such a device, defined as a *continuously* fed electrochemical cell capable of producing electrical energy directly from a fuel.

Fuel cells are operated isothermally and not as heat engines, so that the maximum energy theoretically available for conversion into electrical energy is ΔG, and not ΔH. It is customary to express the theoretical efficiency of a fuel cell by the ratio

$$\frac{\Delta G}{\Delta H} = \frac{\Delta H - T\,\Delta S}{\Delta H} = 1 - T\,\frac{\Delta S}{\Delta H} \qquad (8-9)$$

This definition of efficiency is somewhat unusual, because with it situations exist in which the theoretical efficiency is larger than 1. To see how this can arise, we consider first the heat q_{rev} that must be transferred into the system—here the fuel cell—during the progression of the isothermal reversible cell reaction. For a reaction with zero net work w', this heat would be equal to ΔH, as derived in Section 2–3. But in the present case w' is not zero, being in fact the electrical energy produced, and q_{rev} is thus not equal to ΔH. However, since the process is reversible and isothermal, $\Delta S = q_{\mathrm{rev}}/T$, so that q_{rev} is simply $T\,\Delta S$.

Turning back to the case wherein (8–9) is larger than 1, we see that this occurs when ΔS and ΔH have opposite signs. Since ΔH is usually the major source of the electrical energy, the cell must lose enthalpy during its performance, which makes ΔH negative. Under these circumstances $\Delta G/\Delta H$ is larger than unity when ΔS, and thus $T\,\Delta S$, is positive: the heat $T\,\Delta S$ must flow into the cell; it is added to the enthalpy converted into electrical energy.

When ΔS is negative, the heat $|T\,\Delta S|$ is transferred by the cell to the surroundings during its operation. Part of ΔH is thus not converted into electrical energy, and the theoretical efficiency is less than unity. All preceding considerations assume reversibility, and in actual operation the cell efficiency is less than the theoretical efficiency defined by (8–9).

The case of positive ΔS has further advantages, because by (8–9) the theoretical efficiency increases with temperature in this case. Furthermore, by (7–59), $(\partial \mathcal{E}/\partial T)_P = \Delta S/n\mathfrak{F}$, so that for a positive ΔS the cell emf increases with temperature.

For reaction (8–8) $\Delta G/\Delta H$ happens to be almost equal to 1— just 0.2 per cent larger. Because ΔS is almost zero, the ratio is also almost temperature-independent. A reaction for which $\Delta G/\Delta H$ is substantially larger than 1 is

$$C(s) + \tfrac{1}{2}O_2(g) = CO(g) \qquad (8\text{–}10)$$

for which $\Delta H = -26.42$ kcal, $\Delta G = -32.81$ kcal, and $\Delta G/\Delta H = 1.24$. At 600°K the theoretical efficiency is even larger, about 1.5. Reaction (8–10) would, of course, make use only of about one-third of the energy available in carbon as a fuel [by reaction (8–8)].

Among currently operating fuel cells is the hydrogen-oxygen cell, based on the reaction

$$2H_2(g) + O_2(g) = 2H_2O(g)$$

for which $\Delta G/\Delta H$ is $(-109.28)/(-115.60) = 0.945$ at 25°C and 1 atm. A version of this cell developed by Union Carbide has electrodes made of porous carbon, the anode being coated with platinum catalyst, and a 50 per cent aqueous KOH solution as electrolyte. Its efficiency is about 0.8. The anode is fed with H_2, the cathode with O_2 or air, and the cell is run at temperatures from 20 to 80°C and at pressures between 0.1 and 1 atm. The oxygen at the cathode is reduced to OH^-,

$$O_2 + 2H^+ + 4e^- = 2OH^-$$

The hydroxyl ions migrate to the anode and react there with hydrogen adsorbed on the platinum catalyst,

$$OH^- + H_{ads} = H_2O + e^-$$

There exist other versions of the hydrogen-oxygen cell.   In the Bacon cell, for example, the electrodes consist of porous nickel, and the cell is run at about 200°C and 27 atm, with a much higher power output than the Union Carbide cell.   However, the oxygen electrode corrodes more rapidly.

Fuel cells based on carbon monoxide, methanol, methane, and other hydrocarbons have shown little promise so far, except for the Allis-Chalmers cell, in which the fuel used is reported to consist of about 75 per cent propane.   No details on the operation of this cell have yet been published.

8–3   LIQUEFACTION OF GASES AND GENERATION OF LOW TEMPERATURES

Basic to an understanding of gas liquefaction is the **Joule-Thomson effect.**   Figure 8–1 shows schematically a device in which

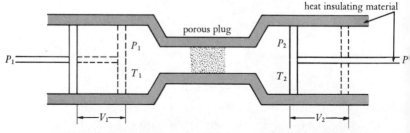

Figure 8–1 The Joule-Thomson experiment. In the device shown a volume V_1 of a gas of temperature T_1 is pushed through the porous plug at a pressure that is maintained at P_1. On the other side the pressure is maintained at P_2, which is below P_1, and the emerging gas assumes a volume V_2 and a temperature T_2. The porous plug prevents turbulent, disorderly expansion of the gas.   The analysis in the text shows that for a perfect gas T_2 is equal to T_1, whereas for a real gas T_2 may be below or above T_1. This is called Joule-Thomson cooling or heating.   In actual practice the device is run continuously, the piston on the left being replaced by a pump and that on the right by a valve that maintains a constant pressure P_2 below P_1.

the pressure P_1 of a gas may be reduced to a pressure P_2 by letting it pass through a porous plug. The plug and all other parts of the device are made of heat-insulating materials. The pressures P_1 and P_2 are kept constant ($P_2 < P_1$) and the flow of gas is continued until a steady state is reached. In this steady state the temperature of the gas is T_1 on the left, T_2 on the right. The gas flow is so slow that the kinetic energy of the gas stream is negligible on both sides. The point of interest is how the temperatures T_1 and T_2 are related. Are they equal or not? This will be examined now.

Suppose that n moles of gas pass from the chamber on the left to that on the right, and that the volume taken up by the n moles is V_1 on the left and V_2 on the right. Because of the heat insulation, q is zero. The work performed on the left is P_1V_1, on the right it is $-P_2V_2$, so that

$$w = P_1V_1 - P_2V_2 \qquad (8\text{--}11)$$

By the first law,

$$\Delta U = U_2 - U_1 = P_1V_1 - P_2V_2 \qquad (8\text{--}12)$$

and by rearrangement,

$$U_2 + P_2V_2 = U_1 + P_1V_1 \qquad (8\text{--}13)$$

Since $U + PV = H$, we conclude that $H_1 = H_2$, or that

$$\Delta H = 0 \qquad (8\text{--}14)$$

for the Joule-Thomson experiment.

When the gas involved is perfect, H is a function of T only, and $\Delta H = 0$ implies $\Delta T = 0$ or $T_2 = T_1$. There is thus no temperature change for a perfect gas. For an imperfect gas it generally depends on T_1 as to whether T_2 is larger or smaller than T_1, or, in other words, whether the gas is heated or cooled in the Joule-Thomson experi-

Table 8–2
Some Joule-Thomson Coefficients[a]

	373°K	273°K
H_2	−0.039	−0.013
N_2	0.159	0.333
O_2	0.193	0.366

[a] The units are °K/atm

ment. The crucial temperature is called the **Joule-Thomson inversion temperature.** Above it there is heating; below there is cooling upon Joule-Thomson expansion.

The Joule-Thomson effect provides a very sensitive means of studying gas imperfection by measuring the temperature changes caused by a given pressure drop. It is of great technical value, because important methods of gas liquefaction, such as the Linde process, are based on it. In it gas that has been cooled by expansion through a throttle is used to decrease the temperature of incoming compressed gas; eventually the incoming gas is cold enough so that a fraction of it is liquefied upon expansion. For most gases the Joule-Thomson inversion temperature lies above room temperature so that no precooling is required before they are expanded through a throttle. Exceptions are H_2 and He, which are heated when Joule-Thomson expansion occurs at room temperature. The ratio $\delta T/\delta P$, where δT is the temperature decrease that is caused by the pressure drop δP, extrapolated to $\delta P = 0$, is called the **Joule-Thomson coefficient.**[1] Table 8–2 lists typical values for this quantity. It is seen that at room temperature N_2 and O_2 are cooled by the Joule-Thomson effect while H_2 is heated.

The inversion temperature of H_2 is −80°C or 193°K, that of He −173°C or 100°K. To liquefy hydrogen it must first be cooled

---

[1] The δ's in δT and δP imply that δT and δP are small.

by liquid air to 193°K or less, whence it can be cooled below its boiling point, 20°K, by Joule-Thomson expansion in the Linde process. To liquefy He it is cooled first with liquid H_2, and then cooled to or below its boiling point at 4.2°K by Joule-Thomson expansion. This was done first by Kammerlingh-Onnes, in 1908. Liquid He is now produced more easily by a method pioneered by Kapitza, in which no liquid H_2 is used, avoiding thus a large fire hazard. Helium is precooled with liquid nitrogen, and made to perform work under adiabatic conditions. The energy loss is compensated by temperature lowering. Below the inversion point final cooling is achieved by Joule-Thomson expansion.

Temperatures of about 1°K are reached by attaching a container with liquid helium to a vacuum pump. Some of the helium evaporates and the loss of enthalpy of vaporization results in cooling. This causes the vapor pressure of helium to drop, and the decrease in temperature comes to a halt when the vapor pressure has reached whatever low pressure the pump is capable of sustaining. The lowest temperature that can be reached in this way depends on the effectiveness of the pump and the details of the temperature dependence of the vapor pressure.

A recent innovation is the use of the rare He^3 isotope, which has become available in sufficient amounts as a by-product of nuclear reactions. Even though He^3 and He^4 are similar in many respects, there are large differences in others. For example, the boiling point of He^3 is 1° below that of He^4. At 1°K the vapor pressure of He^3 is 73 times larger than that of He^4, and at 0.7°K it is 460 times larger. This allows lower temperatures to be reached by pumping on liquid He^3 instead of on liquid natural He, which contains only 10^{-9} per cent He^3. The pump size needed is also reduced. However, He^3 is very expensive (about \$70,000/liter of liquid He^3 in 1964), and pumping must therefore be done in a closed system. In practice, about 0.3°K can be reached in this way.

Still lower temperatures are reached by the method of **adiabatic demagnetization** proposed independently by Debye and by Giauque. It uses a paramagnetic salt such as potassium chromium alum, $KCr(SO_4)_2 \cdot 12H_2O$, in which the chromium atoms have a permanent magnetic moment. Since these magnetic ions are well

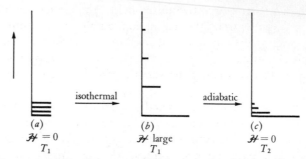

Figure 8–2 Cooling by adiabatic demagnetization, I. The levels shown correspond to different orientations of the magnetic moments of atoms. In a large external magnetic field $\mathcal{H}$ [see (*b*)] the level spacing is much larger than in the absence of such a field [(*a*) and (*c*)]. The three situations shown are the following: (*a*) The temperature T_1 is about 1°K and the level occupancies are approximately equal, because the level spacing is small compared to the average thermal energy of the atoms—this energy is of the order kT_1. (*b*) A large magnetic field $\mathcal{H}$ is now applied, the temperature T_1 being maintained. The occupancies change drastically, because the level spacing is now large compared to kT_1. (*c*) Thermal contact with the environment is broken and the magnetic field decreased reversibly to zero. The entropy cannot change in this adiabatic reversible process, so that the level occupancies of (*b*) are maintained. This corresponds to an average thermal energy of the atoms that is small compared to the level spacing at (*c*). Thus, kT_2 is now small compared to this spacing, so that T_2 is much smaller than T_1.

separated by other ions and the water of crystallization, they interact with one another only weakly, and their orientations are random in the absence of an external magnetic field. The energy levels corresponding to different orientations are close to each other and have almost equal occupancy [Fig. 8–2(*a*)].

When a strong external magnetic field is applied, the spacing of the energy levels is greatly increased, and there are drastic changes in the level occupancies, provided the temperature is kept at around 1°K [Fig. 8–2(*b*)]. These levels correspond to different orientations of the atomic magnets relative to the field—the higher the level, the larger the angle between the magnetic moment of the atom and the field. The new occupancies are thus equivalent to a lining up of the elementary magnets by the external field. There is a parallel lowering of the entropy, because the spread over the energy levels is decreased.

As the magnetic field is applied, it performs work on the system, and heat must be removed to keep the temperature constant. To see this in another way we note that the entropy of the system could not decrease if the magnetization were to be carried out adiabatically. The distribution over the different levels would then be the same in Fig. 8–2(*b*) as in Fig. 8–2(*a*), and this is equivalent to a temperature increase. Thermal contact must therefore be maintained with a constant-temperature bath during the magnetization.

Finally, the thermal contact is broken and the field removed reversibly so that the entropy of the system of magnets stays constant. The distribution of magnetic moments remains thus unchanged, even though the spacing of the different levels becomes again very close. To the maintained entropy at the new level spacing corresponds a new decreased temperature of the system of atomic magnets.

This is not the whole story, however, because there is also energy in the lattice vibrations of the crystal. This energy still corresponds to the original 1°K temperature, but the cold system of atomic chromium magnets now absorbs most of it. Fortunately, at 1°K there is very little lattice energy left, and the redistribution of energy does not markedly increase the temperature of the system of chromium magnets. The over-all result is substantial cooling.

In practice the salt is cooled to about 1°K by being in thermal contact with a liquid-helium bath of this temperature. This contact between salt and liquid-helium bath is maintained by a jacket containing helium gas of low pressure. For the final adiabatic demagnetization the salt is thermally insulated by pumping off the He gas (Fig. 8–3).

The lowest temperature that has been reached by this method is 0.0014°K. Still lower temperatures may be obtained by applying the same principle of magnetic cooling to nuclear magnetic moments, rather than to atomic moments. The lowest temperature achieved

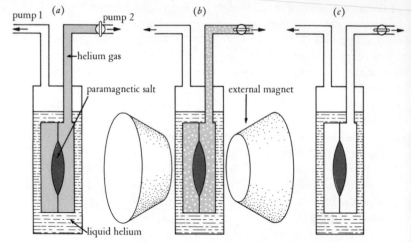

Figure 8–3 Cooling by adiabatic demagnetization, II.
These are the experimental aspects of the situations (*a*), (*b*), and
(*c*) diagrammed in Fig. 8–2. (*a*) Pump 1 keeps pumping on the
liquid helium, thus maintaining the temperature at the boiling
point of liquid helium at whatever pressure the pump is able to
maintain. The helium gas surrounding the paramagnetic salt
serves to maintain thermal contact between the salt and the liquid
helium that acts as a constant-temperature bath. (*b*) The magnetic field is applied. After the field has reached full strength, the
helium gas is pumped off by pump 2, so that the paramagnetic
salt becomes thermally insulated. (*c*) The magnetic field is slowly
removed, and the salt assumes a lower temperature.

to date is 2×10^{-5}°K, which was obtained in several stages of cooling, the last of which involved nuclear magnetic moments.

8–4 VAN DER WAALS GAS

The behavior of real gases, including liquefaction and critical
phenomena, is represented with fair accuracy by the van der Waals
equation. The main virtue of this equation is that it permits the
discussion of many deviations from perfect gas behavior with rela-

Table 8–4
van der Waals Constants

Gas	a, atm-liter^2	$100b$, liters	T_b, °K
H_2	0.245	2.67	20.4
He	0.034	2.36	4.2
N_2	1.38	3.94	77.4
O_2	1.32	3.12	90.2
CO	1.49	4.00	81.6
CO_2	3.60	4.28	194.7[a]
HCl	3.8	4.1	188.1
NH_3	4.0	3.6	239.7
SO_2	6.7	5.6	263.1

[a] Sublimation point.

tively simple algebra. More involved equations are needed to describe real gases *accurately*.

For 1 mole of gas, the van der Waals equation specifies

$$\left(P + \frac{a}{\tilde{V}^2}\right)(\tilde{V} - b) = RT \qquad (8\text{--}15)$$

where a and b are characteristic constants of the gas. The term $a/\tilde{V}^2$ corrects for the **cohesion pressure** that is caused by forces of attraction between molecules called **van der Waals forces.** The cohesion pressure acts in conjunction with the *outside* pressure, effectively increasing it. The constant b takes into account the fact that the space in which each molecule may roam freely is less than $\tilde{V}$, because of the space occupied by other molecules. Table 8–3 contains the constants a and b for a number of gases. As expected, the constants a run more or less parallel to the boiling temperatures at 1 atm, a larger a indicating larger cohesion forces, which make vaporization more difficult. The constants b reflect the sizes that have come to be associated with molecules from X-ray diffraction and other data.

To describe the behavior of complex equations, a mathematical procedure called **expansion in terms of small quantities** is often very useful. The van der Waals equation provides a good example that is therefore treated in some detail. We shall be interested in a pressure range in which $a/\tilde{V}^2 \ll P$ and a volume range in which $b \ll \tilde{V}$. In other words, the cohesion pressure is to constitute a small correction compared to the outside pressure, and the volume proper of the molecules is to be small compared to the volume available to the gas; deviations from ideal gas behavior are expected to be small. In this range of $\tilde{V}$ and P,

$$\frac{a}{\tilde{V}^2 P} \ll 1 \qquad \text{and} \qquad \frac{b}{\tilde{V}} \ll 1$$

These quantities are called **small of the first order,** or **first-order terms,** and the squares of these quantities and their product are said to be small of the second order or terms of the second kind, etc. Frequently one is satisfied with a **first-order approximation** in which terms of second and higher order are neglected.

For example, (8–15) can be rearranged into

$$P\tilde{V} = RT - \frac{a}{\tilde{V}} + bP + \frac{ab}{\tilde{V}^2}$$

Compared to RT the second and third terms on the right are of first order, and the fourth term is of the second order. This can be seen by dividing the equation by $P\tilde{V}$,

$$1 = \frac{RT}{P\tilde{V}} - \frac{a}{\tilde{V}^2 P} + \frac{b}{\tilde{V}} + \left(\frac{a}{\tilde{V}^2 P}\right)\left(\frac{b}{\tilde{V}}\right)$$

because this permits comparison of all terms with the 1 on the left side. By assumption the second and third terms on the right are small of the first order, and the fourth small of the second order. Thus $RT/P\tilde{V}$ must be of the order 1, which proves the contention. We shall neglect the fourth term, being satisfied with first-order approximation, so that

$$P\tilde{V} \approx RT - \frac{a}{\tilde{V}} + bP \qquad\qquad (8\text{–}16)$$

Another fact that will be used is that in all first-order terms it is permissible to replace $P\tilde{V}$ by RT, or P by $RT/\tilde{V}$, etc., because the error made by such replacements is of first order in first-order terms and thus of second order. It may therefore be neglected.

It is an important mathematical theorem that expansions such as ours are unique and thus do not depend on the particular way the expansion is effected. For example, an alternative way to expand (8–15) is to write

$$P = \frac{RT}{\tilde{V} - b} - \frac{a}{\tilde{V}^2} \qquad (8\text{–}17)$$

and to use the expansion $(1 - \delta)^{-1} = 1 + \delta + \delta^2 + \cdots$, where $\delta \ll 1$, in the first term on the right,

$$\frac{1}{\tilde{V} - b} = \frac{1}{\tilde{V}(1 - b/\tilde{V})} = \frac{1}{\tilde{V}}\left(1 + \frac{b}{\tilde{V}} + \frac{b^2}{\tilde{V}^2} + \cdots\right) \approx \frac{1}{\tilde{V}} + \frac{b}{\tilde{V}^2}$$

Terms of higher order than the first are neglected. Insertion in (8–17) yields

$$P = \frac{RT}{\tilde{V}} + \frac{bRT}{\tilde{V}^2} - \frac{a}{\tilde{V}^2} \qquad (8\text{–}18)$$

Replacing $RT/\tilde{V}$ by P in the second term on the right and multiplying the equation by $\tilde{V}$ again yields (8–16).

Although for a perfect gas U and H are functions of the temperature alone, this is not true for the van der Waals gas. It is therefore of interest to derive explicit expansions for U and H for the van der Waals gas. This will be done with the assumption that $\tilde{C}_V$ is constant, even though this is not always a good approximation. These expressions are then used to find the difference between C_P and $\tilde{C}_V$ and to discuss the Joule-Thomson effect for the van der Waals gas.

First, by (2–2), $(\partial U/\partial T)_V = C_V$, so that a temperature increase at constant volume by dT leads to an increase of $\tilde{U}$ by

$$(d\tilde{U})_V = C_V \, dT \qquad (8\text{–}19)$$

Next, we use the relationship derived in (5–41),

$$\left(\frac{\partial U}{\partial V}\right)_T = -P + T\left(\frac{\partial P}{\partial T}\right)_V \qquad (8\text{–}20)$$

Differentiating (8–18) at constant volume, we obtain

$$\left(\frac{\partial P}{\partial T}\right)_V = \frac{R}{\tilde{V}} + \frac{Rb}{\tilde{V}^2} \qquad (8\text{–}21)$$

correct to the first order. Combining with (8–18) and (8–20),

$$\left(\frac{\partial U}{\partial V}\right)_T = \frac{a}{\tilde{V}^2} \qquad (8\text{–}22)$$

Note that $(\partial U/\partial V)_T$ was zero for a perfect gas.

An explanation of (8–22) can be given on the molecular plane. When the van der Waals gas is expanded isothermally, work against the cohesion forces must be performed. This increases the internal energy of the gas, the increased average distance between the molecules implying a gain in potential energy. No such storage of potential energy is possible for perfect gases because there are no intermolecular forces. For 1 mole of van der Waals gas and an isothermal volume increase of $d\tilde{V}$ the work performed against the cohesion pressure $a/\tilde{V}^2$ (p. 229) is $Dw = (a/\tilde{V}^2)\, d\tilde{V}$, corresponding to

$$(d\tilde{U})_T = \left(\frac{a}{\tilde{V}^2}\right) d\tilde{V} \qquad (8\text{–}23)$$

This relationship is equivalent to (8–22).

It is now assumed that because of the smallness of a, the contributions to $\tilde{U}$ arising through (8–19) and (8–23) are additive even for a finite change in volume and temperature. Therefore, with $\tilde{C}_V = \text{const}$,

$$\tilde{U} = \int \tilde{C}_V\, dT + \int \frac{a}{\tilde{V}^2}\, d\tilde{V}$$

or

$$\tilde{U} = \tilde{U}_0 + \tilde{C}_V T - \frac{a}{\tilde{V}} \qquad (8\text{–}24)$$

where $\tilde{U}_0$ is a constant of integration.

To find $\tilde{H}$ we add (8–16) and rearrange:

$$\tilde{H} = \tilde{U} + P\tilde{V} \approx \tilde{U}_0 + \tilde{C}_V T - \frac{a}{\tilde{V}} + RT - \frac{a}{\tilde{V}} + bP$$

$$= \tilde{U}_0 + (\tilde{C}_V + R)T - \frac{2a}{\tilde{V}} + bP$$

It is convenient to express H as function of T and P. Thus, replacing $\tilde{V}$ by RT/P in the second last term,

$$\tilde{H} \approx \tilde{U}_0 + (\tilde{C}_V + R)T + \left(b - \frac{2a}{RT}\right)P \qquad (8\text{–}25)$$

As a first application, we find the difference between $\tilde{C}_P$ and $\tilde{C}_V$ for a van der Waals gas. By (2–14),

$$\tilde{C}_P = \left(\frac{\partial \tilde{H}}{\partial T}\right)_P \approx \tilde{C}_V + R + \frac{2aP}{RT^2} \qquad (8\text{–}26)$$

so that

$$\tilde{C}_P - \tilde{C}_V \approx R + \frac{2aP}{RT^2} \approx R + \frac{2a}{\tilde{V}T} \qquad (8\text{–}27)$$

both parts of the equation accurate to the first order.

As second application, we consider the temperature change δT obtained when 1 mole of a van der Waals gas is subjected to a Joule-Thomson expansion with the pressure change δP. Thus we assume the pressure and temperature in the left chamber of Fig. 8–1 to be $P_1 = P + \delta P$ and $T_1 = T + \delta T$, while for the right chamber we set $P_2 = P$, and $T_2 = T$. We recall that the enthalpy remains unchanged, so that

$$H(T + \delta T, P + \delta P) = H(T, P) \qquad (8\text{–}28)$$

It is assumed that $\delta T/T$ and $\delta P/P$ are both small compared to 1.

By Taylor expansion,

$$\tilde{H}(T + \delta T, P + \delta P) \approx \tilde{H}(T, P) + \left(\frac{\partial \tilde{H}}{\partial T}\right)_P \delta T + \left(\frac{\partial \tilde{H}}{\partial P}\right)_T \delta P$$

or, using (8–28) and rearranging,

$$\frac{\delta T}{\delta P} \approx -\left(\frac{\partial \tilde{H}}{\partial P}\right)_T \bigg/ \left(\frac{\partial \tilde{H}}{\partial T}\right)_P \qquad (8\text{–}29)$$

However, by (8–26), $(\partial \tilde{H}/\partial T)_P$ is just $\tilde{C}_P$, whereas, from (8–25),

$$\left(\frac{\partial \tilde{H}}{\partial P}\right)_T = b - \frac{2a}{RT}$$

Therefore,

$$\frac{\delta T}{\delta P} \approx \frac{(2a/RT) - b}{\tilde{C}_P} \qquad (8\text{–}30)$$

for the Joule-Thomson effect of 1 mole of van der Waals gas.

Three points are worthy of note:

(1) Since δP is always negative for an expansion, δT is positive or negative, depending on whether $2a/RT$ is smaller or larger than b. Thus there is Joule-Thomson heating when $2a/RT < b$, and cooling when $2a/RT > b$.

(2) For given values of a and b, the Joule-Thomson inversion temperature is

$$T_i = \frac{2a}{Rb} \qquad (8\text{–}31)$$

At this temperature the Joule-Thomson effect is zero and no temperature change occurs on expansion; above T_i there is heating, below it, cooling for Joule-Thomson expansion.

(3) The Joule-Thomson effect depends on both a and b, even though it might be expected to depend just on a, seeing that it is the cohesion pressure $a/\tilde{V}^2$ against which work must be performed. The thermodynamic investigation shows that more subtleties are involved. This is a good example of the power of the thermodynamic analysis of the implications of a molecular model.

8–5   ENTROPY OF MIXING

Consider a container like that shown in Fig. 8–4. In the compartment on the left are n_1 moles of perfect gas 1, in the compart-

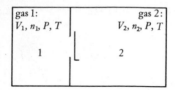

Figure 8–4   Mixing of two gases.   Initially the two compartments are filled with different ideal gases, at the same temperature
T and pressure P.   When the valve is opened the gases mix.   What
is ΔS for this irreversible process?

ment on the right n_2 moles of gas 2, both at the same pressure and
temperature, P and T.   The volumes occupied by them are

$$V_i = \frac{n_i RT}{P} \qquad (i = 1, 2) \tag{8–32}$$

A hole in the partition is opened and the gases are permitted to mix.
The question is: What is the entropy increase for this irreversible
process?   To answer it, a path must be specified along which mixing
can be performed reversibly.   This is achieved by the following
three-step procedure:

(1) Gas 1 is expanded isothermally and reversibly from $V_1 =
n_1 RT/P$ to the total volume $V = V_1 + V_2 = (n_1 + n_2)RT/P$. By
(3–8), the corresponding entropy increase is

$$\Delta S_{(1)} = n_1 R \ln \frac{V}{V_1} = n_1 R \ln \frac{n_1 + n_2}{n_1} = -n_1 R \ln x_1 \tag{8–33}$$

where x_1 is the mole faction of gas 1, $x_1 = n_1/(n_1 + n_2)$.

(2) Gas 2 is expanded in the same way from V_2 to V, with an
entropy increase of

$$\Delta S_{(2)} = -n_2 R \ln x_2 \tag{8–34}$$

(3) The two gases are combined isothermally by the use of a
device such as that shown in Fig. 8–5 and suggested by Planck.
It consists of two concentric cylindrical containers, one of volume
$2V$ with a diaphragm B in the middle, and the other of volume V,

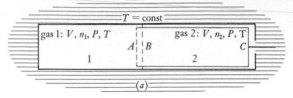

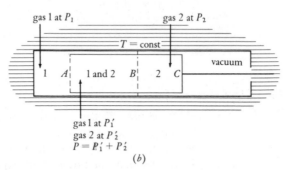

Figure 8–5   Reversible mixing. This device permits reversible mixing (or separation) of two gases. It consists of a stationary part with a diaphragm B that is permeable to gas 2 only, and a movable part with a diaphragm A permeable to gas 1 only. At (a) gases 1 and 2 are not mixed; at (b) partial mixing has been accomplished.

movable in the first container and with a diaphragm A on the left. Diaphragm B is permeable to gas 2, but not to gas 1, diaphragm A to gas 1 but not to gas 2. The device is used for a thought experiment only, but it can be constructed in principle. Diaphragm B may, for example, be attached to a ring of iron and held in its position at the middle of the outside container by magnets. The diaphragms represent an idealization inasmuch as semipermeable diaphragms for gases have been realized experimentally for a few gases only. For example, H_2 can pass through a heated foil of Pt, and He is known to leak through glass.

The left compartment of the device in the position shown in Fig. 8–5(a) is filled with gas 1 and the right compartment with gas 2.

The mixing proceeds at constant temperature and reversibly, by pushing the inside container to the left so slowly that equilibrium between the two sides of each diaphragm exists at all times.

The nature of the equilibrium across a semipermeable diaphragm is such that the partial pressure of the gas able to pass through it must be the same on both sides. This is a corollary of Dalton's law of partial pressures, by which any component gas behaves as if the other gases were absent. In the absence of other gases there is no difference between the two sides of the membrane, and the pressure of the gas able to pass the membrane must be the same on both sides. Thus at all times [see Fig. 8–5(b)]

$$P_1' = P_1 \qquad \text{and} \qquad P_2' = P_2 \tag{8–35}$$

We compute the work performed on the system when the inside container is moved to the left, so that diaphragm A sweeps out a volume dV. The following work is done by diaphragm A: compression against pressure P_1 in the left compartment, and expansion at a pressure $P = P_1' + P_2' = P_1 + P_2$ in the middle compartment. Thus $Dw_A = (P_1 - P)\,dV = -P_2\,dV$. The right wall C of the inside container performs compression work against the pressure P_2, $Dw_C = P_2\,dV$. Thus $Dw = Dw_A + Dw_C = -P_2\,dV + P_2\,dV = 0$. No work is transferred to the system when the inside container is moved reversibly to the right or the left. The energy of the two perfect gases and of their mixture depends on T only, there being no intermolecular forces. It remains constant, and therefore Dq is also zero. Finally, $dS = Dq/T$ is zero also, so that for the third step, the isothermal combination of the gases,

$$\Delta S_{(3)} = 0 \tag{8–36}$$

This result is very interesting. The entropy of each component gas remains the same whether it occupies the volume V alone or not. This can be extended to mixtures of more than two gases. The entropy of the mixture is the sum of the entropies each component gas would have if it were to occupy the total volume alone. Therefore, Daltons' law, by which each component gas in a perfect gas mixture behaves as if it were present alone, applies to entropy as well as to pressure. It also applies to the energies and enthalpies of the components, and therefore also to the free energies. All these quantities are seen to be additive.

To return to the original question, we find that the entropy of mixing of volumes V_1 and V_2 of two gases at equal T and P is the sum of the three contributions (8–33), (8–34), and (8–36):

$$\Delta S_{\mathrm{mix}} = -n_1 R \ln x_1 - n_2 R \ln x_2 = -nR(x_1 \ln x_1 + x_2 \ln x_2) \quad (8\text{–}37)$$

where n is the total number of moles of gas. For more than two components the entropy of mixing is

$$\Delta S_{\mathrm{mix}} = -nR \sum_i x_i \ln x_i \qquad (8\text{–}38)$$

where the x_i are the mole fractions of the component gases and n is the total number of moles of gas. In the sense that the contribution (8–36) from the actual mixing along the path chosen is zero, we may consider the entropy of mixing to be the entropy of changing the volumes of the component gases to the total volume.

Note that ΔS_{mix} [(8–37) and (8–38)] is always positive, because all x_i are fractions by definition, so that $\ln x_i$ is always negative. Equations (8–37) and (8–38) can be shown to apply to the mixing of liquids also, provided the mixed liquids form a perfect solution— that is, provided Raoult's law applies.

Equation (8–37) is valid for the mixing of any two gases, even of gases that differ only because their molecules contain different isotopes of the same element. It applies, for example, when the two gases are He^3 and He^4 or $U^{235}F_6$ and $U^{238}F_6$. It may not be possible to find suitable membranes for mixing or separating these gases reversibly, but other methods of reversible separation may be used. It has, for example, been proved by Schrödinger that step (3) of the preceding discussion may be performed reversibly by a gravity field, with the same result, that is, with $\Delta S_{(3)} = 0$.

What happens then, upon opening the hole in the wall, when the two gases in the compartments in Fig. 8–4 are identical? Molecules that were originally in chamber 1 may now diffuse into chamber 2 and conversely. However, seeing that all molecules are of the same kind, we conclude that there is no macroscopic change so that

$\Delta S_{mix} = 0$, even though (8–37), applied blindly, suggests a positive ΔS. Note that for gases that are as close in their properties as are $U^{235}F_6$ and $U^{238}F_6$, ΔS_{mix} is positive and thus nonzero, whereas for identical gases ΔS_{mix} is suddenly zero. This discontinuity is the noted **Gibbs' paradox.** Gibbs felt that it should be possible to choose gases that would be more and more alike, so that identity of the two gases could be considered to be a limiting case—in other words, that there should be a continuous transition between different and identical gases. It was therefore disturbing that (8–37) did not depend on any property of the gas molecules, such as their masses, but rather depended only on the mole fractions of the gases involved.

Although not recognized as such, this discontinuity was one of the harbingers of quantum mechanics, in which there is a fundamental difference between the treatment of particles of the same kind and that of particles of a different kind, because there is no way to tell particles of the same kind apart. Different isotopes of the same element may *behave* very similarly, but they are fundamentally different: They can be told apart. If we could, for example, fill the two compartments of Fig. 8–4 with the same gas but mark all molecules in compartment 1 with green paint, the entropy increase upon opening the hole in the partition would be given by (8–37), while for unmarked molecules in both compartments ΔS_{mix} would be zero. There is simply no way of marking molecules, be it ever so subtle, without making them fundamentally different. If they are different, (8–37) applies; if they are identical in nature, $\Delta S_{mix} = 0$.

This matter is closely related to the fact that, by quantum mechanics, two microstates in which particles of the same kind have been interchanged are indistinguishable, even microscopically. They are one and the same microstate and cannot be counted separately when counting up microstates. However, two microstates in which particles of different kinds have been interchanged must be so counted. This subject is discussed further in Appendix 3–1.

PROBLEMS

8–1. *Enthalpy of reaction.* The equilibrium constant of the reaction $N_2(g) + O_2(g) = 2NO(g)$ is given by the empirical equation $\log K = 2.692 - 9451/T$ in the range of 2000 to 3000°K. Find $\Delta H^0(T)$ in the same temperature interval for the reaction as written.

8–2. *Temperature dependence of the equilibrium constant.* For the reaction $N_2O_4(g) = 2NO_2(g)$ the enthalpy has been found to follow the equation $\Delta H^0(T) = (12306 - 3.48T - 22.079 \times 10^{-3}T^2 + 65.313 \times 10^{-6}T^3)$ cal. The value of K at 400°K is 47.29. Find $\log K$ as a function of T, and in particular the value of K at 300°K.

8–3. *The water-gas equilibrium.* The enthalpy of the reaction $H_2O(g) + CO(g) = H_2(g) + CO_2(g)$ is -7.8 kcal between 1000 and 2000°C, and the equilibrium constant K equals 0.363 at 1500°K. What is the value of K at 1750°K?

8–4. *Enthalpy of reaction.* The equilibrium constant of the reaction $2SO_2(g) + O_2(g) = 2SO_3(g)$ has been determined to follow the equation $\log K = 5219.1/T^2 + (1.1180 \log T)/T - 7.338/T$. Find $\Delta H^0(T)$ for the reaction as a function of the temperature and in particular $\Delta H^0(1000)$.

8–5. *Fuel cell.* A fuel cell uses CO as fuel and is based on the reaction

$$CO(g) + \tfrac{1}{2}O_2(g) = CO_2(g)$$

taking place at 1000°K in a melt of five parts K_2CO_3 and one part Li_2CO_3. At this temperature the equilibrium constant has the value 1.58×10^{10} atm$^{-1/2}$ and equilibrium is established almost immediately. Calculate a voltage for the cell at zero current, assuming that at existing flow rates two volumes of CO and one volume of O_2 react, that 97 per cent of the CO is used up, and that the total pressure is 1 atm.

8–6. *Van der Waals equation.* Write the van der Waals equation for n moles of gas. What are the modifications needed for the constants a and b? Write (8–24) and (8–25) for n moles of gas and satisfy yourself that the same changes for a and b apply.

8–7. *Van der Waals gas.* A van der Waals gas of volume V_1 is compressed reversibly and isothermally to half its volume. Calculate ΔU, ΔH, and ΔS in the approximation used in (8–18), (8–24), and (8–25). Compare ΔS with that obtained for an ideal gas.

appendix

1 Glossary of Symbols

ln	natural logarithm, 17
mp	melting point, 7
M	concentration in moles per liter; molar, 49
μ	chemical potential, 145
n	number of moles, 9
$\mathcal{N}$	Avogadro's number, 83
ν_i	stochiometric coefficients, 159
Ω	number of realizations, 82
P	pressure, 9
Π	osmotic pressure, 156
q	heat, 24
Q	quotient in mass-action and Nernst equations, 161
$\mathcal{Q}$	electric charge, 22, 186
R	gas constant, 9
$\mathcal{R}$	electrical resistance, 189
s	solid, 42
S	entropy, 71
$\tilde{S}_f^0$	standard molar entropy, 106
Σ_i	sum operator, 50
t	temperature, °C, 7
T	temperature, °K, 8
U	energy, 34
v	velocity, 89
V	volume, 7
$\mathcal{U}$	cell potential, 14, 186
w	work, 15
w'	net work, 40
x	mole fraction, 155
ξ	reaction variable, 159

OTHER SYMBOLS USED

square brackets, as in [H$^+$]	molarity of molecular or ionic species, 146
tilde, as in $\tilde{H}$	quantities per mole, 25
zero, super, as in G^0	standard quantities, 46

appendix

2 The Handling of Inequalities

Inequalities often occur in thermodynamics. The same algebraic operations that are used on equations may also be used on inequalities, but care must be taken because such operations may or may not change a "smaller than" into a "larger than" and conversely. For this reason a number of different cases will be considered in detail.

Inequalities that involve negative quantities are particularly hazardous. It is helpful to visualize them as positional relationships on a line. The meaning of $<$ is then "lies to the left of" and of $>$, "lies to the right of." For example, $-4 < +3$ means that -4 is on the left of $+3$ on the number line, and similarly $-4 > -6$ means that -4 is on the right of -6.

Operations that *do not change* the original inequality sign are:

(1) *Adding or subtracting the same positive or negative quantity on both sides:* When $a > b$, then $(a + c) > (b + c)$. Similarly, when $e < f$, then $(e - g) < (f - g)$.

(2) *Multiplying and dividing both sides by the same positive quantity:* When $a > b$, then $a|c| > b|c|$ and $a/|c| > b/|c|$.

Operations that *do change* the original inequality sign to its opposite are:

(1) *Interchanging sides:* When $a < b$, then $b > a$.

(2) *Changing sign on both sides:* From $a > b$ follows $-a < -b$. This is true whether a and b are both positive, both negative, or mixed.

(3) *Taking the reciprocal on both sides:* From $a > b$ follows $(1/a) < (1/b)$.

(4) *Multiplying or dividing both sides by the same negative quantity:* From $a > b$ follows $a(-|c|) < b(-|c|)$ and $a/(-|c|) < b/(-|c|)$.

When going from quantities with signs to their *absolute values*, considerable care must be taken, as can be seen from the following parallel columns:

$$-2 > -4 \quad \text{but} \quad 2 < 4$$
$$-2 < 4 \quad \text{and} \quad 2 < 4$$
$$-6 < 4 \quad \text{but} \quad 6 > 4$$
$$-6 < -4 \quad \text{but} \quad 6 > 4$$

appendix

3 The
Relationship
between
Ω and S

A3–1   THE BOLTZMANN FORMULA

As explained on page 83, if two independent systems have associated with them the quantities S_1, S_2, Ω_1, and Ω_2, the analogous quantities associated with the combined system are $S = S_1 + S_2$ and $\Omega = \Omega_1 \Omega_2$. To see what functional relationship between S and Ω is implied by these facts, we set $\Omega = f(S)$ and thus also $\Omega_1 = f(S_1)$ and $\Omega_2 = f(S_2)$. The requirements of f are thus that $f(S) = f(S_1 + S_2) = \Omega = \Omega_1 \Omega_2 = f(S_1)f(S_2)$, or, relabeling S_1 and S_2 as x and y, that

$$f(x + y) = f(x)f(y) \tag{A3–1}$$

for all x and y. Differentiation relative to x but with y treated as a constant yields

$$\frac{d[f(x + y)]}{d(x + y)} \frac{d(x + y)}{dx} = f(y)\frac{df(x)}{dx} \tag{A3–2}$$

Similarly, by differentiation relative to y at constant x,

$$\frac{d[f(x + y)]}{d(x + y)} \frac{d(x + y)}{dy} = f(x)\frac{df(y)}{dy} \tag{A3–3}$$

However, the left sides of (A3–2) and (A3–3) are identical, because $d(x + y)/dx$ at constant y and $d(x + y)/dy$ at constant x are both equal to 1. Hence the right sides of (A3–2) and (A3–3) are also equal.

$$f(y)\frac{df(x)}{dx} = f(x)\frac{df(y)}{ay}$$

By rearrangement,

$$\frac{df(x)/dx}{f(x)} = \frac{df(y)/dy}{f(y)} \qquad \text{(A3–4)}$$

The left side of (A3–4) is a function of y only and the right side a function of x only. This is possible only if both sides are constant. For let y be constant for the moment and vary x arbitrarily. The right side remains constant and so must the left. Similarly, when y is varied at constant x, the left side remains constant and so must the right. Let the constant be a:

$$\frac{df(x)/dx}{f(x)} = a$$

By rearrangement,

$$\frac{df(x)}{f(x)} = a \, dx$$

Integration yields

$$\ln f(x) = ax + b \qquad \text{(A3–5)}$$

where b is another constant. For $f(x)$ we thus obtain

$$f(x) = \exp (ax + b) = c \exp ax \qquad \text{(A3–6)}$$

where $c = \exp b$ is a new constant. To see whether this form of $f(x)$ fits the original requirement, we check whether $f(x + y)$ is equal to $f(x)f(y)$. We find

$$f(x + y) = c \exp a(x + y) = c(\exp ax)(\exp ay)$$
$$= c^{-1}f(x)f(y)$$

It is seen that c must equal 1, which corresponds to $b = 0$, since $c = \exp b$ or $b = \ln c$. But x stands for S and $f(x)$ for Ω, so that from (A3–6) it follows, with $b = 0$, that

$$\ln \Omega = aS$$

This is the Boltzmann relationship (4–1) between Ω and S,

$$S = k \ln \Omega$$

with the particular value k^{-1} for a.

Another matter has been deferred until now, so as not to burden the development that led to (4–5), for the ratio Ω_1/Ω_2 for a perfect gas at volumes V_1 and V_2.

According to the quantum theory molecules of the same kind are indistinguishable from each other. Microstates in which the spatial coordinates, velocities, etc., of all molecules are identical but in which two or more molecules are interchanged cannot therefore be distinguished from one another and must be counted as *one* microstate. A closer look shows that in the derivation of (4–5) such microstates were treated as being different, and since $\mathcal{N}'$ molecules can be interchanged $(\mathcal{N}')!$ number of ways there are actually $(\mathcal{N}')!$ times fewer states than were counted. However, the factor $(\mathcal{N}')!$ appears in both the number of realizations of the original state and the number of realizations of the final state, that is, in Ω_1 and Ω_2. In the ratio Ω/Ω_2 it therefore cancels, so that (4–5) is not affected by the indistinguishability of molecules of the same kind. The indistinguishability of particles of the same kind is also important for an understanding of the Gibbs' paradox explained in Section 8–5.

A3–2 STATISTICAL TREATMENT OF THE TWO-LEVEL SYSTEM

A valuable illustration of the relationship between the statistical and the thermodynamic definitions of entropy is afforded by the treatment of a simple system consisting of 1 mole of distinct molecules that have available two energy levels only, one at zero, the other at ϵ (Figure A3–1). Let n_1 and n_2 be the numbers of molecules in the lower and upper levels, respectively. The ratio n_2/n_1 is given by what is known as the Boltzmann factor,

$$\frac{n_2}{n_1} = \exp\left(\frac{-\epsilon}{kT}\right) \tag{A3–7}$$

where $k = R/\mathcal{N}$ is the Boltzmann constant (see also Figure 4–4 and 5–2). As T goes to zero, the right side approaches $\exp(-\infty) = 0$,

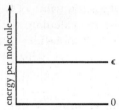

Figure A3-1 System of two energy levels. We consider hypothetical molecules that are able to assume only one of two energies, 0 and ϵ. At zero temperature all molecules are at zero energy; at infinite temperature the two levels are equally occupied.

so that at $T = 0$ all molecules are at zero energy. When kT becomes large compared to ϵ, the right side of (A3-7) approaches exp $0 = 1$, so that at infinite temperature there is equal occupancy of the two energy levels, and $n_1 = n_2 = \mathcal{N}/2$.

We are interested in the entropy gain ΔS when going from $T = 0$ (state 1) to $T = \infty$ (state 2) and shall calculate this entropy gain in two ways: statistically by using (4-1) and thermodynamically by using (4-8).

At $T = 0$ all $\mathcal{N}$ molecules are in the same zero energy level. There is only one microstate, and thus for state 1

$$\Omega_1 = 1 \qquad (A3-8)$$

When $T = \infty$, there are $\mathcal{N}/2$ molecules in each level, at least approximately. Suppose for the moment that at $T = \infty$ each molecule has the choice of occupying the upper or lower energy level, independent of what levels all the other molecules are in. The number of microstates would be equal to $2 \cdot 2 \cdot 2 \cdot \ldots \cdot 2$, the 2 repeated $\mathcal{N}$ times, or 2^N. This includes too many microstates for state 2 because microstates are included in which the occupancies of the two levels are substantially different from $\mathcal{N}/2$, such as the microstate in which all molecules are in the upper level and the one in which all are in the lower level. In fact, 2^N is the number of *all possible* microstates with no restrictions on the occupancies, and we shall call this number Ω_{tot},

$$\Omega_{\text{tot}} = 2^N \qquad (A3-9)$$

Since Ω_{tot} is larger than the value of Ω for state 2 we need another approach. Suppose we calculate the number of microstates that correspond to *exactly* $N/2$ molecules in either of the two levels. This number is $N!/(N/2)!\,(N/2)!$, which may be seen as follows. Imagine the existence of $N/2$ boxes at energy zero and $N/2$ boxes at energy ϵ (Figure A3–2), each box having space for one molecule. There are $N!$ ways of distributing N molecules over these boxes, each of them satisfying the condition of having exactly $N/2$ molecules in either level. This is not the number of microstates, however, because all that matters for a given microstate is that $N/2$ *specified* molecules are in the upper level and the remaining $N/2$ molecules in the lower level, regardless of which box they are in. In other words the specified molecules in the top level can be redistributed in all possible ways over the $N/2$ upper boxes, there being $(N/2)!$ such ways, and independently the remaining molecules in $(N/2)!$ ways in the lower level, without any of this leading to a new microstate. This means that $N!$ must be divided by $[(N/2)!]^2$ to give the number of microstates, which proves the original contention.

The situation just discussed is the *most probable* one for state 2 and

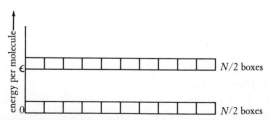

Figure A3–2   System of boxes at two energy levels. To determine how many microstates exist in which both levels have equal occupancy, the N hypothetical molecules are distributed over the boxes shown, one per box, with the understanding that a molecule is to have the energy ϵ when in an upper box and the energy zero when in a lower box. There are $N!$ ways to distribute the molecules over all boxes, but the $(N/2)!$ ways of redistributing $N/2$ specified molecules over the lower boxes does not lead to a new microstate, nor does the redistribution of the remaining $N/2$ molecules over the upper boxes. There are thus $N!/[(N/2)!]^2$ microstates of the required kind.

we therefore denote the number of microstates just calculated by Ω_{mp},

$$\Omega_{mp} = \frac{\mathcal{N}!}{[(\mathcal{N}/2)!]^2} \tag{A3-10}$$

There are, however, more microstates than Ω_{mp} representing state 2, because situations in which the number of molecules in the upper level is slightly larger or smaller than $\mathcal{N}/2$ are not distinguishable from an occupancy that is exactly $\mathcal{N}/2$, $\mathcal{N}$ being so large. Thus Ω_2 for state 2 lies between Ω_{tot} and Ω_{mp}.

To represent the value of Ω_{mp} in a form that does not involve factorials we use **Stirling's approximation,** which states that

$$\ln n! \approx (n + \tfrac{1}{2}) \ln n - n + \tfrac{1}{2}\ln 2\pi \tag{A3-11}$$

Since Avogadro's number $\mathcal{N}$ is very large, the $\tfrac{1}{2}$ in $n + \tfrac{1}{2}$ and the last term can be dropped, so that $\ln \mathcal{N}! \approx \mathcal{N} \ln \mathcal{N} - \mathcal{N}$, and $\ln[(\mathcal{N}/2)!]^2 \approx 2[(\mathcal{N}/2) \times \ln (\mathcal{N}/2) - \mathcal{N}/2] = \mathcal{N} \ln (\mathcal{N}/2) - \mathcal{N} = \mathcal{N} \ln \mathcal{N} - \mathcal{N} \ln 2 - \mathcal{N}$. Subtracting the second expression from the first we obtain $\ln \Omega_{mp} \approx \mathcal{N} \ln 2$, so that

$$\Omega_{mp} \approx 2^N \tag{A3-12}$$

To our amazement Ω_{mp} turns out to be the same as Ω_{tot} in the approximation considered. Or put more accurately, the difference between the logarithms of Ω_{tot} and Ω_{mp} is negligible. It turns out that this is generally true for statistical considerations of this nature, as was stated on page 85.

Finally, because Ω_2 is between Ω_{tot} and Ω_{mp},

$$\Omega_2 \approx 2^N \tag{A3-13}$$

Using the Boltzmann formula for the entropy we obtain

$$\Delta S = \tilde{S}_2 - \tilde{S}_1 = k \ln \Omega_2 - k \ln \Omega_1 = k \ln 2^N = \mathcal{N}k \ln 2$$
$$\Delta S = R \ln 2 \tag{A3-14}$$

This is the *statistical result*.

For the thermodynamic computation we need C_V as a function of T and therefore $U(T)$, because $\tilde{C}_V = d\tilde{U}/dT$. (No volume considerations are involved and the subscript V is not actually needed.) There are n_1 molecules of energy 0 and n_2 of energy ϵ, so that

$$\tilde{U} = n_1 \times 0 + n_2\epsilon = n_2\epsilon \qquad \text{(A3–15)}$$

where $n_1 + n_2 = N$. By (A3–7), $n_2 = n_1 \exp(-\epsilon/kT)$, and thus $n_1[1 + \exp(-\epsilon/kT)] = N$, whence

$$n_1 = \frac{N}{1 + \exp(-\epsilon/kT)} \qquad \text{(A3–16)}$$

$$n_2 = \frac{N \exp(-\epsilon/kT)}{1 + \exp(-\epsilon/kT)} \qquad \text{(A3–17)}$$

Inserted into (A3–15), we see that

$$\tilde{U}(T) = \frac{N\epsilon \exp(-\epsilon/kT)}{1 + \exp(-\epsilon/kT)} = \frac{N\epsilon \exp y}{1 + \exp y} \qquad \text{(A3–18)}$$

where we have set $y = -\epsilon/kT$ for purposes of abbreviation. Differentiation with respect to T yields $\tilde{C}_V$,

$$\tilde{C}_V = \frac{d\tilde{U}}{dT} = \left(\frac{d\tilde{U}}{dy}\right)\left(\frac{dy}{dT}\right) = R\,\frac{y^2 \exp y}{(1 + \exp y)^2} \qquad \text{(A3–19)}$$

Use of $R = Nk$ has been made. Finally,

$$\tilde{S}(T) = \int_0^T \left(\frac{\tilde{C}_V}{T}\right) dT \qquad \text{(A3–20)}$$

where $S(0)$ has been set equal to zero. Noting that $y = -\infty$ at $T = 0$, making the proper changes from T to y, and noting that $dT/T = -dy/y$ we find

$$\tilde{S}(T) = -R \int_{-\infty}^y \frac{y \exp y\, dy}{(1 + \exp y)^2}$$

The indefinite integral has the value $[(y \exp y)/(1 + \exp y)] - \ln(1 + \exp y)$, as can be proved by differentiation. Inserting the limits we obtain

$$\tilde{S}(T) = R\left[\frac{-y \exp y}{1 + \exp y} + \ln(1 + \exp y)\right]$$

or

$$\frac{\tilde{S}}{R} = \frac{(\epsilon/kT) \exp(-\epsilon/kT)}{1 + \exp(-\epsilon/kT)} + \ln[1 + \exp(-\epsilon/kT)]$$

$$(A3-21)$$

Finally as T approaches ∞, $\tilde{S}(T)$ goes to $R \ln 2$. The final *thermodynamic result* is thus

$$\Delta\tilde{S} = \tilde{S}(\infty) - \tilde{S}(0) = R \ln 2 \qquad (A3-22)$$

which is identical with the statistical result. Figure A3–3 shows

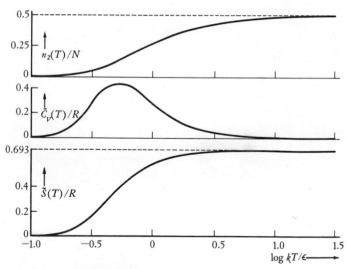

Figure A3–3   Upper-level occupancy n_2/N, **molar heat capacity** $\tilde{C}_V$, **and entropy** $\tilde{S}$ **for the two-level system.** When $kT \ll \epsilon$, n_2/N, $\tilde{C}_V$, and $\tilde{S}$ are all small. As the temperature is raised the upper level begins to be filled, causing the appearance of a characteristic hump in $\tilde{C}_V$. When $kT = \epsilon$ the upper level is about two-thirds from being half-filled. When $kT \gg \epsilon$, n_2/N is close to 0.5, $\tilde{C}_V$ is going back to zero, and $\tilde{S}$ is close to $R \ln 2$.

n_2/N and $\tilde{C}_V$ as functions of T and how $S(T)$ approaches the value $R \ln 2$. Although the example described is simple, it has traits in common with real cases—for example, the hump in $\tilde{C}_V$ that appears when a substantial number of our hypothetical molecules assume the energy ϵ is a general characteristic of the filling of molecular energy levels.

appendix

4 Values of Thermodynamic Functions and Half-Cell emf's

Table A4–1

Values of $\tilde{H}_f^0$, $\tilde{G}_f^0$, $\tilde{S}^0$, and $\tilde{C}_P$

Substance	$\tilde{H}_f^0$, kcal/mole	$\tilde{G}_f^0$, kcal/mole	$\tilde{S}^0$, cal/mole-deg	$\tilde{C}_P$, cal/mole-deg
$Ag(s)$	0.00	0.00	10.21	6.09
$Ag^+(aq)$	25.31	18.43	17.67	
$AgCl(s)$	−30.36	−26.22	22.97	12.14
$Ba(s)$	0.00	0.00	15.1	6.30
$Ba^{2+}(aq)$	−128.67		3.0	
$Br(g)$	26.71	19.69	41.81	4.97
$Br^-(aq)$	−28.90	−24.57	19.29	
$Br_2(g)$	7.34	0.75	58.64	8.60
$Br_2(l)$	0.00	0.00	36.4	
$C(g)$	171.70	160.84	37.76	4.98
$C(diamond)$	0.45	0.68	0.58	1.45
$C(graphite)$	0.00	0.00	1.36	2.07
$CCl_4(g)$	−25.5	−15.3	73.95	19.96
$CCl_4(l)$	−33.3	−16.4	51.25	31.49
$CHCl_3(l)$	−31.5	−17.1	48.5	27.8
$CH_4(g)$	−17.89	−12.14	44.50	8.54
$CO(g)$	−26.42	−32.81	47.30	6.96
$CO_2(g)$	−94.05	−94.26	51.06	8.87
$CO_3^{2-}(aq)$	−161.63	−126.22	−12.7	
$H_2CO_3(aq)$	−167.0	−149.0	45.7	
$HCO_3^-(aq)$	−165.18	−140.31	22.7	
$C_2H_2(g)$	54.19	50.00	48.00	10.50
$C_2H_4(g)$	12.50	16.28	52.45	10.41
$C_2H_6(g)$	−20.24	−7.86	54.85	12.58
$C_3H_8(g)$	−24.82	−5.61	64.5	
$CH_3OH(l)$	−57.02	−39.73	30.3	19.5
$C_2H_5OH(l)$	−66.36	−41.77	38.4	26.64

258

Table A4-1 (continued)
Values of $\tilde{H}_f^0$, $\tilde{G}_f^0$, $\tilde{S}^0$, and $\tilde{C}_P$

Substance	$\tilde{H}_f^0$, kcal/mole	$\tilde{G}_f^0$, kcal/mole	$\tilde{S}^0$, cal/mole-deg	$\tilde{C}_P$, cal/mole-deg
HCOOH(aq)	−98.0	−85.1	39.1	
HCOO$^-$(aq)	−98.0	−80.0	21.9	
CH$_3$COOH(l)	−116.4	−93.8	38.2	29.5
C$_6$H$_6$(l)	11.72	29.76	41.3	32.53
C$_6$H$_6$(g)	19.82	30.99	64.34	19.52
Ca(s)	0.00	0.00	9.95	6.28
Ca^{2+}(aq)	−129.77	−132.18	−13.2	
CaCO$_3$(calcite)	−288.45	−269.78	22.2	19.57
CaCO$_3$(aragonite)	−288.49	−269.53	21.2	19.42
CaO(s)	−151.9	−144.4	9.5	10.23
Ca(OH)$_2$(s)	−235.80	−214.33	18.2	20.2
Cl(g)	29.01	25.19	39.46	5.22
Cl$^-$(aq)	−40.02	−31.35	13.17	
Cl$_2$(g)	0.00	0.00	53.29	8.11
Cr(s)	0.00	0.00	5.68	5.58
Cr^{3+}(aq)	−61.2	−51.5	−73.5	
Cr$_2$O^{2-}(aq)	−364.0	−315.4	51.5	
Cu(s)	0.00	0.00	7.96	5.85
Cu^{2+}(aq)	15.39	15.53	−23.6	
CuCl(s)	−32.2	−28.4	21.9	
Fe(s)	0.00	0.00	6.49	6.03
Fe^{2+}(aq)	−21.0	−20.30	−27.1	
Fe^{3+}(aq)	−11.4	−2.52	−70.1	
Fe$_2$O$_3$(s)	−196.5	−177.1	21.5	25.0
Fe$_3$O$_4$(s)	−267.0	−242.4	35.0	34.3
H(g)	52.09	48.58	27.39	4.97
H$^+$(aq)	0.00	0.00	0.00	0.00
HBr(g)	−8.66	−12.72	47.44	6.96
HCl(g)	−22.06	−22.77	44.62	6.96
HI(g)	6.20	0.31	49.31	6.97
H$_2$(g)	0.00	0.00	31.21	6.89
H$_2$O(g)	−57.80	−54.64	45.11	8.02
H$_2$O(l)	−68.32	−56.69	16.72	18.00
H$_2$O$_2$(l)	−44.84	−27.24		

Table A4–1 (*continued*)
Values of $\tilde{H}_f^0$, $\tilde{G}_f^0$, $\tilde{S}^0$, and $\tilde{C}_P$

Substance	$\tilde{H}_f^0$, kcal/mole	$\tilde{G}_f^0$, kcal/mole	$\tilde{S}^0$, cal/mole-deg	$\tilde{C}_P$, cal/mole-deg
$H_2O_2(aq)$	-45.68	-31.47		
$H_2S(g)$	-4.82	-7.89	49.15	8.12
$HS^-(aq)$	-4.22	3.01	14.6	
$S^{2-}(aq)$	10.0	20.0	5.3	
$Hg(g)$	14.54	7.59	41.80	4.97
$Hg(l)$	0.00	0.00	18.5	6.65
$Hg_2Cl_2(s)$	-63.32	-50.35	46.8	24.3
$I(g)$	25.48	16.77	43.18	4.97
$I^-(aq)$	-13.37	-12.35	26.14	
$I_2(g)$	14.88	4.63	62.28	8.81
$I_2(s)$	0.00	0.00	27.9	13.14
$K(s)$	0.00	0.00	15.2	6.97
$K^+(aq)$	-60.04	-67.47	24.5	
$KCl(s)$	-104.18	-97.59	19.76	12.31
$KNO_3(s)$	-117.76	-93.96	68.87	23.01
$Mg(s)$	0.00	0.00	7.77	5.71
$Mg^{2+}(aq)$	-110.41	-108.99	-28.2	
$MgCl_2(s)$	-153.40	-141.57	21.4	17.04
$Mn(s)$	0.00	0.00	7.59	6.29
$Mn^{2+}(aq)$	-52.3	-53.4	-20	
$MnO_2(s)$	-124.2	-111.1	12.7	12.91
$MnO_4^-(aq)$	-129.7	-107.4	45.4	
$N(g)$	112.98	108.88	36.62	4.97
$NH_3(g)$	-11.04	-3.98	46.01	8.52
$NH_4^+(aq)$	-31.74	-19.00	26.97	
$NO(g)$	21.60	20.72	50.34	7.14
$NO_2(g)$	8.09	12.39	57.47	9.06
$N_2(g)$	0.00	0.00	45.77	6.96
$N_2O(g)$	19.49	24.76	52.58	9.25
$N_2O_4(g)$	2.31	23.49	72.73	18.90
$Na(s)$	0.00	0.00	12.2	6.79
$Na^+(aq)$	-57.28	-62.59	14.4	11.88
$NaCl(s)$	-98.23	-91.78	17.30	11.88
$NaHCO_3(s)$	-226.5	-203.6	24.4	20.94

Table A4–1 (continued)
Values of $\tilde{H}_f^0$, $\tilde{G}_f^0$, $\tilde{S}^0$, and $\tilde{C}_P$

Substance	$\tilde{H}_f^0$, kcal/mole	$\tilde{G}_f^0$, kcal/mole	$\tilde{S}^0$, cal/mole-deg	$\tilde{C}_P$, cal/mole-deg
$Na_2CO_3(s)$	−270.3	−250.4	32.5	26.41
$ONCl(g)$	12.57	15.86	63.0	9.37
$O(g)$	59.16	55.00	38.47	5.24
$OH^-(aq)$	−54.96	−37.60	−2.52	
$O_2(g)$	0.00	0.00	49.00	7.02
$O_3(g)$	34.0	39.06	56.8	9.37
$Pb(s)$	0.00	0.00	15.51	6.41
$PbCl_2(s)$	−85.85	−75.04	32.6	18.4
$S(s, \text{rhombic})$	0.00	0.00	7.62	5.40
$S(s, \text{monoclinic})$	0.071	0.023	7.78	5.65
$SO_2(g)$	−70.96	−71.79	59.40	9.51
$SO_3(g)$	−94.45	−88.52	61.24	12.10
$SO_4^{2-}(aq)$	−216.90	−177.34	4.1	
$Zn(s)$	0.00	0.00	9.95	5.99
$Zn^{2+}(aq)$	−36.43	−35.18	−25.4	
$ZnCl_2(s)$	−99.40	−88.26	25.9	18.3
$ZnO(s)$	−83.17	−76.05	10.5	9.62

Table A4–2
Standard Half-Cell emf Values

Reaction	$\mathcal{E}^0$, volts
$F_2(g) + 2e^- = 2F^-$	2.87
$H_2O_2 + 2H^+ + 2e^- = 2H_2O$	1.77
$PbO_2(s) + 4H^+ + 2e^- = Pb^{2+} + 2H_2O$	1.47
$MnO_4^- + 8H^+ + 5e^- = Mn^{2+} + 4H_2O$	1.51
$Cl_2(g) + 2e^- = 2Cl^-$	1.359
$Cr_2O_7^{2-} + 14H^+ + 6e^- = 2Cr^{3+} + 7H_2O$	1.33
$O_2(g) + 4H^+ + 4e^- = 2H_2O$	1.229
$2IO_3^- + 12H^+ + 10e^- = I_2(s) + 3H_2O$	1.19

Table A4–2 (*continued*)
Standard Half-Cell emf Values

Reaction	ε^0, volts
$Br_2(l) + 2e^- = 2Br^-$	1.0652
$Cu^{2+} + I^- + e^- = CuI(s)$	0.85
$Ag^+ + e^- = Ag(s)$	0.7994
$Fe^{3+} + e^- = Fe^{2+}$	0.771
$O_2(g) + 2H^+ + 2e^- = H_2O_2$	0.69
$I_3^- + 2e^- = 3I^-$	0.535
$I_2(s) + 2e^- = 2I^-$	0.534
$Cu^{2+} + 2e^- = Cu(s)$	0.337
$Hg_2Cl_2(s) + 2e^- = 2Hg(l) + 2Cl^-$	0.2680
$AgCl(s) + e^- = Ag(s) + Cl^-$	0.2224
$Cu^{2+} + e^- = Cu^+$	0.153
$S(s) + 2H^+ + 2e^- = H_2S$	0.14
$HSO_4^- + 3H^+ + 2e^- = SO_2(g) + 2H_2O$	0.14
$TiO^{2+} + 2H^+ + e^- = Ti^{3+} + H_2O$	0.1
$S_4O_6^{2-} + 2e^- = 2S_2O_3^{2-}$	0.09
$2H^+ + 2e^- = H_2(g)$	0.000
$Pb^{2+} + 2e^- = Pb(s)$	−0.126
$Ni^{2+} + 2e^- = Ni(s)$	−0.23
$V^{3+} + e^- = V^{2+}$	−0.255
$Fe^{2+} + 2e^- = Fe(s)$	−0.440
$Zn^{2+} + 2e^- = Zn(s)$	−0.7628
$Na^+ + e^- = Na(s)$	−2.698
$K^+ + e^- = K(s)$	−2.925
$Li^+ + e^- = Li(s)$	−3.03

Sources for Tables A 4–1 and A 4–2

Charlot, G., *Selected Constants Oxydo-Reduction Potentials*, Pergamon Press, New York, 1958;

F. D. Rossini, D. D. Wagman, W. H. Evans, S. Levine, and I. Jaffe, *Selected Values of Chemical Thermodynamic Properties*, Circular of the National Bureau of Standards 500, February 2, 1952.

Gray, Dwight E., Coordinating Editor, *American Institute of Physics Handbook, Part 4: Heat*, 2nd ed., McGraw-Hill, New York, 1963.

Landolt-Börnstein, K. Schäfer and E. Lax, ed., *Zahlenwerte und Funktionen, Vol. II-1 Kalorische Zustandsgrössen*, Springer, Berlin, 1961.

Latimer, W. M., *Oxidation Potentials*, 2nd ed., Prentice-Hall, Englewood Cliffs, N.J., 1952.

appendix

5 Solutions

of

Problems

1–1. 491.67° Rankine and 671.67° Rankine

1–2. −272.3°C

1–3. 21.4°C

1–4. 35.8°C

1–5. 4.619 joules/mole-deg Rankine

1–6. −961 cal, −39.71 liter-atm

2–1. 0.23°C

2–2. 186.7°C

2–3. 25.14°C

2–4. $w = -1.341$ kcal $= -q$; $\Delta E = \Delta H = 0$

2–5. −81°C

2–8. 35 per cent NaCl

2–9. (*a*) −92.00 kcal; (*b*) −224.17 kcal

2–10. (*a*) 4.12 kcal; (*b*) −50.0 kcal; (*c*) −6.6 cal

2–11. −312.4 kcal

2–12. $\Delta H = -212.80$ kcal; $\Delta U = -211.6$ kcal

2–13. −326.70 kcal

2–14. −15.14 kcal

2–15. −66.48 kcal

2–16. −26.27 kcal

2–17. 113 kcal

2–18. 137°C

2–19. 38.0°C

2–20. 3000°C

2–21. 0.0319 weight per cent

2–22. 380°C

2–23. 1300°C

2–24. 55.6°C

2–25. $\Delta U = 0$; $\Delta T = 0.67$°K; $\Delta H = -30$ cal

2–26. 20.1°C

2–27. 7200°C (!); 45,000 atm (!)

2–28. 77.1°C; 1.53 atm

2–29. 2.54×10^{-3} cal

4–1. 6.85 cal/deg

4–2. 15.0°C; 0.230 cal/deg

4–4. 25.0 cal/deg

4–6. −1.38 cal/deg

4–7. (a) $T_3 = 596°K$; $T_4 = 93.25°K$; $T_5 = 149°K$

   (b) (1) $w = -261.3$ cal; $q = 37.8$ cal; $\Delta U = -223.5$ cal; $\Delta S = 0.263$ cal/deg

      (2) $w = -443.8$ cal; $q = 220.3$ cal

      (3) $w = -110.9$ cal; $q = -112.6$ cal

4–9. 28.0 cal/mole

4–10. 0.125; 0.0125 cal/deg

4–11. 0.123 kwhr

4–13. −0.067°C

4–14. 9.42 kcal

4–15. 8.1 kcal

4–16. 6.62 kcal

4–17. 0.06 atm

4–19. (a) 27.1 cal/deg; (b) 28.8 cal/deg

4–20. (a) 23.9 cal/deg; (b) 26.3 cal/deg

4–21. 0.633 mole

4–22. (a) 21.5 liters; (b) 320 torr; all

5–2. $\Delta H_{sub} = 12.203$ kcal; $\Delta S_{sub} = 44.674$ cal/deg; $\Delta G_{sub} = 0$

5–3. $q = 9.25$ kcal; $w = -0.70$ kcal; $\Delta U = 8.55$ kcal; $\Delta S = 26.32$ cal/deg; $\Delta G = 0$

5–4. 95.6 torr

5–5. $\Delta H^0 = 55.5$ kcal, $\Delta G^0 = 46.5$ kcal, $\Delta S^0 = 30.0$ cal/deg; Fe_2O_3 more stable

5–6. $\Delta H^9 = -495.82$ kcal; $\Delta S^0 = -295.72$ cal/deg; $T \Delta S^0 = -88.17$ kcal; $\Delta G^0 = -407.61$ kcal

5–7. $\Delta U = 8.98$ kcal; $\Delta H = 9.71$ kcal; $\Delta S = 26.1$ cal/deg; $\Delta G = 0$

5–8. 8300°K

5–9. $\Delta U = 4.55$ kcal; $\Delta S = 17.2$ cal/deg; $\Delta G = 0$

5–10. (a) $\Delta H = -74.7$ cal; $\Delta S = -0.273$ cal/deg; $\Delta G = -2.8$ cal

   (b) $\Delta G = -2.83$ cal

5–11. $w = 0$; $\Delta H = 10.52$ kcal; $\Delta U = 9.9$ kcal $= q$; $\Delta S = 35.3$ cal/deg; $\Delta G = 0$

6–4. ΔG^0, kcal: (a) −54.72; (b) −6.92; (c) −49.48; (d) −82.95

   K: (a) 1.3×10^{40}; (b) 1.2×10^5; (c) 1.8×10^{36}; (d) 6.2×10^{60}

6–5. $(b) K_X = P_{HX}^2 / P_{H_2} P_{X_2}$; log $K_{Cl} = 33.37$; log $K_I = 0.45$

6–6. (a) 2.5×10^{-10}; (b) 5.0×10^{-13}; (c) 8.1×10^{-17}

6–7. 4×10^{-19} atm

6–8. 27 atm

6–9. 3.0×10^{10} atm $^{1/2}$; 4.8×10^{20}; 1.91 atm

6–10. -14.70 kcal; 26.98 kcal; to left

6–11. 698 cal

6–12. (a) zero; (b) 3.07 kcal

6–13. 2.79 kcal

6–14. $P_{CO} = 0.983$ atm; $P_{CO_2} = 0.0169$ atm; $K = 57.19$ atm; $\Delta G^0 = -9.65$ kcal

6–15. (a) -42.94 kcal; (b) -52.09 kcal

6–17. 1.0×10^{-12}

6–18. $\Delta G^0 = 5.11$ kcal; $\Delta H^0 = 0$; $\Delta S^0 = -17.1$ cal/deg

6–19. $K_1 = 6.3 \times 10^{-7}$; $d \log K_1 / dT = 4.5 \times 10^{-3}$; $K_2 = 4.7 \times 10^{-11}$; $d \log K_2 / dT = 8.7 \times 10^{-3}$

6–20. $\tilde{S}_f^0 = 21.80$ cal/deg; $\tilde{H}_f^0 = -26.13$ kcal

6–21. (a) $\Delta G = -35.08$ kcal, $\Delta H = -52.23$ kcal, using $H_2O(l)$ and $H_2(g)$; ethanol strongly favored; at higher temperatures less so; pressure increase advantageous. (b) $\Delta G = -1.36$ kcal, $\Delta H = -10.54$ kcal, using $H_2O(l)$; ethanol favored; temperature increase not favorable; pressure increase favorable

7–2. (a) $2Fe^{3+} + 2Cl^- = Cl_2(g) + 2Fe^{2+}$; $n = 2$; $\mathcal{E}$ negative
  (b) $2H^+ + 2Hg(l) + 2Cl^- = H_2(g) + Hg_2Cl_2(s)$; $n = 2$; $\mathcal{E}$ negative
  (c) $PbO_2(s) + Pb(s) + 2H_2SO_4 = 2PbSO_4(s) + 2H_2O(l)$; $n = 2$; $\mathcal{E}$ positive

7–3. $Zn^{2+} + Ni(s) = Zn(s) + Ni^{2+}$; $\mathcal{E} = -0.52$ volt; $\Delta G = 24.0$ kcal; Ni positive

7–4. 1.0×10^{15}

7–5. $H_5IO_6 + H^+ + 2e^- = IO_3^- + 3H_2O$; $\mathcal{E}^0 = 1.54$ volts

7–6. 9×10^{34}

7–7. -52.42 kcal $(Q = 1)$

7–8. 15.54 kcal/mole; -20.29 kcal/mole; -2.51 kcal/mole

7–9. -2.71 volts; 1.51 volts; 1.229 volts

7–10. 0.626 volt

7–11. 0.42 volt

7–12. 1.108 volts; 5.1×10^{-5} volt/deg; Cu positive

7–13. $Cd(amalgam) + Hg_2SO_4(s) = 2Hg(l) + Cd^{2+} + SO_4^{2-}$; $\Delta G^0 = -46.96$ kcal; $\Delta S^0 = -1.87$ cal/deg; $\Delta H^0 = -47.52$ kcal

7–14. $2Ag(s) + Hg_2Cl_2(s) = 2Hg(l) + 2AgCl(s)$; $\Delta G^0 = -2.09$ kcal; $\Delta S^0 = 15.6$ cal/deg; $\Delta H^0 = 2.55$ kcal

7–15. (a) $Mg(OH)_2(s)$, -199.27 kcal; (b) $Mg^{2+}(aq)$, -109.00 kcal; (c) -2.363 volts

7–16. 1.8×10^{-12}

7–17. 0.74 volt

7–18. $\Delta G = 88.528$ kcal; $\Delta S = -5.078$ cal/deg; $\Delta H = 87.014$ kcal

8–1. 43.25 kcal

8–2. $\log K = -2689/T + 1.751 \log T + 4.825 \times 10^{-3} T - 7.137 \times 10^{-6} T^2 + 3.053$; $K(300) = 0.170$

8–3. 0.250

8–4. $(-47464 + 2.428T)$ cal; -45.04 kcal

8–5. 0.77 volt

8–6. replace a by n^2a and b by nb

8–7. $\Delta U = -n^2a/V_1$; $\Delta H = n^2(bRT - 2a)/V_1$; $dU = n^2a\, dV/V$; $Dq_{rev} = dU + P\, dV = (nRT/V + n^2bRT/V^2)\, dV$; $\Delta S = -nR \ln 2 - n^2bR/V_1$

Bibliography

The following texts are elementary and on a level similar to the present text:

B. H. Mahan, *Elementary Chemical Thermodynamics*, Benjamin, New York, 1963.

L. K. Nash, *Elements of Chemical Thermodynamics*, Addison-Wesley, Reading, Mass., 1962.

Still on an elementary level but more extensive and going farther than the present text are:

W. J. Moore, *Physical Chemistry*, 3rd ed., Prentice-Hall, Englewood Cliffs, N.J., 1962.

F. W. Sears, *An Introduction to Thermodynamics, the Kinetic Theory of Gases, and Statistical Mechanics*, 3rd ed., Addison-Wesley, Reading, Mass., 1965.

The following classical texts are recommended particularly for their clarity:

P. S. Epstein, *Textbook of Thermodynamics*, Wiley, New York, 1937.

E. A. Guggenheim, *Thermodynamics*, 4th ed., Wiley (Interscience), New York, 1960.

I. M. Klotz, *Chemical Thermodynamics*, Benjamin, New York, 1964.

G. N. Lewis and M. Randall, *Thermodynamics*, 2nd ed. revised by K. S. Pitzer and L. Brewer, McGraw-Hill, New York, 1961.

I. Prigogine and R. Defay, *Chemical Thermodynamics*, Longman Green and Co., London, 1954

F. T. Wall, *Chemical Thermodynamics*, 2nd ed., Freeman, San Francisco, 1965.

A good text with particular emphasis on the second law is:

J. D. Fast, *Entropy*, McGraw-Hill, New York, 1963.

Treatment of low-temperature phenomena may be found in:

F. E. Simon, N. Kurti, J. F. Allen, and K. Mendelssohn, *Low Temperature Physics*, Pergamon Press, London, 1952.

Thermodynamics is applied to biological energy transfer in:

A. Lehninger, *Bioenergetics*, Benjamin, New York, 1965.

Many additional references may be found in:

L. K. Nash, *J. Chem. Educa.*, **42,** 64, (1965).

Index